The Mythology of Modern Dating Methods

John Woodmorappe

M.A., Geology

B.A., Biology

The Mythology of Modern Dating Methods
John Woodmorappe

ISBN 0-932766-57-9
Library of Congress 99-073040

Institute for Creation Research
P.O. Box 2667
El Cajon, California 92021

Printed in the United States of America

Table of Contents

Foreword .... *v*

Introduction .... *vii*

1. Rebuttal to Critics' Misrepresentations of my Previous Work 1
2. Overview of this New Book 5
3. Bogus Arguments for the Overall Validity of Isotopic Dating Methods 7
   A. Geologic Implications of Dating Results 7
   B. On "Conspiracies" and Data Manipulation 13
   C. "Stratigraphic Trends" in Isotopic Dates 18
   D. "Dating Consensus" on Earth's 4.5 Ga Age 24
4. "Malfunctioning Watches:" False Claims about the Rarity of Discrepant Dates 27
   A. Assessing the Frequency of Dates not Accepted as the Age of the Rock 27
   B. "Rigorous Testing" of Geochronometric Systems: Past and Present 33
5. "Reliability Criteria:" Are Isotopic Systems Truly Self-Checking? 37
   A. "Self-Checking:" Proved or Assumed? 37
   B. Credible/Non-Credible Dates: A Real or Contrived Dichotomy? 42
   C. Arguments Based on Consistency and Concordance of Dating Results 49
   D. "Mutually Corroborated" Biostratigraphic, Magnetostratigraphic, and Geochronometric Systems 54
   E. Do High "Closure Temperatures" Accredit Prolonged Closed Systems? 57
6. Isochron Methods (Rb-Sr, Sm-Nd, Lu-Hf, Re-Os, Pb-Pb, and Some K-Ar) 61
   A. Analytic Data and the Collinearity of Points on Isochron Plots 61
   B. The "Inherent Geologic Reliability" of Isochron Dates 65
   C. "Distinctions" Between "True" and Non-Chronometric Isochrons 70
7. The $^{40}Ar/^{39}Ar$ Method and its Imagined Diagnostic Properties 73
8. Single-Grain U-Pb Dating of Zircons 81
9. How Often do Dating Methods Agree by Chance? An Exploratory Study 87
10. Future Research 93
11. Conclusion 95
    References 97
    Study Questions 109
    Index 113

This work is dedicated to the memory of Robert Witter who, while in the process of researching isotopic dating in graduate school and courageously writing about its fatal flaws, was forced to endure open discrimination for doing so. May his rewards in Heaven be great.

Foreword

My friend John Woodmorappe has a wonderful God-given talent for exhaustive literature research in almost any given scientific field, combined with in-depth probing and insightful (and critical) analysis of the data sifted from that research. His two previous monographs (*Studies in Flood Geology* and *Noah's Ark: A Feasibility Study*) have already been invaluable contributions to the rapidly evolving (pardon the expression!) paradigm of scientific Biblical creationism.

The evolutionist paradigm (or worldview, if preferred) is steadily disintegrating. Not only is it Biblically indefensible for Christians, but also its scientific foundations have been almost fatally eroded. No real organic evolution has ever been observed during the period of human history and no true evolutionary transitional forms have ever been found among the billions of fossils from the past. The evidence of design is overwhelming in even the simplest living organism: the laws of probability and thermodynamics seem to make macro-evolution not only non-existent but also not possible. The evidence of creative design seems (to us, at least) to be overwhelming.

The only remaining argument that seems to make evolution appear feasible is the alleged immense age of the earth and the cosmos. That immense age, as far as the earth is concerned, is based almost entirely on the evidence from the radioactive decay of certain minerals in its crust. These are widely claimed by evolutionary geologists and others to yield "absolute" ages for various rocks and even for the earth itself—now said to be about 4.6 billion years old.

Now, if the earth really is that old, we Christians are really in a bind. There is not even a hint of such long ages in the teachings of Christ or anywhere else in the Bible, which has always been the basis of our Christian faith. The Bible very clearly teaches that all things (including man) were created and made in six days several thousand years ago, (*days*, not ages!—see Genesis 1; Exodus 20:8-11; Mark 10:6; etc.). It also teaches, clearly and unequivocally, that a worldwide cataclysmic deluge devastated the entire planet as a result of divine judgment on the demonic wickedness and violence of those first generations (Genesis 6:13; 7:17-23; Matthew 24:37-39; II Peter 3:3-6; etc.). There is no room at all for 4.6 billion years of geologic ages in the Biblical worldview, assuming that the Bible (God's written Word) means what it says.

Nevertheless, anti-creationists (both ancient pantheists and modern naturalists) have always maintained that the earth is almost infinitely old. The evolutionary worldview in its modern form is built around a series of long geological eras and periods, which supposedly are identified by the remains of multi-billions of dead animals now preserved as fossils in the sedimentary rocks formed in those periods. In this scenario, the fossils speak of animals that lived and died long ages before man ever evolved from his animal ancestry.

But this concept also negates the Biblical revelation of earth history. The Bible teaches that suffering and death entered the world only when human sin brought God's curse on man and his dominion (Genesis 3:17-19; Romans 5:12-21; 8:20-22; I Corinthians 15:21-22; etc.). The fossil record, therefore, instead of recording the evolutionary development of life over many ages, must be reminding us primarily of the cataclysmic destruction of life in one age, the age of the great deluge and its after-effects. Even apart from the Biblical record of *true* history, the very idea of a "god" who would "create" by a billion-year process of struggle and death, natural selection and survival of the fittest, extermination of the weak and unfortunate, is untenable to the Christian—or to anyone else who believes in an omnipotent, omniscient, purposeful, loving God who created and controls the world. Thus, the idea of long geological ages not only supports belief in evolution but also atheism and/or pantheism.

But geologists and their evolutionary colleagues insist that radiometric dating of the minerals in the rocks has proved irrefutably that these rocks are millions and billions of years old and, therefore, that we must (they say) believe in the geologic ages and their record of evolution.

There are, of course, many weaknesses in this argument, scientifically as well as Biblically and theologically, and these have been developed in many books and papers by creationist scientists in recent decades. But there is no question that the argument from the decay of radioactive isotopes still remains the main "proof" of the great ages of geology. Creationists, therefore, need to show, finally and unequivocally, that this argument proves no such thing.

That is what Woodmorappe has done in this monograph. He has demonstrated that the various assumptions on which radioactive dating techniques are based are all wrong, and he has done this masterfully and overwhelmingly—by citations (almost 500 separate articles) from evolutionists who specialize in this field, not from other creationists who already agree with his worldview.

He has entitled this study *The Mythology of Modern Dating Methods*, and has structured it around the many assumptions which he calls "myths"—and what he then calls "reality checks," which document the fact that they really are mythical and not real. He does this so thoroughly that the term "overkill" almost comes to mind!

The monograph is quite technical and is not easy to read, although its interesting "myth/reality check? structure makes it about as easy to follow as possible with such a subject. He assumes the reader will come to it with at least some knowledge of the terminology and techniques of radiometric dating in order to be able to follow the devastating critiques of these techniques and the assumptions on which they are based. Any evolutionist or progressive creationist who has been assuming that isotopic dating has proved the long-age scenario owes it to himself (and those whom he influences) to read carefully Woodmorappe's monograph (and refute it if he can), before continuing with his belief and advocacy of the old-earth scenario.

John Woodmorappe is very positive (and sometimes rather abrasive—though never as abrasive as evolutionists are when they attack creationists) in his strong rejection of all these isotopic dating methods. Yet the more one absorbs the significance of his copiously documented arguments, the more he will agree with his strong denunciations of evolutionary uniformitarians and compromising evangelicals. His language is not intemperate at all in view of the importance of the subject and the overwhelming evidence he amasses against the validity of radiometric dating.

He has, in this monograph, rendered a valuable service to the Christian and the cause of truth, and I believe God will honor and use it to that end.

Henry M. Morris, President Emeritus
Institute for Creation Research

Introduction

Isotopic (radiometric) dating is the cornerstone of the uniformitarian belief that the earth is very old. There seems to be no end to the dogmatic claims which are incessantly repeated in favor of these dating methods. Both the humanists and their compromising, evangelical devotees have, with no small amount of intellectual arrogance, attempted to hammer home the absolute factuality of the dates derived from these methods—all the while ignoring and belittling the fatal flaws inherent in them.

The present author did an extensive critique of isotopic dating, and this study was published in the September 1979 issue of the *Creation Research Society Quarterly*, and then reprinted in my 1993 (and 1999, 2nd edition) book *Studies in Flood Geology*. While scientific creationists have done individual studies on the isotopic dating methods in recent years, no one has performed an overall review of isotopic dating. This particular book accomplishes just that, while offering a broad-based, yet incisive, rebuttal to the status of these presumed geochronometers.

Much has changed in isotopic dating in the last 20 years, but, as shown throughout this book, these "advances" actually serve to highlight the invalidity of these dating methods. In addition, a wealth of silly arguments have been advanced by apologists for isotopic dating. I address the various bogus claims based on the alleged rarity of discrepant dates, the imagined self-checking properties of these dating methods, the supposed discrediting of the Gospel by questioning the old earth, ostensible "conspiracies" to fabricate agreement on "good" dates, alleged "younging up"

trends in isotopic dates, alleged mutual corroboration of biostratigraphic/magnetostratigraphic/isotopic-dating information, concordances between different dating methods, and much more. I also delve into the question of the measurements of decay constants, the alleged convergence of dating results at 4.5 billion years for the age of the earth, and the questionable significance of extinct radioactivity.

There are now several isochron-based methods of isotopic dating in widespread use. Because of the fact that the principles (and fallacies) of the isochron-based methods are essentially the same, I discuss all of these methods in a single chapter. This includes an exposé of some little-known fatal flaws pertinent to all of these methods.

The Ar-Ar method has been widely touted for its presumed ability to distinguish valid vs. invalid dates by analytic criteria alone. I devote an entire chapter demonstrating how widespread acceptance of this method has actually forced its users to abandon such rosy claims. Likewise, the U-Pb method has been revolutionized by the dating of individual zircon grains, inadvertently betraying the composite "ages" of most zircons.

Finally, I tackle the question of how often results of different dating methods can agree by chance. A variety of simple analyses using random numbers clearly shows that fortuitous concordances are not at all unlikely.

A comprehensive index provides the reader with extensive cross references to miscellaneous geologic topics.

Acknowledgments

I wish to thank Dr. Andrew Snelling and Dr. Donald DeYoung for reviewing the manuscript, and Dr. Steven Austin and Marvin Ross for finalizing the art cover (and the latter for artwork). For editoral work, I am indebted to Mrs. Mary Smith, daughter of Dr. Henry M. Morris. I also thank Kristopher Schmitt, grandson of Dr. Henry M. Morris, for drafting the figures in the text.

Chapter 1

Rebuttal to Critics' Misrepresentations of my Previous Work

Although many of the early dates cited in my earlier paper (Woodmorappe, 1979, 1993) have been superceded by more recent ones, there should be no concern about the bulk of the data being outdated in any substantive sense of the word:

> An individual K-Ar date can only rarely be considered to have a gross precision greater than about 3% when it is compared to dates by other methods and from other laboratories. The analytical methods and precision of conventional K-Ar dates have been only slightly refined since the mid 1950's, so *the vintage of a date is rarely of concern* in its use for time scale calibration (Harland *et al.* 1990, p. 76) [emphasis added].

What of the reactions of uniformitarians to my previous work? Most critics have an obviously very superficial understanding of it (if that). They often characterize it by stereotypes such as "Woodmorappe's list of bad dates." In fact, I also had spent a fair amount of time discussing "good" dates, reliability criteria, and concordance—all of which have been conveniently ignored by the critics. Worse yet, there are many cases where I have been accused of being unaware of something when I had discussed *that very thing* in my previous paper (for examples, see Woodmorappe 1985).

Not surprisingly, apologists for isotopic dating have tried to belittle the fatal flaws of isotopic dating by trying to spin them as "merely a few malfunctioning watches" or "merely a few rotten apples." Consider the following, for example:

> In fact, the number of "wrong" ages amounts to only a few percent of the total, and nearly all of these are due to unrecognized geologic factors, to unintentional misapplication of the techniques, or to technical difficulties (Dalrymple 1984, p. 76).

One wonders, first of all, if "unrecognized geologic factors" do in fact exist, how is one supposed to *know* that they exist? What sorts of powers of omniscience are being arrogated? Or, more seriously, what egregious circular reasoning is being employed?

And what of the "few percent" claim? Based on the literature searches that I have conducted, discussions with geology professors who have used isotopic dating, etc., I find Dalrymple's claim totally fantastic. In fact, I have never read anyone other than Dalrymple make a comparable claim in any of the thousands of scientific articles that I have read on isotopic dating. If Dalrymple can produce a published study in some scientific journal that makes and documents his claim, I would love to see it. He does not, however, cite any study or studies to back up his assertion. Until such a study is forthcoming, and adequately proves such a high rate of dating success on a variety of commonly-used dating materials and in a variety of geologic environments, I think that we best reckon Dalrymple's claim on par with statements by other anti-creationists (who say one thing in the professional literature and another in anti-creationist writings). I am not alone in this conclusion. Richard Milton, a British science journalist and amateur geologist who is neither a creationist nor a religious believer, expresses the following opinion:

> Dalrymple's writings are often strong on rhetoric but weak on scientific fact (Milton 1997, p. 264).

In a chapter of this new paper, I present several lines of direct and indirect evidence which make it all but impossible to accept any argument that suggests that discrepant results amount to only a tiny fraction of all dating results. I also cite a number of qualified geochronologists who openly contradict Dalrymple's "few percent" claim and candidly acknowledge the considerable frequency of discrepancies in isotopic dating. In fact, if anything, it appears that it is closer to the truth to consider the "good" results to be the ones which amount to only a small percentage of all results!

Sounding as if they had just discovered the world, some critics have suggested that a systematic study be done of the relative numbers of "good" and "bad" dates. The trouble with this intellectual-sounding suggestion is this: I *had already considered* such an approach in the opening paragraphs of my 1979 paper, showing that it is unworkable because most discrepant results are not published. I also made it clear, by a citation, that most isotopic-dating work is done on a "non-experimental, nonstatistical basis." In fact, as anyone with even a cursory familiarity with geologic literature is aware, very little isotopic-dating work is experimental in nature. The vast majority of dating results is simply interpreted on a posterioritic basis in the context of the local geology (and uniformitarian presuppositions, of course).

Apologists for isotopic dating have also tried to convince us that there are objective criteria which guarantee the reliability of the dates they obtain. As shown in the previous paper, and in more detail in this one, this self-serving claim is no more correct than the one about the existence of only a "few percent" discrepant results. Unfortunately, however, whatever it is that the apologists for isotopic dating have to say, compromising evangelicals will swallow it hook, line, and sinker. Then again, this is far from the only way that compromising evangelicals have shown themselves to be no less steeped in rationalism than the card-carrying atheistic humanists.

There is no point in responding to every single paper that has been written to try to obfuscate the findings of my previous paper. After all, these papers are all clones of Dalrymple (1984). Most of the objections are either trivial or simply wrong, as discussed elsewhere (Woodmorappe 1985). As a further example of this, Dalrymple (1984, p. 78) complains that I had not mentioned the fact that an anomalous result by K-Ar dating had given the "correct" date by $^{39}Ar/^{40}Ar$. I had, in fact, discussed the $^{39}Ar/^{40}Ar$ method in my 1979 paper, and concluded that it was flawed. In the twenty years since, much more evidence has surfaced to substantiate this fact, as is discussed in a chapter below. That was and is the reason for my lack of regard for the method.

As to Dalrymple's (1984, pp. 77-78) argument about the excellence of most of Evernden's glauconite-dating results, there is more to this than has already been discussed (Woodmorappe 1985). The trend of depth-burial discussed by Evernden has been vitiated by other evidence (Odin 1982, pp. 310-311). It is now recognized that there is no regularly-discernable cause for the "rejuvenation" of glauconites—whether solely by depth of burial, tectonic action, or thermodynamic effects (Odin 1982, p. 311; Morton and Long 1984, p. 505).

On the Internet, some anti-creationists have tried to embellish Dalrymple's original argument by accusing me of being deceptive in citing "experimental" dates done on a now-discredited material (glauconite). Such insinuations only show how little the critics know what they are talking about. While it is true that some geochronologists (e. g., Obradovich 1988, 1993) consider dates on glauconite inherently unreliable, there are others (Amireh *et al.* 1998; Craig *et al.* 1989; Gradstein *et al.* 1994, 1995; Haq *et al.* 1988; Smith *et al.* 1998; and many others) who to this very date still use glauconite dates for time-scale calibration if the results agree with other "reliable" values. Thus, when it comes to the isotopic dating of glauconites, we are at very much the same place where we were 30-40 years ago. Some geochronologists accept them as potentially reliable if certain reliability criteria are met; others don't.

Both Dalrymple (1984, p. 78-79) and those who parrot him have made much of the fact that the points defining a 3.2 Ga date, from the Pahrump diabase, do not define a statistically-valid isochron. In fact, if the samples do not closely line up to form a statistically-valid isochron, geochronologists can draw a reference isochron to show an overall trend of the points (for example, see figure 6 in Barovich and Patchett 1992, p. 390). And, of course, if it fits with their ideas, they accept its chronometric validity:

> As the reference age A is within the known age range for members of the Gamsberg Granite suite (see above), it possibly represents a reset age induced by the intrusion of Gamsberg magmas in the area (Ziegler and Stoessel 1993, p. 48).

So, for Dalrymple to object to my use of the reference line for a Rb-Sr age of 3.2 or 3.4 Ga is to object to something widely used by his fellow uniformitarians, who freely use reference lines whenever the "ages" agree with their ideas. So what is so terrible about me using it when the result most certainly does not agree with uniformitarian ideas? Of course, this whole discussion is rather pointless in view of the many other dates that have been found which exceed the agreed-upon 4.5 Ga age of the earth, and which in no sense depend upon reference isochrons. Several new examples of "older than Earth" results are provided in this paper.

Some of the criticisms of my previous paper are nothing short of laughable. For instance, Arthur N. Strahler (1987) has written a widely-quoted anti-creationist geology book. Apart from being replete with uniformitarian dogmas masquerading as facts (for some examples, see Snelling and Woodmorappe 1998), Strahler's tome contains statements that have no semblance of reality. For instance, this is what he would have his readers believe about the content of my previous paper:

> Generally, the description of the incident offered by Woodmorappe turns out to be a misrepresentation or misstatement of what the original text actually stated. For example, in the case of a wide range in radiometric ages of "Hawaiian" basalts, it turns out that the deviating ages were from basalt samples on other islands of the Hawaiian chain (Strahler 1987, pp. 135-136).

The upshot of Strahler's complaint is this: *A discussion of Hawaiian basalts, and their dates, exists **nowhere** in my 1979 paper!* If Strahler is genuinely concerned about those who propound misrepresentations and misstatements of quoted authors, he would do well to look himself in the mirror.

Enough said. I think it is more productive to examine the styles of argumentation used by the critics rather than jump at every single trivial argument. Indeed, the fallacious reasoning used by apologists for isotopic dating boils down into three central fallacies. The first one is **CDMBN** [Credit **D**ating **M**ethods (for ostensible successes); **B**lame **N**ature (for failures)]. Heads, I win; tails, you lose. This exempts isotopic dating itself from rational criticism (i. e., the dating method is never wrong—only the initial conditions have not been met) and protects it from falsification (figure 1).

Figure 1: Because "open systems" are freely invoked on an *ad hoc* basis, no observation can ever count as evidence against the validity of isotopic dating. The wheel of evidence is thus allowed to turn only in a direction favorable to the claims of isotopic dating.

The second fallacy is the **ATM** (Appeal To Marginalization) fallacy. It attempts to belittle the significance of contrary evidence by spinning it as rare and/or occurring only under limited geologic circumstances. A classic use of the **ATM** is the oft-repeated false claim about "a few malfunctioning watches." A more subtle use of it, however, involves the reluctance or refusal to acknowledge the broad implications of a discrepancy. For instance, an apologist for isotopic dating might try to marginalize a given dating discrepancy by asserting that it is a problem only in ultramafic intrusives. Soon, however, he has to backpedal and say that it is a problem in only ultramafic intrusives as well as mafic intrusives. Failing that, he backpedals once again and admits that it is a problem only in ultramafic intrusives, mafic intrusives, and mafic extrusives. With each cycle of special pleading, the "only" becomes less and less meaningful, and the attempt to marginalize the problem becomes more and more vacuous. The uniformitarian geochronologist, of course, will never admit that his method itself has failed. A classic example of the use of the **ATM** fallacy involves the attempts to minimize the significance of excess argon. As described by Dickin (1997, p. 248-249), excess argon was first marginalized by being thought of as a potential problem only in exotic minerals such as beryl. To these, the following were successively added: pyroxenes, subaqueus lavas, then subaerial lavas. All of a sudden, a marginal problem turned out to be not so marginal after all.

Owing to the fact that isotopic dating, in its geologic context, is highly interpretative (a fact which itself is testimony to its frequent recalcitrance as an indicator of the age of the rock), this can only facilitate the usage of the **ATM** and **CDMBN** fallacies. The rationalizations can always be covered with geologic interpretations, as is obvious from the following:

> In conclusion, it should be noted that dating with nuclear methods, though rather simple in principle and really quantitative, may give data which are extremely difficult to interpret, in particular when the geologic

history is long and multi-staged. But, as a consequence, this complexity may give many useful data on heritage and the succession of thermal phenomena. Obtaining not only one age, which is too often what the geologist is asking for, but a sequence of values, interpretable sometimes in a rock or region, is in the end very attractive for the geologist (Poty 1989, p. 40).

A third fallacy is the **ATT** (Appeal To Technicalities) fallacy. An unwelcome date is rejected, and its rejection is excused on some technicality, usually an after-the-fact one. For instance, one might learn that a given discrepancy was expected because the host rock showed traces of alteration. Yet, since almost *all* rocks show some alteration (Harland 1990), there would be almost no rocks left to date if the hidden premise behind this fallacy was taken to its logical conclusion. Furthermore, as we shall see, uniformitarians have no problem accepting results from slightly-altered (and often from more-than-slightly-altered) rock so long as it agrees with their ideas. Thanks to widespread use of the **ATT** fallacy, all isotopic dates are trial balloons, to be accepted or to be rejected and rationalized, at will. Williams (1992) has provided an excellent review of this type of posterioritic reasoning which is endemic to uniformitarian historical geology in general and isotopic dating in particular.

"But wait a minute!" says the uniformitarian, "Even if some (or even most) dates are questionable, there are other dates which are reasonable. Therefore, they must be believed, and so the earth's rocks must necessarily be measured in the millions to billions of years." Let us examine the fallacies of this reasoning by substituting dreams for isotopic dates. "Even if some (or most) dreams fail to predict the future, some of them appear to do so. Therefore, dreaming is a valid means of ascertaining the future at least some of the time." Obviously, this is contrary to scientific reasoning. Dreaming is not accepted as a valid means of predicting the future just because it appears to "work" sometimes. To the contrary: the fact that most dreams don't come true leads scientists to the conclusion that those which do "come true" are either of psychogenic origin, or are coincidences (e. g., Martin 1998). So it is with isotopic dating. Just because some of them appear to "work," or even coincide with uniformitarians' predictions, does not validate them. Were skeptics to apply the same standards of their investigation and reasoning to isotopic dating as they do to evaluating dreams, astrology, clairvoyance, etc., they would have recommended the discarding of isotopic-dating methods a long time ago.

There are those who insist that criticism of isotopic-dating methods is "being negative." To the contrary: the criticism of hypotheses and methodologies is a major part of science. Criticism is positive because it advances scientific knowledge. This is as true for the Bible-believing scientist as well as for the uniformitarian one. Finally, I also include, in this work, a "strictly positive" chapter—one which demonstrates that fortuitous concordances between results of different dating methods should be fairly common.

Chapter 2

Overview of this New Book

The topic in question is most commonly called isotopic dating, although some geologists use radiometric dating (e. g., Dickin 1988), or simply radiometry (Gradstein 1985, p. 18). In this book, special emphasis is devoted to those dating methods which have come into fairly widespread use in the last 20 years. These include the FT (fission track), Sm-Nd (samarium-neodymium), and Lu-Hf (lutetium-hafnium) methods. A special chapter each is devoted to the rise and fall of the ^{39}Ar/^{40}Ar method, as well as the consequences of single-grain dating of zircons (and related minerals) by the U-Pb method. Other chapters expose the fallacious, propagandistic claims of apologists for isotopic dating. In particular, I demonstrate the fact that isotopic dating methods are not self-checking, nor are discrepancies in any way limited to just a few "malfunctioning watches," as claimed by Dalrymple (1984, p. 76).

Before going any further, I would first like to dispose of some commonly-repeated anti-creationist misconceptions:

Myth: Questioning of such things as isotopic dating and the old earth brings discredit to the Christian faith, and hinders others from accepting the Gospel.

Reality Check: This baseless canard is constantly repeated by compromising evangelicals. But at least they are in good company, as this transparently bogus argument has been repeated by the compromising evangelicals of yore for well over a century. In actuality, compromise with the uniformitarian old-age system has the *precise opposite* effect of keeping the Gospel credible, as noted long ago by William Robert Gordon. He described how unbelievers *actually* react to such compromise:

> Moreover, they are greatly encouraged in their hope of success by the writings of certain Christian geologists, who having adopted their theory of the vast age of the earth, have attempted to force the cosmogony of Moses into harmony with it. Such efforts have not only failed, but have yielded all that infidelity cares to ask for the logical subversion of the Scriptures as the inspired Word of God given to man as his only rule of faith and practice. This advantage bestowed upon modern infidelity was by no means meant; on the contrary, it was intended to take away the infidel's objection to the Bible, aris-

ing from his theoretical geology. But it has had the contrary effect, and elicited his contempt instead of his admiration, while he rejoices in the concessions made (Gordon 1878, p. 7).

So the more things change, the more they remain the same. Unbelievers today are not at all impressed by the Scripture-twisting antics of the compromising evangelicals, any more than their 19th-century counterparts had been. And, when one looks at virulent anti-creationist writings, one does not see a flock of converts as a result of the forcing of Scripture to conform to old-age beliefs. To the contrary: All one finds is the exploitation of compromising evangelicals as weapons against true Bible believers, just as had been the case 120 years ago. Thus, then and now, both modernists and compromising evangelicals serve as useful tools of the humanists. *That* is the consequence of currying favor with the humanists and their ideas.

Finally, the canard about the young earth being a stumbling block to acceptance of the Gospel is soundly refuted by the many testimonies of individuals (including scientists) who have been won to the Lord as a result of creation evangelism. Ken Ham (1998) has published many such testimonies. He also tells of many others who would not accept the Gospel until the compromising-evangelical distortions of the Bible (e. g., old-earth beliefs) had been dispelled in their minds, thus allowing them to take the Bible's authority seriously for the first time.

Myth: Scientific creationists are obligated to explain isotopic dating methods before anyone can begin to seriously doubt the validity of these methods.

Reality Check: Creationists are under no such obligation, for the simple reason that the burden of proof is on the uniformitarian and not the creationist. This stems from the fact that it is not creationists who are trying to have it taught as fact that the earth is young: It is uniformitarians who are dogmatically claiming that the great antiquity of the earth is virtually proven fact, and doing it with no small amount of intellectual arrogance. As a result, it is the uniformitarians, not the scientific creationists, who have placed themselves at the mercy of the highest standards of evidence. This fact only serves to magnify the significance of all of the flaws of isotopic dating. Therefore, creationists can point out the fatal flaws

	Evidentiary Considerations		Socio-Political Considerations				Theological Considerations
	Rigorously tested for overall validity?	Dogmatic claims of factuality?	Scientific criticisms discouraged by "ruling theory" mentality?	Research funded by public monies?	Promoted by mass media?	Taught to unsuspecting children in schools?	Conflict with Scripture?
Long-Age Dating Methods	No	Yes	Yes	Yes	Yes	Yes	Yes
Young-Earth Position	In progress	No	No	No	No	No	No

Table 1. Because of their unjustified dominant position in science and society, isotopic dating methods deserve the highest level of scrutiny, and the critic of these methods does not "have" to provide an alternative.

of these dating methods without being under any sort of "obligation" to propose and defend alternative theories of their own.

Of course, scientific creationists can and should develop alternative theories for isotopic systems—not due to some sort of mythical obligation to uniformitarians, but as a matter of their own scientific curiosity. In fact, research efforts are now underway to understand isotopic systems in the light of the creationist-diluvialist paradigm (Vardiman 1997, 1998, Austin and Snelling 1998, etc.). The present author is of the opinion that all avenues of understanding (particularly geochemical ones) should be investigated. It should not be assumed that a drastic increase in radioactive decay rates is the only viable route to understanding these isotopic systems in the light of the young earth. I analyze the likelihood of fortuitous concordances in a later chapter.

Myth: Criticism of isotopic dating by Woodmorappe involves intemperate language.

Reality Check: If evolutionists and uniformitarians want respect from me, let them first show some respect to the creationist position. And to those that do, I return the respect. To the extent that I had gone too far in what I had said, there had been a good reason for it. Recall the words of the immortal Martin Luther:

> I cannot deny that I am more vehement than I should be. . . . But they assail me and God's Word so atrociously and criminally that . . . these monsters are pushing me beyond the bounds of moderation (Gritsch 1993, p. 35).

Moreover, if my critics are interested in *really* intemperate language, they need look no further than their own ilk. This includes vile and scurrilous anti-religious bigotry exhibited in infidel tabloids. (For example, *Free Inquiry*, which I had—no kidding—begun to write as *Free Iniquity* (Whether or not this was a Freudian slip, I do not know). The summer 1993 issue (Volume 13, No. 3) contains the article: "Is religion a form of mental illness?") Now imagine the outcry in the liberal media if some Christian publication had the following article: "Is atheism a form of mental illness?" We believers would get another stern lecture on tolerance.

More subtle forms of bigotry also occur in respectable professional publications such as the *American Biology Teacher* and the *Journal of Geoscience Education*. These include transparently abusive remarks such as: "Creationism rears its ugly head," etc. Why all this innuendo? Simple. Some individuals just cannot face reality and come to terms with the fact that many intelligent believers have dared to question the sacred cows of rationalism (not the least of which is the great antiquity of the earth). Since this is just too much for some rationalists to bear, they must resort to the denigration of the intellectual capabilities of those who disagree with them.

Myth: Bad dates are dates that geologists would never use.

Fact: A half-truth. Obviously, absurd dates are rejected out of hand, and no geologist would think of using them. But so are many "reasonable" ones. That is, many "reasonable" dates are *accepted* as valid by uniformitarians—until they fall out of favor for reasons extraneous to the dates themselves [as discussed elsewhere (Woodmorappe, 1979, 1993), and throughout this work]. Finally, the multitude of rejected dates, be they absurd or "reasonable," never-accepted or once-accepted, can only deprive the remaining accepted dates of credibility.

Chapter 3

Bogus Arguments for the Overall Validity of Isotopic Dating Methods

A. Geologic Implications of Dating Results

Myth: As analytical tools improve, the validity of isotopic dating is strengthened.

Fact: From a strictly analytic point of view, this is not the case. Consider K-Ar dating, and the significance of the nonradiogenic argon correction (which is the most important source of error):

> Errors in many single analyses reported in the past have been based on theoretical equations and commonly have been optimistically small (Tabor *et al.* 1985, p. 1).

Moreover, Fleck *et al.* (1996b) have demonstrated that there exists a measurable bias between different laboratories which perform K-Ar dating. This especially aggravates the problems of dating rocks with a large nonradiogenic argon correction and ostensibly-young rocks:

> Young basaltic rocks are among the most difficult for K-Ar age dating, often resulting in greater dispersion in the analytical results than associated with

older rocks with higher K_2O (Fleck *et al.* 1996b, p. 205).

Of course, the foregoing discussion concerns analytic matters only. When it comes to geological interpretations, the need for rationalizations to cope with unwanted results has not diminished as dates have become more and more precise. To the contrary: new layers of rationalizations have had to be invented even as single grains of minerals have themselves become datable. This fact is discussed in the section on $^{40}Ar/^{39}Ar$ dating, as well as the U-Pb dating of individual zircon grains. In addition, let us consider the state of the Phanerozoic time scale:

> The past decade has seen tremendous advances in the ability of the geochronological community to produce very precise and accurate (analytically speaking) radiometric ages for minerals and whole-rock systems. Yet a perusal of the numerous time scales proposed solely during the last decade clearly reveals that, despite the great advances in geochronometry and the increased data base, there is still not a single time scale that is universally accepted. Interlab bias

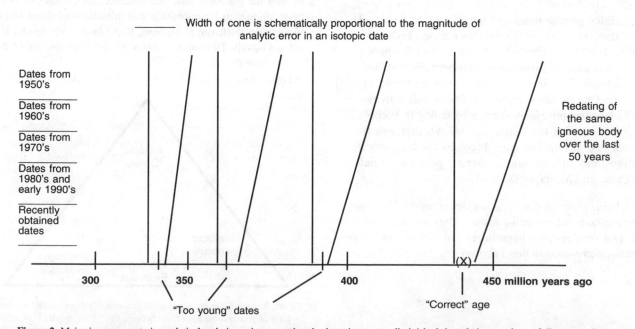

Width of cone is schematically proportional to the magnitude of analytic error in an isotopic date

Dates from 1950's

Dates from 1960's

Dates from 1970's

Dates from 1980's and early 1990's

Recently obtained dates

Redating of the same igneous body over the last 50 years

300   350   400   450 million years ago

"Too young" dates   "Correct" age

(X)

Figure 2. Major improvements in analytical techniques in recent decades have in no way diminished the relative numbers of discrepant dates.

and subtle but unrecognized open system behavior of the various chronometers can be cited as two of the numerous reasons. It is well to remember that analytic precision and accuracy need not be synonymous with geologic accuracy (Obradovich 1984, p. 11).

Myth: Uniformitarian geochronology rests upon rigorous, objective methodology.

Reality Check: A case can be made for the opposite conclusion:

> Subjective and, in many instances, incorrect use of radiometric data has become endemic in the earth science literature. Mathematical analysis of imperfect and, in many cases, highly subjective data sets leads to dubious conclusions (Baksi 1990, p. 985).

> Subjective influences on a scientist are clearly exposed when evaluating an experiment design and deciding which parameters are constant and which are variable. Because of the extreme challenge of geological time, geologists are often confronted with more ambiguous scenarios than the norm, amplifying the contribution of personal taste or philosophy. . . . It can be surprising how different are the approaches of geochronologists to essentially identical problems, and not surprising that many misunderstandings arise as a result (Harrison 1990, p. 227).

Myth: Isotopic geochronology leads to testable hypotheses.

Reality Check: Let us take a closer look at an example of what is actually meant by testable hypotheses:

> Major geochronological hypotheses to be tested by these samples are (1) whether plutonic bodies are coeval with the exposed volcanic rocks, (2) whether a resolvable age difference exists between previously hypothesized intrusive events (e. g., gabbroic, intermediate anorthositic, and later troctolitic activity), (3) whether intrusions show a tendency to become young towards the south, and (4) whether significant age differences exist between the hypabyssal dikes and sills versus the deeper plutonic bodies (Paces and Miller 1993, p. 14,001).

Note what is tested and what is not being tested. The isotopic dating methods are not being tested. They are *assumed* to be valid, and the "testable hypotheses" in uniformitarian geochronology *presuppose* this validity.

Myth: All discrepant isotopic results have a rational geologic explanation that corresponds closely with the known geology of the region.

Reality Check: The first part of the premise is partly correct, but meaningless. *Any* unwanted result can be explained away, *at will*, on an after-the-fact basis. The second part of the premise is very questionable. As noted in the previous papers (Woodmorappe 1979, 1993) and this book, geologically-based rationalizations for discrepant results are used inconsistently by uniformitarians. That is, they are prone to accept dates which agree with their ideas *in spite of* showing clear geologic evidences of potential open-system behavior:

> In conclusion we note that, although collected in tectonically disturbed series and very poor in K, the two biotites from the Woodbury Quarry appear to give coherent results. From these results it may be concluded that the base of the Ludlovian is older than 420 Ma (Odin *et al.* 1986, p. 131).

No doubt if the results had turned out to be unacceptable for this trial balloon, the low K-content and tectonically-disturbed environment would have been immediately appealed to as a legitimization for the rejection of the results. Heads, I win; tails, you lose.

In other instances (e.g., Bingen, Demaiffe, and van Breemen 1998), inferred geologic events (metamorphic overprints, rifting and creation of new oceans) fail to "register" on the dated samples.

More to the point, there are also cases where isotopic results are accepted as the age of the rock, but the isotopic age is *completely at variance* with previous geologic judgments of its age. In such situations, the geochronometric tail is allowed to wag the geologic dog. For instance, an igneous stock had been mapped as Late Jurassic, and thus dates of about 140 Ma were expected from it. Instead, K-Ar and U-Pb results indicated a Middle Devonian age of around 400 Ma from it (Albers

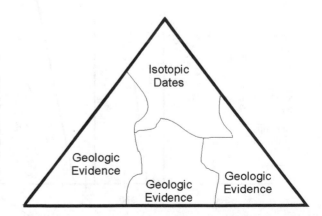

Figure 3. Aren't isotopic dates valid if ostensibly corroborated by several lines of geologic evidence? No, because the "fitting together" of different lines of evidence can always be later discounted if the interpretations change.

et al. 1984). Such instances have apparently been generalized:

> It also is now clear that neither proximity nor similarity in chemistry and (or) mineralogy implies contemporaneity of intrusions. This point is well illustrated by the difference in the ages of the Lincoln Porphyry (64 m. y.) . . . and the petrographically and texturally similar coarse-grained porphyritic quartz monzonite of the Breckenridge district at locality 1, which has an age of about 35 m. y. The latter was correlated with the Lincoln Porphyry by Ransome (1911) and Lovering (1934) (Bryant *et al.* 1981, p. 23).

In another example, two lines of empirical geologic evidence (structure and petrology) had to be overthrown by two interpretive lines of evidence (paleomagnetism and geochronometry). A dike had at one time been assigned to the Tertiary based on the parallelism of its trend to Tertiary mineralized faults, as well as its chemical similarity to Paleocene lava flows. This was until both paleomagnetic and isotopic determinations placed it in the Proterozoic (Braddock and Peterman 1989, p. 97), thus suddenly aging it by a factor of twenty-five. Such contradictions between the field evidence of dike emplacement, and the isotopic dates obtained, have occurred elsewhere (e.g., Scotland), prompting the following generalization:

> They [isotopic dates] demonstrate that caution should be exercised in assuming that all dykes in the same location with similar orientations have identical emplacement ages (Heaman and Tarney 1989), p. 707).

In still another example of the isotopic-dating tail being allowed to wag the geologic dog, several ostensibly independent lines of geologic evidence had to be set aside to accommodate some discrepantly-old U-Pb dates from plutons in the Yucatan Peninsula (Steiner and Walker 1996). A series of intrusives showed contact metamorphic relations with faunally-dated Permo-Carboniferous sediments. A Triassic age for the plutons appeared to be corroborated not only by the age of the intruded sediments, but also by the following lines of evidence: (1) internally-consistent Triassic K-Ar dates, (2) then-believed sequence of folded strata and undeformed pluton, and (3) broad agreement of the ostensibly-Triassic post-tectonic plutons with similar temporal sequence of folding and intrusion seen throughout orogenic belts of Central America (Steiner and Walker 1996, p. 17, 729). Later, however, a series of U-Pb dates indicated a Silurian age for the plutons. This created a major conflict with earlier geologic interpretations:

> The presence of a Late Silurian granite in contact with contact-metamorphosed Pennsylvanian-Permian sedimentary rocks necessitates a reconsideration of the nature of the alteration of the sedimentary rocks at these pluton margins (Steiner and Walker 1996, p. 17,732).

Since the U-Pb results appeared to be reliable to the authors, this could only suggest two possibilities: (1) the contact-metamorphic zone had mistakenly been attributed to the Permo-Carboniferous sedimentary rocks instead of some supposed look-alike Silurian or pre-Silurian strata, or (2) the contact metamorphic zone in the Permo-Carboniferous sedimentary rocks had been mistaken as such by many geologists, and had actually originated from a later hydrothermal event that was unrelated to the intrusion of the Silurian granites. The latter rationalization was adopted, thus overturning what had previously been accepted as several independent lines of geologic evidence.

We thus have examined several situations where isotopic dating results have created unexpected and artificial difficulties for field geologists. Conversely, as if to mock the uniformitarian geochronologist, isotopic results sometimes blur the differences which appear to be very real based on field geology:

> Despite field evidence for two generations, all have an equivalent isotopic age of 89±3 Ma. Moreover, the plutons, though not strictly comagmatic, are sufficiently similar in composition to allow treatment as one magmatic entity (Anderson and Cullers 1990, p. 49).

The following describes an example wherein geologists' predictions of intrusives' heterochroneity had been contradicted, if not falsified, by U-Pb dating results:

> The close fit of these analyses to a single discordia line is surprising given that field relationships show the dykes to be structurally, and therefore temporally, distinct (Ketchum *et al.* 1998, p. 33).

As noted earlier, and contrary to earlier uniformitarian beliefs, no straightforward relationship exists between glauconite-date "rejuvenation" and the timing of tectonic or thermal effects. Ironically, an inferred period of hydrothermal activity has failed to "register" in the form of "reset" glauconite dates (Morton and Long 1984).

What can we conclude from all this? Geologic interpretations are used inconsistently and with their own set of special pleadings. Therefore, it can hardly be claimed that geologic environment provides a coherent basis for the rejection of discrepant isotopic-dating results. For this reason, we should remain utterly unimpressed with the **ATT** (**A**ppeal **T**o **T**echnicality) rationalizations which are presumably based on geologic evidence.

Myth: "Cooling ages" from plutons are accredited by virtue of the fact that they can be contoured and mapped to indicate geologically-realistic intervals of regional uplift.

Reality Check: Since most K-Ar dates from plutons are discrepantly young, this is routinely blamed on the supposed long delay between the crystallization of magmas and the time when they first became cool enough to retain radiogenic argon. The fact that such "cooling ages" can be pigeonholed into the geology of a region, and even used to draw "contours of uplift" or "contours of cooling" for a pluton (such as the Idaho batholith), does not in itself justify the "cooling age" rationalization:

> Scatter in the conventional K-Ar ages had led to much confusion about the actual age of the Idaho batholith and even has been used to *construct elaborate uplift histories that have no basis in geologic reality* (Snee *et al.* 1995, p. 402) [emphasis added].

In addition, this confusion is further evidence that isotopic systems are not in themselves "self-checking" as to their validity, nor is there such a thing as innately "credible" results.

It is misleading to suppose that, even on uniformitarian terms, so-called cooling ages could be rigorously justified. This owes to the fact that, at least over extensive areas, plutons usually cannot be unambiguously assigned a tightly-constrained relative age to begin with:

> In theory, truly igneous bodies, such as granites, should be a particularly reliable data source, firstly because of their obviously intrusive nature, and secondly because they should display the least ambiguous relative age relationships to tectonic and metamorphic features in the country rocks. In practice, this has often not been the case, mainly due to disagreements over the interpretation of field relationships made by different authors at different times (Holdsworth and Strachan 1988, p. 613).

This allows a built-in plasticity for the interpretation of any isotopic dates obtained, and can only weaken the argument that protracted "cooling ages" are justified by strong independent geologic evidence. In fact, at times it seems that geochronologists are virtually jumping through hoops in order to pigeonhole a discordant array of isotopic dates into an ostensibly geologically-reasonable set of "cooling ages." For instance, in one situation, there was a suite of $^{40}Ar/^{39}Ar$ dates at 293 Ma, another one at about 243 Ma, and some FT apatite dates at only 80 Ma (Lux and Gibson 1998). So it was suggested that the oldest dates were crystallization ages, the 243 Ma dates dated the time when the granite was suddenly uplifted and hence its minerals could retain argon, while the 80 Ma ages reflect the time when the protracted residual cooling ended and the FT tracks could be retained in apatite. Similar "gymnastics" involving a veritable "dance" of geographically

and temporally-variable cooling (and even reheating) trends was invoked to ostensibly account for a complex array of discordant results from a single batholith (Premo *et al.* 1998).

Myth: Fission-track (FT) dates that are "too young" can be unambiguously interpreted in terms of annealing caused by heating events.

Fact: Annealing of tracks is routinely used as a rationalization for FT results that are unacceptably young. While such an interpretation can be straightforwardly applied to some geologic situations, this is not the case with others:

> The AFT (apatite fission track) ages are difficult to interpret directly; the wide range of ages indicates different degrees of track annealing. . . . Indeed, thermal modeling of the fission track data cannot distinguish between a thermal history that includes a pre-Cenozoic history and one that assumes complete annealing in the Cenozoic. . . (Willett *et al.* 1997, p. 979, 992).

As always, the uniformitarian geochronologist appeals to the complexity of geologic history whenever he wants to do so, while citing the simplicity of geologic history when the data fits his ideas (that is, the **CDMBN** fallacy). Ironically, this whole process has come full-circle. FT apatite dates are now used to actually *invent* heating events on a purely *ad hoc* basis:

> No previous evidence of such uplift in Northern England has been reported, and the study reported here highlights the unique potential of apatite fission track analysis for the detection of mild thermotectonic events, *often in areas where no other evidence exists* (Green 1986, p. 493) [emphasis added].

In a similar example from the United States, unexpectedly-young (Tertiary-age) FT results were blamed on a hypothesized strong hydrothermal activity during that time. Why not "rejuvenation?" Answer: The nearest Tertiary intrusives were deemed to be too far away (50 km) (Roden 1991, p. 49-50).

A recently developed algorithm for interpreting FT dates likewise must be used in conjunction with uniformitarian premises and interpretations:

> The CRS algorithm is effective in finding the global minimum or optimum fit to the data, although this must be interpreted with caution as considerable variability may be permitted by typical fission track data . . . with the CRS method or any search technique, careful application of prior constants and careful interpretation of the resulting set of solutions is important to maximize the information gained while avoiding over-interpretation (Willett 1997, p. 965).

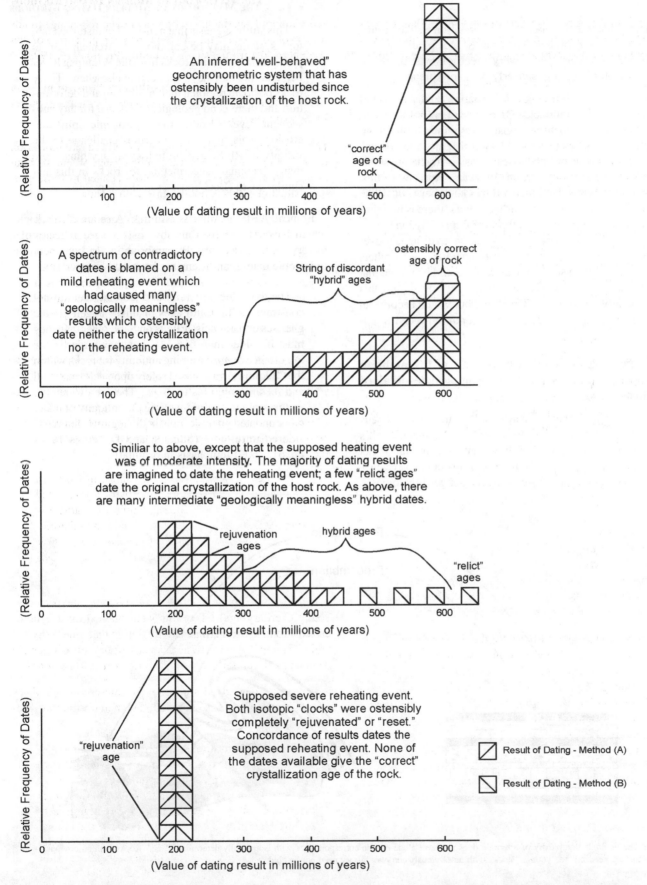

Figure 4: Any conceivable pattern of isotopic dates can be fitted-in *a posteriori* into one of the categories above. In the examples above, the believed crystalliza-tion age is late Precambrian (600 Ma ago) and the believed reheating event took place in the Triassic (200 Ma ago).

Of course, what is and is not over-interpretation is, like beauty, in the eye of the beholder. To someone not predisposed to believe in an old earth, very, very much of what passes as science in isotopic dating is clearly over-interpretation.

There is some intriguing new information on the subject of the annealing of fission tracks. On one hand, as noted earlier, the uniformitarian geochronologist always falls back on annealing as a rationalization for FT dates that are "too young." On the other hand, he must believe that fission tracks are stable enough to last for many millions of years. Apropos to this, there now is evidence (summarized by Gallagher *et al.* 1998, pp. 528-529) that, contrary to earlier beliefs, there is no minimum threshold temperature for the annealing of fission tracks. In fact, some of these tracks are now known to disappear over short periods of time even at room temperature, with others apparently remaining stable. Clearly, if it could be shown that fission tracks cannot last over significant periods of time, this would not only destroy the FT method, but would become an argument for a young earth. More research is needed to understand this.

Myth: The geologic complexity and age of Precambrian terranes excuses the discordance of isotopic dates obtained from them.

Fact: To begin with, the "great age" of Precambrian rock begs the question about the age of the earth and the age of earth's rocks! Secondly, it does not follow that Precambrian rocks have invariably experienced a more complex cumulative geologic history than did ostensibly much younger lithologies:

This study suggests that non-ideal or disturbed isotope systems may be common for Archean syn- to post-tectonic plutonic rocks from the Winnipeg River belt and this may have application elsewhere. These rocks postdate regional metamorphism and deformation and there is no geological evidence for any subsequent "events" other than epirogenic uplift and erosion. This represents a serious challenge to the validity of Rb-Sr geochronology as anything more than a reconnaissance method for rocks in this and similar cases (Beakhouse *et al.* 1988, p. 346).

Ironically, the converse is also true. A series of lithologies which have experienced an obviously severe and complex history need not be early Precambrian in age but, according to isotopic dates, can ostensibly be much younger:

The available structural and isotopic data do not constrain the protolith ages of minor augen granite gneisses or paragneissic units on Sark, other than they must be older than 616 Ma, but they underlie the importance of *not* assuming antiquity for rocks within the Cadomia terrane based solely upon deformational and metamorphic features. . . . The use of gneissic features as a means of invoking the antiquity of many other undated gneissic units in the region is thus considered unreliable (Samson and D'Lemos 1998, pp. 617, 609) [emphasis in original].

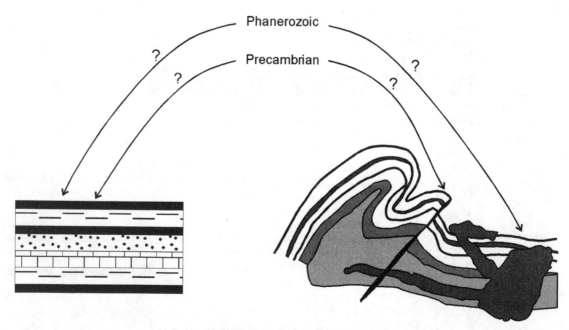

Figure 5: The geologic complexity of a terrane does not have a one-on-one correspondence with isotopically-determined "age." Rocks with an obviously-simple history need not be "young." Rocks with an obviously complex history need not be "old."

B. On "Conspiracies" and Data Manipulation

Myth: The "tight consensus of results" for the Phanerozoic geologic column means that geochronologists would have needed to conspire in order to come up with the agreed-upon arbitrary values.

Hayward (1985), among other apologists for isotopic dating, would have us believe this.

Reality Check: To begin with, talk of a "tight consensus of results" is laughable. Any self-congratulatory claim of "internal consistency" for K-Ar (or *any* method) must come while the apologist for isotopic dating is conveniently glossing over the numerous dates that have been arbitrarily disregarded:

> There is a *minimal* spread of 40 MYBP [Million Years Before Present] for the base of the Permian Period and 20 MY for the top of the Permian, for example, and these figures are only obtained by *omitting, with no objective reason, the much broader deviations* (Waterhouse 1979, p. 499) [first emphasis in original, second one added].

This fact can obviously be generalized:

> Often it is not easy to reconcile different isotopic dates, and many age determinations which do not agree with currently accepted time scales are simply rejected as wrong without our fully understanding why (Paul 1980, p. 184).

The considerable scatter *even in results already selected for ostensible validity* is particularly glaring in certain parts of the geologic column. For instance, currently-accepted dates for the Cambrian-Precambrian boundary span the large range of 530 to 610 million years (Compston *et al.* 1992; Jie-Dong *et al.* 1996). Furthermore, the interesting thing about this range of values is that it has not changed much over an entire century! In 1893, based on inferred sedimentation rates, Reade had suggested that the Cambrian began about 600 Ma ago (Schuchert 1931, p. 21). Similar estimates by others had suggested a range of plausible dates from 550 to 820 Ma (Schuchert 1931, p. 53). What about early isotopic dates? Consider the 1917 time scale by Barrell:

> His version of the Phanerozoic geologic time scale (Holmes' detailed versions were to come later) has stood the test of time—his range of values for Era boundaries include today's best values (Armstrong 1991b, p. 5).

The 1937 time scale of Holmes placed the Cambrian-Precambrian boundary at 470 Ma, and the 1947 version of his scale raised it to 510 Ma [for a tabular comparison of proposed Phanerozoic time scales from 1937 through 1990, see figure 1.5 of Harland *et al.* 1990].

The early dating methods gave results which spanned virtually the entire range of values, applicable to the Precambrian/Cambrian boundary, that had seemed plausible in the light of the old sedimentation-rate studies. This was also true of dating results up to the late 1950's (reviewed by Whitcomb and Morris 1961, pp. 362-366). *To this day*, ostensibly reliable methods (such as the highly-touted U-Pb method on zircons in bentonites), give "dates" for the Precambrian/Cambrian boundary covering a comparably wide range of values (370-600 Ma; studies reviewed by Jie-Dong *et al.* 1996, p. 58), with circa-540 Ma currently favored (Landing *et al.* 1998).

Let us return to the discussion of Reade's 1893 estimate of the base of the Cambrian at 600 million years ago:

> Reade's figures therefore show a rather remarkable agreement with what radioactivity teaches us now [in 1999 no less than in 1931] (Schuchert 1931, p. 21).

They most certainly do. And all the more so when we consider the fact that, as currently recognized, sedimentation rates have little value for dating even short segments of the Phanerozoic (Gale *et al.* 1980, p. 13; Tucker and McKerrow 1995, p. 369; and many others), let alone the *entire alleged time span* of the Phanerozoic. As if to highlight this fact, a comprehensive study of sedimentation rates in modern environments (Sadler and Strauss 1990) shows a large variance in sedimentation rates. The inference of sedimentation rates going back into the past, of course, presupposes the validity of actualism and thus begs the question about the age of the earth.

Yet the inescapable fact is this: values for the duration of Phanerozoic time, some of which go as far back as 1893, show "remarkable agreement" not only with decades-old dates which have long since been discarded (Whitcomb and Morris 1961, p. 335), but also with currently-accepted values. What are we to make of all this? Is this some sort of amazing coincidence, *or have isotopic dates always been "checked" for "correctness," first directly against this sedimentation-rate based column, and then against earlier dates that had been checked against this column?*

There are a number of direct and indirect evidences which indicate that this is in fact the case. Yet in no sense was a conspiracy necessary for this to have occurred. Early time scales (such as that of Holmes in the 1940's) relied upon a small number of dating results checked by, and interpolated against, dates derived from sedimentary thicknesses and sedimentation rates, such as those of Schuchert (1931, and citations). For openly-acknowledged examples of this, see Burchfield (1975, p. 205), Urry (1936) [reprinted in Harper (1973)], and Zeuner (1950, pp. 338-339). The use of "probable values" derived from sedimentation rates was also combined with an obviously-subjective "assessing the most probable age" (Zeuner 1950, p. 328; see also Whitcomb and Morris 1961). We thus can clearly see that, right from the beginning, there has been a "tracking effect" in existence which had arbitrated the acceptance of isotopic dates. With the explosion of K-Ar and Rb-Sr dates in the 1950's, this "tracking effect," or reinforcement syndrome, only became more obvious:

> With Cormier's first Rb-Sr determination on "glauconite" (1956) began the study of authigenic minerals that were enriched in Rb and depleted in Sr. The results were encouraging, as the ages were *reasonable* compared to the suggested time scale (Clauer 1982, p. 245) [emphasis in original].

Another line of evidence for the existence of a "tracking effect" is the fact that some isotopic dates and their stratigraphic placement "corroborated" each other *and* "agreed" with the absolute determinations of the geologic column, despite the fact that *both* the isotopic results and their stratigraphic placement were later shown to be invalid. Consider, for instance, the Crocker Well (Australia) mineral deposit, which once was stratigraphically placed at the Cambrian-Precambrian boundary and from which a "corroborative" U-Pb date of 600 Ma had once been obtained (which is in striking contrast to both the presently-accepted well-before-Cambrian stratigraphic date and its presently-accepted 1.7 Ga U-Pb date):

> Also, uranium minerals (brannerite and davidite) from this area were used for determination of some of the very early isotopic ages, which were for several years considered to be of great importance in assigning the age of the Cambrian-Precambrian boundary. . . . Curiously, these data were used by Holmes (1960) to place limits on the age of the base of the Cambrian, due to a misunderstanding of the actual stratigraphic relationships of nearby Adelaidean tillite. Even more curiously, Holmes' estimate of the base of the Cambrian, based on quite invalid stratigraphic assumptions, has proved to be reasonably accurate (Ludwig and Cooper 1984, pp. 299-300).

Curious indeed. Was this set of simultaneous errors, and its agreement with the currently-accepted circa 600-Ma date for the Precambrian-Cambrian boundary, some sort of an amazing coincidence? Or is the reinforcement syndrome in operation?

While on the subject of the dating of the Cambrian system, it is interesting to note that various forms of data manipulation are evident in other studies. For instance, the contact between a granophyre and the host Lower Cambrian sediments has been reinterpreted from an intrusive one to an unconformable one, instantly reversing the status of "spurious" and "well-founded" U-Pb dates from the igneous body (Cowie and Harland 1989, p. 194). In a recent study, clusters of internally-concordant but contradictory U-Pb zircon dates have been blamed on inheritance, with a miscorrelation within a Cambrian shale and "time transgressive" first-appearance of

trilobites also coming into play as potential rationalizations (Landing *et al.* 1998).

In conclusion, it should be obvious that dating results were and are evaluated based on their "reasonableness" compared with existing time scales, and no "conspiracy of geochronologists acting as cheating schoolboys" (Hayward 1985) had ever been necessary (or is necessary even today) to have created any manner of "consensus of results" for the Phanerozoic Time Scale.

Myth: If isotopic dating methods were false, some sort of a massive conspiracy would have to be in existence to suppress this fact.

Reality Check: A conspiracy is not needed for the simple reason that the peer pressures within geology are sufficient to dissuade and suppress any potential dissent. Particular isotopic dates, and interpretations of them, come and go. But the central belief in their overall validity, and in the validity of the multibillion year age of the earth, is never open to serious re-examination. Any and all discrepant data is simply explained away as part of the very geologic methodology of interpreting isotopic results.

Accuracy often takes a back seat to a consensus-mentality among uniformitarian geochronologists. This makes it all the more unnecessary for a conspiracy to exist in order to discourage the appearance of divergent thinking. The existence of a consensus-mentality, in this case surrounding zeta, the poorly-constrained proportionality constant in FT (fission-track dating), is obvious from the following statements and the attitudes they reveal:

> So what now of the basic calibration of the FT method? The pragmatist might say that the method and its basic calibration, in particular zeta, are working well so why consider anything further? A *plausible argument* is that discussion about alternative calibration strategies *might undermine confidence in the existing calibration and in the method*, at worst returning it to the position of the 1970's. Counter to that, scientific argument would maintain that zeta is comprised of many factors: physical constants, variables which could be determined empirically and other variables which are neither easily defined nor quantified (Hurford 1998, p. 27) [emphasis added].

It goes without saying that, in science, accuracy should always take precedence over pragmatism. Yet, according to the statements above, it may be more important for geochronologists to maintain a consensus-mentality than to re-open questions about their dating methods! With all of this peer pressure, who needs a conspiracy?

To a large extent, the same holds true for other areas of conventional geologic thought, and in areas of study as diverse as plate tectonics, crustal growth, and coastal erosion.

Let us examine and demonstrate how this peer pressure (not some sort of nefarious conspiracy) serves to repress alternative viewpoints within each of these respective areas of study:

> The hard core of belief in plate tectonics is protected from direct assault by auxiliary hypotheses that are still being generated (Saull 1986, p. 536).

> Then as now, peer review can represent the tyranny of the majority. I have run the peer-review gauntlet perhaps a hundred times. My papers describing and interpreting geology in more or less conventional terms have progressed smoothly, whereas publication of my manuscripts challenging accepted concepts has often been impeded, and occasionally blocked (Hamilton 1998, p. 3).

> The idea of steady growth of continental crust survives, as does any myth, by distortion of facts, repetition, and self-citation. Its adherents, who still are a majority of geochemists, are reluctant to abandon cherished concepts they grew up with and have vigorously defended during their education and research careers. . . . It is a dogma that has distorted thinking about the Earth for decades. In science this is an old story, likely to be repeated again, as *the defenders of common wisdom are seldom treated with the same skepticism as the challengers of the status quo.* . . . In science, conventional wisdom is difficult to overturn (Armstrong 1991a, p. 625, 613) [emphasis added].

> Criticism of modeling is usually not well received by modelers. . . . Critical reviews of models of earth surface processes can be difficult to publish. A common reviewer's response is that "we are already aware of these problems" (Pilkey 1996, p. 12).

It should be obvious that issues surrounding such matters as plate tectonics, crustal growth, and the behavior of beaches are quite innocent from an ideological point of view compared with something like the age of the earth. If, as is vividly evident, peer pressure is so strong when it comes to relatively mundane matters such as plate tectonics, one can only imagine how many orders more magnitude stronger must it be when it comes to foundational rationalistic dogmas such as the "fact" of isotopic dating and the "fact" of the great antiquity of the earth! Why would organized suppression of dissent (that is, an actual conspiracy) even be necessary? Furthermore, considering the vast web of rationalizations which exist to cover every eventuality in the interpretation of isotopic dating results, one can readily see how the isotopic dating methods, and the great ages they imply, are most certainly protected from falsification!

There are also a variety of lesser factors which hinder an objective, critical assessment of isotopic dating as a whole. One of these is the well-known tendency of scientists to see what they expect to see. Hetherington (1983) provides many examples of this, showing how previous scientific measurements and observations had been biased by theoretical expectations. Considering the fact that he is a specialist in scientific measurements, Hayward (1985) displays nothing short of naivete in his disregard of these facts as well as his "you-would-have-to-believe-in-a-conspiracy" argumentation against scientific creationists.

Furthermore, there exists the matter of funding (as if scientific peer pressures, and the straitjacket effects of theories, were not enough). Funding for research tends to be funneled into areas of accepted lines of thinking within science. This is obvious from the following:

> Scientists cannot risk (or gain funding for) research without a high probability that a "successful" result will be obtained. Having been convinced of the credibility of the good-genes theory, could it be possible that researchers have felt more inclined to conduct heritability studies on systems that they believe will yield orthodox results? (Tregenza and Wedell 1997, p. 234).

One can also readily appreciate the fact that funding for geochronometric studies will tend to become available for studies that tacitly accept the validity of isotopic dating!

Myth: Discussions about fudging, and the selective publication of dating results, are tantamount to accusing scientists of being dishonest.

Reality Check: To begin with, were these correct, the onus should be on the scientists who are dishonest, and not on those who expose the dishonesty! Second, the charge of dishonesty implies an accusation of deliberate deceit. This is far from the truth. While nearly everyone agrees that fabrication of data and/or falsification of the same amounts to dishonesty, this appears to be very rare in science. By contrast, there is a large "gray area," which includes some manner of skewing the selection of data, and this is much more common in science (Teich and Frankel 1992, pp. 3-4) than deliberate fraud. This skewing of data is what is endemic to studies in isotopic dating. The uniformitarian geochronologist, in good conscience believing that certain results have no geologic meaning, chooses not to publish them. No dishonesty is involved.

What about "trimming" and fudging of data? Probably most fudging that takes place in the laboratory is not deliberate:

> Put more bluntly, scientists are just about as pseudoscientific when it comes to their own behavior (in and outside of the laboratory) as the crackpots are. For example, more than 30 years ago, Robert Rosenthal showed that scientists tend rather systematically to bias their laboratory observations. CSICOP often takes psi [related to ESP] researchers to task for not providing safeguards against "experimenter bias," but

I'd guess that less than 10 percent of the published studies *in all fields of science* include the use of similar precautions! I've seen more examples of data-fudging in the lab (most of it unconscious) than I care to mention—and some of the worst instances were by a Nobel Prize laureate in chemistry. Scientists are almost as likely to impose their values and expectations on "objective evidence" as the crackpots are (McConnell 1986, pp. 104-105) [emphasis in original].

In view of the fact that, in isotopic dating, one usually begins with a general prior expectation of the "correct" age, and then subjects the result to after-the-fact interpretations (or rationalizations), McConnell's statements take on more significance. Milton (1997, pp. 15-56) discusses this matter further, to whom I refer the interested reader.

Personally, I do not believe that either selective publication of results, or even a certain fudging of data, is in itself dishonest. However, in my opinion, the extravagant self-congratulatory claims often made for isotopic dating, and the dogmatic claims about their overall factuality, do in fact border on dishonesty, especially when the recipients of this propaganda are unsuspecting laypersons as well as children in the science classroom.

Myth: But surely if geochronometric methods were invalid, they would have been abandoned long ago.

Reality Check: It should be obvious that isotopic dating methods have become non-falsifiable. The ratchet of uniformitarian thinking turns in only one direction. In other words, if a dating result "works," this is counted as evidence for its validity. But if it does not "work," this is not recognized as evidence against validity of the method. We are supposed to think that it only means that initial conditions had not been met (again, the **CDMBN** fallacy). Heads, I win; tails, you lose (recall figure 1, page 3).

As more and more problems have cropped up with dating methods, more and more layers of rationalizations have been invented to explain them away. In time, this became an integral part of the very vocabulary of isotopic dating. For instance, dates which are "too young" to be accepted as the age of the rock are not likely to be called incorrect or anomalous. Instead, they were and are likely to be called by such euphemisms as "cooling ages," "closure temperature ages," "delayed-uplift ages," or some other Orwellian construct. In fact, it has been seriously suggested (Lippolt *et al.* 1994, Zeitler 1987) that the long-abandoned U-Th-He method, which routinely gives discrepantly-young results, not be reckoned invalid, but rather that its use be revived and that its discrepantly-young results be seen as giving "useful measurements of thermal history," that is, cooling ages.

It all boils down to this: If dating methods are in fact invalid, how would the uniformitarian even *know* it? There are now so many forms of special pleading and rationalization, and these are so thoroughly woven into the very thought processes routinely used in isotopic dating, that it is doubtful if the invalidity of radiometric dating could even be *conceived* by uniformitarians. This fact should remind the reader of George Orwell's *1984*, wherein the enslaved population could not even *conceive* of such things as freedom and democracy, because such notions were not even part of the current vocabulary (Newspeak). And it is precisely the newspeak and doublethink in isotopic dating (along with the earlier-discussed peer pressure within establishment science) which makes unnecessary the existence of a conspiracy in order to effectively suppress any potential doubts about the validity of isotopic dating.

Myth: If dates were selectively published, there would be no discrepant dates to cite from the literature.

Fact: This egregious canard presupposes that *no* discrepant results are ever published. No one ever claimed *that*. However, the selective publishing of dating results remains an inescapable fact:

> Garnet and clinopyroxene form a common mineral association in metamorphic rocks. Sm/Nd is partitioned between these two minerals in a way, that this isotopic system should give ideal possibilities for the age measurements. Only in a few cases geologically meaningful ages were obtained. *In the majority of cases the ages are clearly off and the data disappear in a lab-datafile* (Jagoutz 1994, p. 156) [emphasis added].

Another instance of probable selective publication of dates is provided by Snelling (1995), who reported the existence of discrepant results which had been apparently ignored by preceding researchers, even though comparable "good" results had been published by the latter.

Myth: The decay constants used in isotopic dating had been measured completely independently of each other.

Fact: While it is true that the decay rates have presumably been measured accurately in the laboratory, there is more to this story. Earlier creationist literature had demonstrated the fact that choice of the Rb to Sr decay constant had been partly influenced by the value it would need to have in order to maximize agreement with the K-Ar "clock." In view of the fact that creationists have been accused of not telling the truth when discussing this matter, it is worth documenting. Thus, the fact that such Rb-Sr "calibration" had in fact been going on at least as late as the mid-1960's is evident from the following:

Unfortunately, some of the early Sr isotope data in this area were predicated on the assumption that the ages obtained from the K/Ar method reflect the original age of the intrusion (Fairbairn et al. 1964) ... (Magaritz and Taylor 1986).

Also, Gale (1982, p. 114) substantiates the fact that the decay constant of rubidium had been adjusted, for some time, to maximize agreement with U-Pb dates. This matter is not only of historical interest, but raises questions even today. In fact, when Rb-Sr and U-Pb dates are compared, there remains the question about accuracy of decay constants:

Assuming that the discrepancy in Rb-Sr and U-Pb intercept ages cannot be accounted by the analytical uncertainty, the following possibilities to explain this discrepancy may be suggested: 1) the half-lives of the two methods are not closely cross-calibrated; 2)... (Ayuso et al. 1984, p. 123).

A third approach to the determination of the Rb decay constant is to date geological samples whose ages have also been determined by other methods with more reliable decay constants. This method has the disadvantage that it involves geological uncertainties, such as whether all isotopic systems closed at the same time and remained closed. However, *it provides a useful check on the direct laboratory determinations* (Dickin 1997, p. 40) [emphasis added].

It is obvious that laboratory determinations take a back seat to geologic interpretations. Further evidence of the use of one (or more) dating methods to "calibrate" the half-life of another is provided by the FT (fission-track) method. To this day, the spontaneous fission decay-constant of ^{238}U is not accurately known:

A variety of techniques yielded a diverse range of values with marked peaks around 7, 8.5, and 11.75 x 10(E-17)yr(E-1) (Hurford 1998, p. 24).

The smaller of these values is based on obtaining the best agreement of FT with K-Ar and/or Rb-Sr ages, and is used by many authors (e.g., Herz and Garrison 1998). Various technical difficulties hinder the determination of an independently-measured reproducible constant (Van den Haute et al. 1998). In the fission-track (FT) method, a decay constant deduced by concordance with other methods preceded the one determined empirically in the laboratory:

... we assumed ... that the uranium fission decay constant quoted with these data had been used independently to calculate ages, whereas in fact these fission-track ages were essentially calibrated against K-Ar age; were quoted in "K-Ar years" and depended mainly on the ^{40}K decay scheme. (This procedure was not stated in the abbreviated reports of the fission track dating). ... The large errors associated

with the fission-track ages detract considerably from their utility in calibrating the geological time scale (Gale et al. 1980, p. 13).

The same holds for the most recently-developed dating methods. Uncertainty in the measured half-life of ^{138}La (of the La-Ce dating method) has prompted a proposal (Shimizu et al. 1986, p. 145) that the half-life adopted should take on a value which will maximize agreement of La-Ce dates with Sm-Nd dates.

It is widely claimed that current lab measurements on most decay constants are accurate and unbiased. However, in view of the fact that the legacy of isotopic dating is unalterably tainted with the practice of using one method to "calibrate" another prior to actual ostensibly-reliable lab determinations of decay rate, skepticism is in order. There is, in fact, definite evidence that earlier lab measurements of decay rate were, in one way or another, influenced by what then was perceived to be the correct value of the decay constants:

The close agreement between the earlier results of Kovack and Adams (1932, 1955), Curtis et al. (1941), and Kienberger (1949) seems to be fortuitous, and is reminiscent of the similar close agreement of pre-World War II measurements of the velocity of light which subsequently proved to be many standard deviations away from later, more accurate measurements (Gale 1982, p. 113).

Is this in fact actually fortuitous, or was a "tracking effect" or "reinforcement syndrome" in operation at the time? Moreover, is it possible that, *even today*, discrepant lab measurements of decay rate are simply assumed to be in error and are not published? To answer this question, a large series of double-blind experiments, with publication of all results, would be necessary in order to measure the decay constants with complete objectivity, and to rule out the possibility of conscious or unconscious bias in their measurement and/or publication.

Myth: Conscious or unconscious experimenter bias cannot possibly be a factor in the actual computation of particular isotopic dating results.

Reality Check: For at least some isotopic dating systems, a definite experimenter bias is evident. For instance, a bias in counting is recognized to be a factor for FT standard:

... simple agreement with an independent age cannot be taken to validate individually either the neutron dosimetry or the value of Lambda. ... Although these experiments represent a most important attempt at circulating and dating standard material, as an absolute interlaboratory comparison system, it contains two drawbacks. Firstly, the samples were calculated with a known K-Ar age and thus the possibility of inadvertent or deliberate counting bias cannot be overlooked (Hurford and Green 1982, pp. 350-351).

Can counting of the FT tracks themselves be biased? It appears to be possible, at least sometimes:

> . . . the apatite age of 56.4 m. y. is older than the zircon age of 37.6 m. y. In that sample, however, the apatite has many crystal defects that may have been counted as fission tracks (Bryant *et al.* 1981, p. 22).

Further evidence of potential experimenter bias, in this case surrounding the K-Ar method, is evident from the following discussion related to the famous (or infamous) KBS Tuff controversy:

> Every time they were reanalyzed by Fitch and Miller, their ages came out at around 2.4 to 2.6 Ma. Lewin (1987, p. 252) found some of the original crystals and had them reanalyzed by the K-Ar method; their dates came out 1.87±0.04 Ma. Even methods that are supposedly objective and "absolute," such as radiometric dating, can be biased by the expectations of the experimenter. For example, Lewin (1987, p. 246) quotes Hurford on running the fission-track method:
>
>> You can bias your results ten percent either way, easily. You go crystal by crystal, and you begin to see where the rolling average is going. If you need the count to be higher with the crystal you are working on, so that it will fit in, you might include something that is a double track. If you want the count to be lower, you don't include it. That was poor practice.

(Prothero and Schwab 1996, p. 446).

A detailed, and highly-revealing discussion of the KBS tuff controversy is provided by Lubenow (1992, pp. 247-266), to which I refer the interested reader.

C. "Stratigraphic Trends" in Isotopic Dates

Myth: Since results of dating methods typically fall in the millions to billions of years, the correct ages of rocks must be within this general range.

Reality Check: First, let us take this argument to its *reductio ad absurdum*. Let us do this by considering historical lavas. We can find some of them that give an apparent K-Ar age in the few tens of millions of years. Then we compare this with some historic lavas that have fictitious Rb-Sr isochron ages in the few tens of millions of years. Or, we can use the simulated Rb-Sr isochron of twenty-seven million years, derived from Rb-Sr ratios, on modern lavas, (described by Lutz and Srogi 1986, p. 68). Following the logic of those who assert the general correctness of "comparable ages," we could argue that

both dating methods (K-Ar and Rb-Sr in this case) corroborate the "fact" that modern lavas are actually a few tens of millions of years old!

The central premise undergirding the belief in the overall validity of the multimillion/multibillion year ages, as it turns out, is the *assumption* of the validity of the dating methods themselves. What if this assumption was not believed? In such a situation, these isotopic systems would be understood to be little more than geochemical phenomena, and certainly not geochronometers. There would then be no reason to take seriously the inferred multimillion to multibillion year ranges seemingly indicated by these methods. In particular, once we understand that, during the Flood, colossal amounts of magma were generated, and much argon was trapped in the magma (e. g., Austin 1996, Snelling 1998), there is no reason to be surprised by the millions and billions of years apparently indicated by the K-Ar method. Likewise, once we understand the implications of mixing lines, and similar geochemical phenomena, there is no need to take seriously the millions and billions of years apparently indicated by the Rb-Sr method. An analogous line of reasoning holds for the other so-called dating methods.

Myth: Even when discordant (by one or more methods), results are still comparable with each other; therefore isotopic dating results must be generally correct.

Reality Check: While it is true that many data sets of such results are frequently comparable, there are also many instances when they are strongly discordant. For instance, a suite of lamprophyre dykes in the Canadian Shield has yielded a wide range of results ranging from 300 million years all the way to 1.7 billion years (Queen *et al.* 1996, p. 958). In other situations, the isotopic dates disagree by an order of magni-

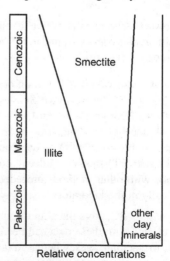

Figure 6. "Younging up" trends in isotopic dates, if they exist, are not evidence for the validity of the dating methods, because a variety of geochemical processes can generate trends in concentrations of mineral or chemical species. For instance, by anyone's reckoning, the changes in clay-mineral ratios in the geologic column have nothing to do with the radioactive decay of some parent element(s) over vast stretches of time.

tude or more. The latter include cases of "rejuvenated" Precambrian basement, examples of which I have provided in the earlier paper (Woodmorappe, 1979, 1993). A recent example of this is provided by the Natal Metamorphic Provinces (Jacobs and Thomas 1996), where the dates "smear" from 1.1 billion years to approximately 180 million years age (Jacobs and Thomas 1996, pp. 971-972), which is nearly an entire order of magnitude of difference. The older results are believed to approximate the age of origin of the lithologies, and the younger results are from periods of reheating (that is, "rejuvenation," and time since the rock temperatures supposedly last fell below the closure temperature of a particular isotopic system). In another instance, a comparable range of "dates" which span an order of magnitude, derived from geographically-coherent lava flows, was blamed on "excess argon" (Seidemann 1988). In this case, it was the Mesozoic dates which were accepted as reliable. Obviously, such reasoning is convincing only to those who already believe the validity of these isotopic dating methods, as it begs the question about the validity of these isotopic dating methods in the first place.

When considering uniformitarian geology in general and isotopic dating in particular, we must watch for "cover words." These include "collage of terranes," which serves as a cover for widely-contradictory dating results from adjacent suites of lithologies:

> In summary, the Rae "craton" appears to be a relatively complex amalgamation of Archean and Proterozoic material of a wide range of ages. A recent model for the evolution of the area has suggested that the "craton" represents a tectonically accreted collage of terranes, overthrust westward unto the Superior craton during east-west convergence between the Main and Superior cratons (Scott 1998, p. 95).

In other instances, this procedure of invoking some form of accreted terranes is not even self-consistent and is, as usual, blamed on geologic complexity:

> Uncertainty over which craton a given zircon age "belongs to" arises from two sources: disagreement over where the boundaries between "true" parts of cratons and (presumed) microcontinents should be drawn; and the realization that unlike other parts of the world, cratons in Eurasia underwent substantial growth and development during the Phanerozoic (Hacker *et al.* 1998, p. 223).

Examples of "rejuvenated" Precambrian igneous bodies, and their wide range of conflicting dates, could be multiplied *ad infinitum*. But even the results of one method can spread over a considerable range of values. For instance, a series of dykes intrude Proterozoic "basement." The hornblende gives K-Ar results all of which are in the Proterozoic range. By contrast, the K-Ar biotite results spread over a range that exceeds an order of magnitude in value: 76 million all the way to 1640

million years (Rex *et al.* 1993, p. 273). At other locations, the discordances can be even greater—approaching three orders of magnitude. Thus, some Precambrian "basement" rock, located in the western Canada sedimentary basin, are believed to be 2.0 billion years old, yet give FT dates as young as 2.2 *million* years old (Willett *et al.* 1997, p. 977).

Discordances, measured in orders of magnitude, between results of a single dating method and/or different dating methods, can also be found in sequences of ostensibly young rocks. For instance, pooled K-Ar and FT ages from the volcanics of the Taiwan-Luzon arc range widely from 0.02 to 49.9 million years (Yang *et al.* 1995). This is over three orders of magnitude, and this huge range is blamed on a combination of xenocrystic contamination, excess Ar, and alteration.

Orogenic belts comprise another source of widely divergent isotopic dates from relatively small geographic areas. One might intuitively suppose that belts of plutons of whatever age (Paleozoic, Mesozoic, and Cenozoic) should trend more-or-less randomly on earth, intersecting each other sporadically and randomly. But this is far from the case. Seldom are areas of Precambrian crust transversely cut by Phanerozoic orogens (Sykes 1978). And orogenic belts of whatever "age," with their associated plutons, tend to occur in the same general areas on earth (Beloussov 1990, Ryan and Dewey 1997; see figure 7, next page). Thus, geographic areas containing Meso-Cenozoic plutons often, if not usually, also contain Paleozoic (and older) plutons. This is explained, by advocates of plate tectonics, as a consequence of suture zones being weak areas of crust that tend to tear apart in the same area over and over again in geologic history.

One implication of this phenomenon is the fact that an investigator often obtains a large diversity of isotopic dates from a series of geographically-proximate plutons. To someone without a prior belief in the great antiquity of the earth, talk of repeatedly-rejuvenated crust is vacuous. Rather, the evidence points to highly-contradictory datasets of isotopic dates from closely-clustered plutons. A uniformitarian can argue about a complex geologic history all he wants, and spin just-so stories about repeated episodes of igneous intrusions and partial "rejuvenation" of older plutons in the area. However, the empirical evidence at hand contradicts his claim that results of different dating methods are generally comparable. Instead, there often exists a string of discordant results, by many different dating methods, and coming from plutons which are not geographically distant from each other. Let us consider, as an example, the Leadville quadrangle in Colorado (Wallace 1995). Closely-neighboring granitic bodies yield results which span nearly two orders of magnitude—from about 20 million years to nearly 2.0 billion years. The Cross Creek Granite itself yields results ranging from 1.7 billion years to 29 million years (Wallace 1995, p. 40).

Finally, if one goes ahead and reckons discrepantly-old Rb-Sr and Sm-Nd isochrons as "ages," this creates a large dataset of situations where results of different dating methods dis-

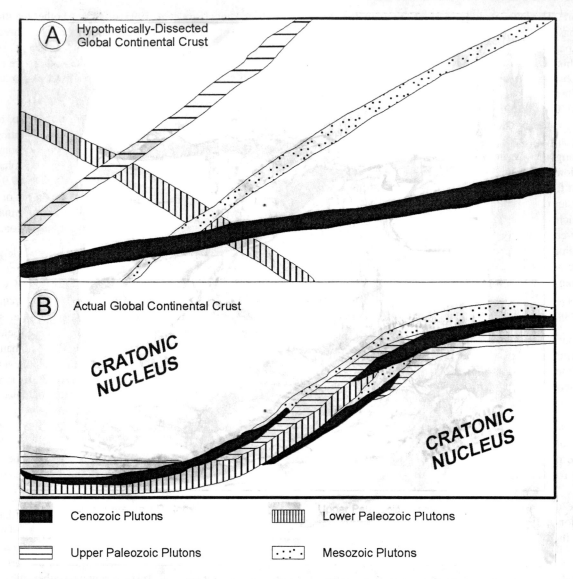

Figure 7: Plutonic belts of given "ages" do not occur just anywhere on Earth, as shown in (A). Instead, they tend to occur in association with plutonic belts of other "ages" (B).

agree by an order of magnitude or more. For instance, plutons in the Yukon Territory (Canada) have yielded K-Ar and Rb-Sr "cooling and crystallization" ages in the 60-100 Ma range, but also "inherited" Rb-Sr isochrons of up to 1380 Ma (Pigage and Anderson 1985). This is also true of presumably-young rocks. For instance, Neogene volcanics in Spain have yielded "true" K-Ar dates of 12 Ma as well as very well-defined ostensibly-inherited Rb-Sr isochrons in the 200-220 Ma range and less well-defined ones as old as 535 Ma (Munksgaard 1984). Quaternary basalts in Japan have yielded Sm-Nd "mantle isochrons" of 1.0 Ga (Togashi *et al.* 1992), amounting to a discordance of three orders of magnitude with other dating methods.

Myth: Locally, isotopic results agree with the law of superposition; therefore, isotopic dating methods must, at least generally, be valid indicators of rocks' ages.

Reality Check: To begin with, when a "stack" of lavas or tuffs shows a trend towards progressively younger isotopic results going upwards, it need not necessarily have anything to do with the actual age or ages of the "stack" of extrusives in question. It may be simply an artifact of one or more of the following: magma chamber zonation, isotope fractioning, differential argon trapping and/or chance for trapped argon to escape, source-area effects, etc.

As it is, there are numerous cases where there is an inverse relationship between local stratigraphic succession and isotopic dates obtained, as discussed in my previous paper

Lava (or tuff) IV	K-Ar date	60 m.y.
Lava (or tuff) III	K-Ar date	50 m.y.
Lava (or tuff) II	K-Ar date	30 m.y.
Lava (or tuff) I	K-Ar date	25 m.y.

Figure 8. Isotopic dates from extrusives need not "obey" the law of superposition. This can be blamed on xenocrystic contamination of the most recent flows, the thermal "rejuvenation" of the most deeply-buried flows, or some other geologic gymnastic.

(Woodmorappe 1979, 1993). A more recent example of an inverse succession of isotopic dates is provided by a series of conventional K-Ar dates from lava flows in Israel:

Whole-rock K-Ar ages previously determined on volcanic rocks from the Atlit-1 borehole systematically *decrease* downhole from 203 Ma near the top to 123 Ma near the bottom. This age range is inconsistent with the Upper Triassic-Lower Jurassic stratigraphic constraints (Kohn *et al.* 1993, p. 17) [emphasis added].

It was claimed that this resulted from a selective thermal "rejuvenation" of the lower part of the "stack" of lavas, based on a uniform $^{40}Ar/^{39}Ar$ result, and petrographic evidence.

Inconsistencies between stratigraphic succession, and a suite of isotopic dates obtained, is a frequent occurrence. The alleged contamination of tuffs, tephras, etc., closely connected with studies of presumed human evolution (notably the KBS tuff controversy of the Koobi Fora area of Lake Turkana), is well known (e. g., Drake *et al.* 1988, Lubenow 1992, Milton 1997, Prothero and Schwab 1996):

The example of the Koobi Fora and related formations of East Africa points out a number of problems typical of this kind of study. The radiometric dates provide the numerical ages, but they are subject to many types of error and so had to be redone many times in several laboratories by three methods over 15 years before all the results were consistent and undisputed (Prothero and Schwab 1996, p. 445).

In addition, the Hadar Formation of Afar, Ethiopia, famous for its *Australopithecus afarensis* fossils, has recently yielded more than just the acceptable $^{40}Ar/^{39}Ar$ and FT dates ranging from 1.6 to 2.9 Ma. It also includes "contaminant" dates, by both methods, which range in age from 5 to 26 Ma (Walter *et al.* 1996, p. 69). Let us move beyond the paleoanthropological implications of these dates and consider them in the light of the law of superposition. Indeed, such inconsistencies are, in and of themselves, *assumed* to be' an indicator of the unreliability of at least some of the dates obtained (or its converse). This fact is obvious from the following:

The presence of *geological* error is evident when repeat samples from the same stratigraphical horizon don't produce consistent ages, and when the ages obtained from a given horizon are incompatible with those from strata immediately above and below (Fitch *et al.* 1985, p. 611) [italics in original].

The regularly-decreasing succession of isotopic ages must follow the stratigraphic succession. When this condition is satisfied, there is a high probability that the calculated ages are indeed those of the deposition dates (Bonhomme 1982, p. 5).

Inversions between local stratigraphy and isotopic-dating results are hardly limited to ostensibly "young" rocks, where one might rationalize the maximized impact of older contaminants on the "young" dates. To the contrary: such inversions also occur in Precambrian rocks. For instance, a dacitic volcanoclastic lithology yielding a U-Pb zircon date of 2697 Ma is overlain by komatiitic-tholeitic lavas which yield an *older* Sm-Nd date of 2826 Ma (Catell *et al.* 1984, p. 280). To explain away this conflict, the Sm-Nd result took the fall. It was relegated to a mixing isochron.

In conclusion, the claim of consistency of gross stratigraphic successions with older-to-younger sequences of isotopic dates, as an argument for the overall validity of isotopic-dating methods, openly begs the question. It is just another use of the **CDMBN** fallacy.

Myth: If isotopic dating methods were invalid, we should not see an overall older to younger progression of isotopic dates relative to biostratigraphy.

Fact: There are two tacit premises in this argument: 1) the trends seen in the literature reflect actual trends in dating results obtained from earth's lithologies, and 2) assuming the validity of premise (1), radioactive decay is the only manner by which a progression of dates could arise. Premise (1) is unlikely to be correct, and premise (2) is egregiously false.

Let us first examine premise (1). The trends seen in the discrepant results themselves (in the table within the previous article—Woodmorappe 1979, 1993) are at least partly an artifact of the selective publication of dating results. Less severely-deviant results are more likely to be published than more severely-deviant ones because the former are easier to assign a geologic meaning than the latter. More importantly, dates which are "too young" are more likely to be published than those which are "too old" for the same reason.

Moreover, the selective acceptance of dates, right from the earliest history from isotopic dating, had been predicated on the *assumption* that dating methods are valid and hence "should" display a stratigraphic older-to-younger progression! This fact is obvious from the following discussion of early 20th-century isotopic dates, and how they had been evaluated for presumed correctness:

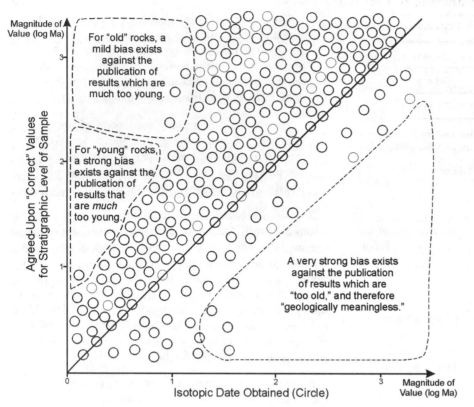

Figure 9: It is often claimed that, despite the scatter in data, there exists a "younging up" trend in dating results. Even if earth's rocks were evenly sampled, such a trend would be questionable at best. Publishing biases occur *precisely* within those regions of the graph where the presence of data points would tend to randomize the entire data set. This is particularly the case for discrepantly-old results.

Apart from this, we would need to account for the biases which exist solely as a result of the unequal abundances of potentially-datable igneous materials throughout the Phanerozoic column. Such biases are particularly glaring for certain segments of the column:

> Fourth, radiometric data for the Cretaceous exceed those for all but late Cenozoic parts of the geologic column because of the abundance of volcanic ash, bentonite beds, and glauconites in global Cretaceous marine sections (Kauffman 1979, p. A445).

Only by fulfilling all of these requirements could we have some basis of deciding if premise (1) is correct. And, if it is, only then could we determine if a progression exists and, if it does, if it is a particularly strong one.

I have my doubts about the existence of a strong progression, particularly when the aforementioned Meso-Cenozoic bias is taken into account. In fact, as noted below, most results of comparative dating methods are discordant. This also means that, were all these dates to be strongly bracketed biostratigraphically, there would only be a welter of contradictions between isotopic dates and biostratigraphy. Thus, if a progression between the two systems surfaced at all, it would probably be a weak one, and then accompanied by a very considerable scatter of data points.

But in the end, he [Schuchert] concluded that the only viable approach was to accept from radioactive dating an age of 500 million years for the lower Cambrian, and to adjust the stratigraphic determinations of the duration of each individual period using that as a standard. He believed that approached in this manner, radioactivity would make it possible to determine the rates of formation of the various strata, *while stratigraphy, in turn, would provide an important check upon radioactive results* (Burchfield 1975, p. 205) [emphasis added].

Clearly, then, to the extent that a "younging-up" trend appears to exist, it is hardly surprising. It may in fact be little more than a self-fulfilling artifact of this procedure.

Let us now turn this discussion to the evaluation of any potential progression. To begin this, we must solve the vexing problem of multiple biases in our dataset.

And this is only the beginning. In order to validate premise (1) we would need to guarantee that the earth's surface is being sampled equally. To do this, we would need sampling of the crust on a grid pattern, as described by Patchett (1992, p. 482). We would subsequently need to correct for the bias caused by the greater overall area of outcrops of Mesozoic and Cenozoic igneous bodies with respect to Paleozoic ones.

Let us now examine a clear-cut case, within uniformitarianism, where an "age" progression *and* agreement with biostratigraphy had *not* been accepted as *ipso facto* evidences for the validity of the dates. For a time in the 1950's and 1960's, sedimentary rocks had been dated directly by using the K-Ar and Rb-Sr methods on certain clay minerals (such as presumably-authigenic illite). With the occasional exception of glauconite dating (discussed earlier), such attempts have been virtually abandoned (for time-scale purposes) since they produce discrepant results in the overwhelming majority of cases (Russell 1995, p. 175). In fact, as noted in my 1979 work, agreements with "reliable" values for the time scale are probably little more than fortuitous (see also Harland 1990, p. 76). Ironically, however, no attempts (at least of which I am aware) have been made to even consider the possibility that dates from igneous minerals (that are biostratigraphically-bracketed, of course) may *also* be fortuitously in agreement with each other and with biostratigraphy.

Now consider premise (2). Is radioactive decay the *only* means by which a trend could arise? Certainly not. For instance, let us consider the relative abundance of the major groups of clay minerals in shales through Phanerozoic time (Weaver 1967). Illite decreases sharply from Paleozoic through Tertiary, while smectite increases even more dramatically from Paleozoic through Tertiary. No one is, of course, suggesting for a moment that this trend constitutes evidence that illite undergoes radioactive decay to smectite over hundreds of millions of years of time! After all, the clay minerals are not radioactive. Yet, if one were to follow the logic of the apologists for isotopic dating, one would almost have to do so (see figure 6)!

What about all the dates from igneous rocks? Here, we need to remember the non-geochronometric means (such as isotope fractioning, magma-chamber zonings, etc.) by which an overall trend could arise (between progressively younger isotopic dating results, and local stratigraphy, and even global biostratigraphy). Some current creationist research (e. g., Austin and Snelling 1998, Snelling 1998) is along these lines.

Myth: If isotopic dating methods were false, we should not expect to see less discordance among younger dates than older ones.

Fact: To my knowledge, this assertion has never been proved. I have seen much discordance among Tertiary rocks just as I have seen it in Precambrian ones. And, to evaluate this claim, we would need to overcome all of the rock-collection and dating biases discussed in the previous entry. In particular, if we were to guarantee the publication of all "inherited" isochrons, we would undoubtedly see many severely discordant results between the "true" Tertiary values and the much-older "inherited" ones.

We would also need to evaluate the geochemical dynamics of inheritance. If it turned out that all "daughter" products tend to become geochemically attenuated with stratigraphic progression, this would not only explain the progressive "younging" of all the dating results, but also any trend in decreased discordance between them.

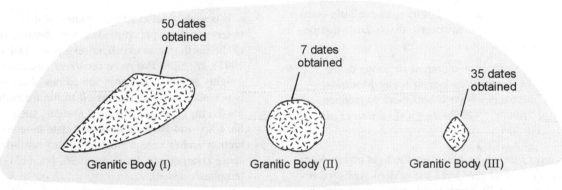

Number of dates obtained bear no necessary relationship to size of pluton

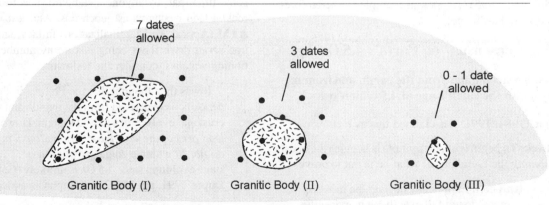

Number of dates tabulated are normalized for size of outcrop of pluton
(although they may still not be normalized for the volume of the igneous body).

Figure 10: Even if all dates were published, a "grocery list" approach to comparing relative frequencies of "good" and "bad" dates would be inadequate. This stems from uneven sampling of igneous bodies (top). To rectify this sampling bias, a normalization scheme would be needed—for example, a grid-network (bottom).

Myth: If isotopic dating methods were false, we would expect to see as many "future" ages as million to billion year ages, and/or as many zero ages as the same.

Reality Check: These arguments may sound intuitively appealing to the uninitiated, but they are actually somewhere between extremely dubious and bogus. In actuality, what kind of "dates" we would obtain on a young earth would very much depend upon many things, not the least of which is the dynamics of inheritance of the isotopic systems. If, as discussed below, the retention of argon in magmas is proportional to rate of the mobilization of the magma, it would not be surprising that most ancient rocks (dating from the Creation or the Flood) have built-in positive ages, and very few have zero or future ages. A similar line of reasoning holds for the inheritance of isotope systematics used in other dating methods.

This is not to say that there are no zero or future ages derived from ancient rocks. Future ages do occur, and are relatively common when geochronologists figure model ages using the Sm-Nd method (Scherer *et al.* 1997, p. 73). In particular, these negative-slope isochrons ("futurechrons") have also been seen in the Sm-Nd dating of garnet (Jagoutz 1994, p. 156). Negative ages also occur among Rb-Sr whole-rock isochrons (Gazis *et al.* 1998, and citations). Future ages are fairly common as a result of the so-called reverse-discordance that occurs in some U-Pb dates:

> Reverse discordance is common in young monazites. . . . For Tertiary and even many Mesozoic monazites, the excess ^{206}Pb is sufficient to produce negative or "future" $^{207}/^{206}Pb$ ages (Mattinson *et al.* 1996, p. 355).

However, most future ages never see the light of day. Very likely, negative ages and zero ages are seldom published because they are not usually considered to have any geologic meaning in the evolutionary-uniformitarian paradigm. For example, Snelling (1995) provides an example of a heretofore-unpublished zero Th-Pb age.

D. "Dating Consensus" on Earth's 4.5 Ga Age

Myth: Lead isochron dates from the earth, and from meteorites, establish the earth's age at 4.5 billion years.

Dalrymple (1984, 1991) has claimed this as fact.

Reality Check: To begin with, Dalrymple is begging the question by *assuming* the factuality of what he is out to prove:

> Although modern Earth leads lie near the meteoritic isochron, many do not fall exactly on it, evidently because many have had complex (multi-stage) histories (Dalrymple 1984, p. 101).

More importantly, Dalrymple's overall claim is *squarely repudiated* by other uniformitarian geochronologists who point

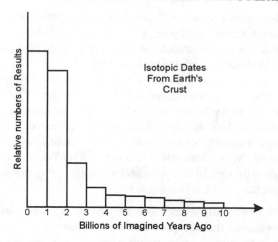

Figure 11. The myth of isotope-date agreement for a 4.5 Ga earth age. In actuality, there is a wide range of "dates" from Earth's crust with a sharp drop-off in abundance for dates in excess of about 2.5 Ga (Bowring and Williams 1999). There also exist a number of dates by different dating methods and from different geographic regions all over the earth, which indicate ages far in excess of the accepted 4.5 billion year age of the earth.

out that any agreement of lead isochrons with the (supposed) 4.5 Ga age of earth is coincidental:

> It is widely believed that studies of lead isotopes in terrestrial samples provide a well-determined age of the Earth (for an excellent review see Dalrymple 1991). *We show this to be incorrect*, even though a roughly accurate answer is sometimes obtained, but is not necessarily related *at all* to the formation of the Earth. Other widely-cited systems such as Rb-Sr, I-Xe, and Pu-Xe also do not date terrestrial accretion and/or core formation in any well-defined sense (Harper and Jacobsen 1996, pp. 1131-1132) [emphasis added].

This is really nothing new, as it has been known for quite some time that, by anyone's standard, it is too simplistic to reckon lead isochrons as geochrons. And lest we hear some **ATM (Appeal To Marginalization)** fallacy, such as that old line about these flaws being just a tiny number of malfunctioning watches, consider the following:

> It was then thought that the Pb ores in these large deposits were derived from the mantle and the lower crust and evolved in a closed system. However, *most lead ores of the world are "anomalous" in that they do not fit* a single-stage growth curve . . . a single-stage evolution since 4.5 Ga is unlikely (Gariepy and Dupre 1991, pp. 216-217) [emphasis added].

Other lead-isotopic evidence which disagrees with the 4.5 Ga claim is discussed by Witter (1974) and Williams (1992, p. 2). This includes discussion of meteorites, whose lead isochrons have been questioned for some time, despite their status of fact in the eyes of apologists for isotopic dating methods.

Myth: On Earth, all dating methods converge on a 4.5 billion year age for our planet.

Reality Check: To begin with, the earth's rocks yield a huge *range* of ages. There is a high frequency of ages in the few tens of millions to few hundreds of millions of years. This is supposed to be the result of an intense burst of Meso-Cenozoic magmatic activity. From that point, there is a steady, asymptotic decline in frequency of ages as they approach a value of 3.8-3.9 Ga (Dalrymple 1991, p. 128), with some recent dates in the 4.0-4.3 Ga age range from Australia (Amelin 1998) and Canada (Bowring and Williams 1999; Stern and Bleeker 1998). The steepness of the asymptotic curve is highest for K-Ar, less for Rb-Sr, and least for Sm-Nd model ages [see figure 3 of McCulloch and Bennett (1994), p. 4722]. Such trends, of course, are explained by the assertion that the earth had widely divergent times of crustal formation and even more widely divergent temporal episodes of tectono-magmatic events. Such reasoning, of course, begs the question about the great age of the earth and the validity of the dating methods.

We must also remember that the presumed differences in billions of years, from dates obtained from rocks of the earth's crust, are largely *ad hoc*: That is, they often have little or no independent basis in local or regional geology. For instance, there often is little or no independent geologic evidence that one Precambrian lithology is, say, one billion years older than another similar lithology. As noted in my previous work, greenstone belts thus unexpectedly yielded very diverse multibillion-year ages. Nor is there some sort of consensus of results from "old" terrane. Recently, a granite-greenstone association, predicted on geologic grounds to be Archean in age (>2.5 Ga) yielded "completely unexpected" U-Pb zircon dates ranging from 1.02 to 1.8 Ga (de Wel *et al.* 1998). Ever since the 1950's, when widespread dating of Precambrian rocks had begun, the artificial imposition of multibillion-year age differences on different crustal regions had been tacitly covered up by supposing that previous geologic interpretations have been erroneous:

> When combined with work from other laboratories, the "geochronological map" of the Precambrian began to fill in. Prior to the advent of these techniques, there was no way, except by often misleading lithological similarities, to correlate Precambrian rocks from one locality to another (Wetherill 1998, p. 8).

And, since there is such a wide variance of isotopic ages from earth's crust, and these decline exponentially in frequency as they get older, it can hardly be claimed that there is some sort of "consensus" of results at 4.5 Ga.

Interestingly, some dating methods do not even yield values, for earth materials, which come anywhere close to 4.5 billion years. Consider, for instance, FT apatite ages. Despite the fact that "thermal annealing" rationalizations are routinely invoked for FT dates which are "too young," such rationalizations cannot explain the rarity of apatite FT results greater than a mere 0.5 billion years:

> Whatever the reason, outcropping rocks with apatite fission-track ages older than 500 Myr are extremely rare in our experience, even from areas which on other evidence would appear to have been tectonically quiescent for much longer periods (Gleadow *et al.* 1986, p. 411).

Another line of evidence against the claim that all methods give an age of the earth of 4.5 billion years is the recurrent appearance of isotopic-dating results in excess of that figure. Some of these have been discussed in the previous article (see Woodmorappe 1979, 1993). I now present some newer examples. These include a Pb-Pb isochron which was rationalized to have undergone "a complex history of both U loss and Pb addition" (Bridgwater 1989, p. 292) because it yielded an age of 4.5 Ga (see also Moorbath *et al.* 1986, p. 73). A suite of Rb-Sr isochrons has indicated ages which are as high as 8.75 billion years (Holland and Lambert 1995, p. 504). Other "super-old" results include K-Ar dates as old as 4.9 billion years from Greenland which are, according to the usual assumptions of the $^{40}Ar/^{39}Ar$ method, corroborated by flat-spectrum results (Pankhurst *et al.* 1973, pp. 163-164). To show that these results are no fluke, it is worth adding that comparable results (4.8-5.2 billion years) have been found on K-Ar biotites from an area in Baltic Russia (Pankhurst *et al.* 1973, p. 168). Similar dates have also been obtained from Australia (Snelling 1998). Of course, no uniformitarian is suggesting that the earth's age has now been increased to 4.9 or 5.2 billion years, even though these results are corroborated from different regions of Precambrian crust. Instead, all the sets of unwanted dating results are simply explained away, as they always have been.

In recent years, so-called model ages have achieved considerable status as supposedly indicative of the time when the local crust was formed. These ages revolve about reference values for depleted mantle (DM) and for chondritic abundances (which obviously presupposes that the earth has undergone geochemical evolution with reference to chondritic meteorites—the so-called CHUR [chondritic uniform reservoir]: Arndt and Goldstein 1987; Intasopa *et al.* 1995). Moreover, consideration of some of these model ages, taken literally, would also imply an earth much older than 4.5 Ga. These include a series of Re-Os model ages up to 11.0 Ma, and a Rb-Sr model age of 8.3 Ga (Pearson *et al.* 1995). Assuming that this is not a misprint, it also includes a Sm-Nd model age of 5.19 Ga (Moller *et al.* 1998, p. 781) from Antarctica.

Following the usual logic employed by proponents of isotopic-dating, we could argue that the earth must be very much older than the accepted 4.5 Ga. After all, this "fact" is corroborated by different dating methods, from different minerals, from different geologic environments, and from very different geographic locations on earth. Such is the *reductio ad absurdum* of the acceptance of multibillion-year values from Earth's crust as valid indicators of age.

Myth: Extinct radioactivity constitutes proof that the earth and universe are old

Reality Check: There are several kinds of extinct radioactivity. One of these involves a set of isotopes whose half-lives are very small in relation to a 4.5 Ga earth, but very large in relation to a 10,000 year-old earth. The presumed basis behind the old-age claim is the alleged absence of these unsupported isotopes in nature. When such isotopes are found on Earth, however, we are told that they were made by recent, secondary processes. But is this fissiogenic or cosmogenic support for the isotopes proved, or is it *assumed*? It often is the latter, as evidenced by this use of ^{129}I (half-life 15.7 million years):

In the case of the Anadarko basin, the host formations are all Paleozoic, thus the age of the I contained in the organic matter, which lived, died and accumulated in the Paleozoic, is at least 300 m. y. This means that the cosmogenic (surface) ^{129}I component decayed to insignificant levels long ago.... these brines probably do not contain an anthropogenic ^{129}I component. The most likely source for the ^{129}I measured in these brines is fissiogenic. . . . the most likely source for I is the Upper Devonian—Lower Mississippian Woodford Shale (Moran 1996, pp. 689, 692).

No consideration is made for the possibility that ^{129}I exists in Paleozoic rocks because they are much younger than 300 million years old. Instead, uniformitarians *presuppose* the fissiogenic origin and secondary status of this relatively short-lived isotope in the rock.

Chapter 4

"Malfunctioning Watches:" False Claims about the Rarity of Discrepant Dates

A. Assessing the Frequency of Dates not Accepted as the Age of the Rock

Myth: Discrepant isotopic dating results are very rare.

Fact: This is the keystone of the myth, propounded by apologists for isotopic dating, which seeks to lead us to believe that discrepant results are "just a tiny number of malfunctioning watches" (e. g., Dalrymple 1984, p. 76). Other uniformitarian geologists puncture this myth by making it clear that discrepant results are sufficiently common to warrant serious attention:

> . . . the assumption that during the whole life of the rock volume being analyzed, neither the radioactive element nor its decay products have moved into or out of this volume is practically unlikely to be realized in nature at all or, if it is, it occurs only in exceptional cases. Therefore, differences (often essential) between data determining absolute age and geologic data are a *usual* phenomenon that surprises nobody; it has always been solved in favour of the latter. In the absence of geological data, determination of absolute age often leads us into great errors (Skobelin *et al.* 1990, p. 25) [emphasis added].

> As research progressed and data accumulated, it became apparent that *many* minerals and rocks presented problems with either trapping large amounts of ^{40}Ar . . . at the time of crystallization, or radiogenic ^{40}Ar loss during slow cooling (Bowring 1998, p. 39) [emphasis added].

For at least some commonly-used dating methods, there is no question about the fact that ostensibly-accurate age-determining results are clearly in the minority:

> Because of the sensitivity to moderately elevated temperatures, apatite fission-track ages *only rarely* give a reliable measure of the age of formation of their host rock (Gleadow *et al.* 1986, p. 405) [emphasis added].

What about other isotopic systems used for dating? As discussed below, they also have yielded a considerable minority, if not outright majority, of dates that have had to be rejected

as indicative of the ostensibly correct age of the rock. Furthermore, all this is on uniformitarians' own terms:

> Most, if not all, isotopic systems of Paleozoic age have been open, to one degree or another, for some period of time since their formation (Kunk and Sutter 1984, p. 13).

This latter statement, of course, is a tacit use of the **CDMBN** (**C**redit **D**ating **M**ethods, **B**lame **N**ature) fallacy, and thus a tacit admission that most Paleozoic dating results are variably discrepant. What about presumably younger igneous bodies, which are ostensibly less likely to have experienced secondary reheating? Consider the use of isotopic dating methods, on Late Paleozoic and Early Mesozoic lavas, for the purpose of time-scale calibration:

> . . . problems of alteration or loss of radiogenic daughter products, which are *so common* in otherwise suitable lava horizons. . . (Forster and Warrington 1985, p. 109) [emphasis added].

And lest the apologist for isotopic dating give us the **ATM** fallacy again, let the broader application of these flaws be noted. Thus, when it comes to the dating of still-younger lavas and granitic bodies (Jurassic to early Tertiary, and then still younger), the K-Ar method, at least, fares no better:

> Secondly, the potassium argon method is complicated by the possibility *if not likelihood* of argon loss (Hallam *et al.* 1985, p. 118) [emphasis added].

> In the Japanese Islands, it is *not rare* for Quaternary and especially Tertiary volcanic rocks that their K-Ar date are not consistent with the stratigraphical relation because of some disturbances in the K-Ar system (Ebihara *et al.* 1989, p. 149) [emphasis added, grammatical errors in original].

But surely, many apologists for isotopic-dating have claimed, even if K-Ar dates are prone to open-system behavior, Rb-Sr ones are nonetheless certainly reliable. Think again:

> The evidence for open-system Rb-Sr systematics in numerous environments has now *discredited the Rb-Sr isochron method as a dating tool for igneous crystallization* (Dickin 1997, p. 53) [emphasis added].

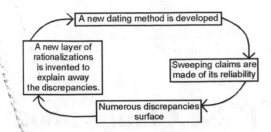

Figure 12. The cycle of inflated claims about isotopic-dating methods.

The U-Pb and Rb-Sr systems are known to be *highly susceptible* to resetting by hydrothermal, diagenetic and metamorphic processes (Toulkeridis *et al.* 1998, p. 138) [emphasis added].

Myth: Isotopic dates give the correct age of the rock in the vast majority of instances.

Fact: This converse of the "tiny number of malfunctioning watches" argument is very questionable. In fact, if the following statements are correct, then it is *flatly untrue*:

> Many glauconite dates do have inherent analytical and geochemical problems, but *so do most high-temperature dates.* We find it regrettable that, whereas low-temperature dates have been criticized widely, often for good reasons, very little is said about equally significant problems with high-temperature dates (Haq *et al.* 1988, pp. 601-602) [emphasis added].

> Geologists currently interpret *most* mineral ages as cooling ages. . . (Zeitler *et al.* 1987, p. 2865) [emphasis added].

There is no escaping the fact that inferred closed-system behavior, as deduced *a posteriori* from the dating results of all methods, is the exception and not the rule:

> Thirdly, to obtain the age of formation of a rock or mineral, the material must have remained a closed chemical system since its formation, with neither gain nor loss of radioactive parent or daughter atoms or, in the case of complex decay chains, of intermediate members. Unfortunately, geological materials and environments *do not often meet this requirement* (Durrance 1986, p. 287) [emphasis added].

Let us now focus on K-Ar dating:

> Nevertheless, it is probably true that the majority of biotites yield reliable cooling ages. . . (McDougall and Harrison 1988, p. 26).

To begin with, "cooling ages" often are tens of millions of years younger than the presumed age of the rock's crystallization. Second, it is difficult to imagine that such tentative wording ("probably true") would be made if even "reliable

cooling ages" were overwhelmingly more common than "unreliable" ones.

Dalrymple (1984, p. 72) would have us believe that geologists know which types of rocks and minerals meet the closed-system requirements for K-Ar dating, and that biotite is one of the minerals "that retain[s] argon well." In light of his claim, consider the following:

> Many studies have demonstrated that the apparent K-Ar ages of biotites in crystalline rocks of orogenic terranes *commonly are younger* than the true ages of metamorphism or pluton emplacement . . . a considerable interval may separate the time of emplacement (or metamorphism) from the time of Ar retention in the minerals. . . (Criss *et al.* 1982, p. 7029) [emphasis added].

> Intrusives are *prone* to slow cooling after emplacement, and may undergo later thermal metamorphism *yet show little evidence of that overprint.* Incipient weathering may go unrecognized (Harland *et al.* 1990, p. 75) [emphasis added].

If words mean things, then this is tacit admission that "too young" results are very common, if not usual, as these must be routinely blamed on protracted cooling and/or *ad hoc* reheating events. Most definitely, they cannot be explained away as a tiny number of malfunctioning watches.

The foregoing concerns hypabyssal and plutonic rocks. What about lavas? Here we have unequivocal evidence that the majority of K-Ar dates, as currently interpreted by uniformitarians themselves, do *not* give the correct age of the lava flow. This is particularly evident from K-Ar datings of flood basalts. Typically, the results have "smeared" over tens or hundreds of millions of years, and this was taken as evidence of protracted episodes of extrusive volcanism. With the widespread use of the presumably-reliable $^{40}Ar/^{39}Ar$ method, however, these new results have ostensibly indicated a short, penecontemporaneous single episode of flood-basalt extrusion. This also implies that *most* of the previously-believed K-Ar dates were *not* reliable. For example:

> Although a wide range of dates between 90 and 193 Ma have been published for the Kirkpatrick Basalt, it is now recognized that the young dates reflect non-ideal behavior of Ar in the matrix (Heimann *et al.* 1994, p. 19; see also Fleming *et al.* 1997).

The currently-accepted date for the areally-extensive Kirkpatrick Basalt is 176.6 Ma. Therefore, on uniformitarians' own terms, what we have is not a tiny number of malfunctioning watches, but a small number of supposedly *properly functioning* watches! In fact, the foregoing example can be generalized, to one degree or another, to all flood basalts:

> Precise dating of flood basalt eruptions is often a difficult task. Paleontological control is usually weak, because the types of fossils usually associated with lava flows (e. g., plant material) do not give precise

zonal ages. Radiometric dating is also difficult because the small grain size of lavas usually precludes the separation of K-or Rb-rich phases for precise K/Ar dates, which are *notoriously susceptible to argon loss*, and in the Thulean Province may be further complicated by inherited argon. In this situation, many conventional K/Ar dates are needed to provide a consensus of results *so that samples displaying high or low ages (corresponding to inherited argon and argon loss respectively) can be rejected* (Dickin 1988, p. 111) [emphasis added].

Of course, as noted earlier, the "consensus of results" approach failed to pin down an accurate date of extrusion for the Kirkpatrick Basalt.

A variety of regional analyses also explode the myth that discrepant results are rare. When it comes to specific regions, it is clear that K-Ar and/or Rb-Sr isochron dates believed to be indicative of the correct age of the rock are *clearly in the minority*. Therefore, talking of discrepantly-young results as just a few rotten apples, as apologists of isotopic dating commonly do, is blatantly self-congratulatory and completely contrary to the evidence. Consider, for instance, the eastern Transverse Ranges of southern California:

> Only a few of the potassium-argon ages obtained may approach emplacement ages; most reflect a complex postintrusive thermal history that affected the entire region sampled (Miller and Morton 1980, p. 2).

Furthermore, this geographic area of discrepantly-young K-Ar dates is probably much larger than previously supposed (Miller and Morton 1980, p. 19). Of course, belief in this "rejuvenation" rationalization is convincing only to those who already presuppose the validity of the K-Ar dating method, as it begs the question about its overall validity. Discrepant Rb-Sr whole-rock dates can also occur from rocks from a large geographic area. For instance, volcanic rocks of the Llyn Peninsula and Snowdonia regions of Wales usually yield discrepantly-young Rb-Sr isochron dates from the entire region (Evans *et al.* 1995).

Further proof that discrepant dates cannot be wished away as "just a few bad apples" is provided by the fact that at least some uniformitarian geologists think that the contents of the apple cart are largely bad, and that this judgment applies to "apples" gathered from large areas of the earth's crust. For instance, in tabulating isotopic dates for the ophiolites of the Middle East, Alsharhan and Nairn (1997, p. 34) warn that the determinations are "*usually of doubtful validity*, except in cases of U-Pb zircon ages." [emphasis added].

Myth: Isotopic-dating results are, generally speaking, internally consistent.

Fact: The contrary has been clearly shown in my previous paper (Woodmorappe 1979, 1993), as well as in this one. However, the circular reasoning involved in disregarding inconsistent results, and then asserting that isotopic results are consistent, should be self-evident. In fact, at times, such circularity is so obvious that it takes on almost comical proportions, as the following criticism of a geochronological study indicates:

> This study essentially showed that: (1) FT dates could be coherent (eliminating a noticeable proportion of calculated ages considered unreliable, i. e., incoherent *a posteriori*); and (2) that there were dateable Ordovician and Silurian bentonites in Great Britain (Odin *et al.* 1986, p. 128).

This is no fluke. Far from it. Earlier (page 13, this work), I had quoted Waterhouse (1979, p. 499), who had made it clear that even accepted results within the Phanerozoic Time Scale are widely contradictory, and even this does not take into account the much more severely deviant results which have already been arbitrarily disregarded.

Ever since the earliest days of K-Ar dating, indiscriminate dating of samples of granitic rock has been avoided. Instead, mineral separates (usually micas and amphiboles) have been extracted from granitic rocks and used for dating:

> However, in general whole rock dating of acid Paleozoic rocks by the K-Ar method is not considered to be reliable (Lippolt *et al.* 1983, p. 273).

This practice is, of course, tacit admission that results from mineral separates and whole-rock samples are *not* usually internally consistent. But surely the Rb-Sr dates on rocks and minerals are consistent. Think again:

> Although the problems of loss of daughter product are far less severe in the ^{87}Rb-^{87}Sr method than in ^{40}K-^{40}Ar dating, they do, as shown, still exist. *Even in igneous rocks, discordant mineral dates are more often encountered than concordant dates* (Durrance 1986, p. 296) [emphasis added].

Myth: When a rock is dated by more than one dating method, the results are usually concordant.

Fact: This oft-repeated self-serving assertion is patently untrue. Consider, for instance, the U-Pb methods:

> ... $^{206}Pb/^{238}U$, $^{207}Pb/^{238}U$, $^{207}Pb/^{206}Pb$, and $^{208}Pb/^{232}Th$ will agree, provided that there are no geologic complications such as xenocrystic material in the sample. However, *rarely do all the calculated ages agree* (Stern *et al.* 1981, p. 5) [emphasis added].

> Natural zircon *typically* displays an inconsistency (discordance) of age values obtained on the basis of the $^{206}Pb/^{238}U$, $^{207}Pb/^{235}U$, and $^{207}Pb/^{206}Pb$ isotopic ratios (Levchenkov *et al.* 1998, p. 1006) [emphasis added].

> The isotopic systematics of zircon populations from most SCT [Salinian composite terrane] granitoids can be described with a single word: discordant (Mattinson 1990, p. 244).

The same situation applies to *all* of the other commonly-used dating methods:

> When determined by several methods (K-Ar, Rb-Sr and fission track) radiometric ages for coexisting minerals in a metamorphic or igneous rock *generally differ* because of different closure temperatures for retention of daughter products or tracks (Itaya and Takasugi 1988, p. 281) [emphasis added].

It should be stressed that this rule (not exception) of discordance also applies to those dating methods which are commonly believed to be highly resistant to open-system behavior:

> It is well documented that Rb-Sr whole-rock dates *tend to be younger* than U-Pb zircon dates from the same rock (Beakhouse *et al.* 1988, p. 346) [emphasis added].

What about the suggestion of performing a controlled experimental determination of the rate of concordance and discordance between results of different dating methods? There are no studies, at least of which the author has knowledge, that rigorously compare the rate of agreement by different dating methods *on a controlled global scale*. However, there are available several compilations of results of many datings, by various dating methods, on a regional scale. Of course, there is no guarantee that all results have been published, or that dating results have been normalized to the area or volume of igneous rock located in the area in question (see figure 10). Nevertheless, let us briefly consider some of these compilations. There are many Meso-Cenozoic dates tabulated, from 19 different granitoid sequences of the central Sierra Nevada Mountains (Stern *et al.* 1981, p. 16). In addition, there has been an evaluation of approximately 3,000 K-Ar, Rb-Sr, and U-Pb dates from numerous granitic rocks from the Canadian Cordillera (Armstrong 1988, Friedman and Armstrong 1995). These compilations clearly indicate that discordant results from different dating methods are overwhelmingly the rule, and not the exception.

Myth: Excess argon occurs only in a few kinds of minerals.

Fact: While this may have been believed in the early days of isotopic dating, it can no longer be held. In my earlier paper (Woodmorappe 1979, 1993) I had given many examples of excess argon in common minerals. This fact can certainly be generalized:

> The excess argon problem arose at the same time as the K-Ar method became widely used because anomalously high ages were obtained for some rocks and minerals. At first, excess argon was found only in materials that are exotic for K-Ar dating such as beryl, cordierite, chlorite, and pyrite, whereas subsequently excess argon was observed in minerals and rocks traditionally used for dating purposes (Rublev 1985, p. 73).

Further documentation of this fact is provided by Dickin (1997).

Myth: The equilibration of magmatic argon gas with atmospheric argon gas, a precondition for K-Ar dating, is a well-founded assumption.

Reality Check. One of the central assumptions of the K-Ar method is that any argon left in the magma is in equilibrium with that in the atmosphere, so that a $^{40}Ar/^{39}Ar$ ratio of 295.5 can be used for atmospheric correction. Of course, whenever K-Ar results are "too old," it is claimed that this assumption has been violated, as discussed shortly. Furthermore, use of these argon-isotope ratios tacitly assumes the validity of the evolutionary-uniformitarian view of the origin of planet Earth and its supposed cosmochemical analogy with other celestial bodies, and begs the question about the validity of the K-Ar method and the great antiquity of the earth:

> Argon, the third most abundant gas in the atmosphere, consists of three isotopes, ^{36}Ar, ^{38}Ar, and ^{40}Ar, of which only ^{40}Ar is of radiogenic origin (^{40}K decay). The ratio of ^{36}Ar to ^{38}Ar is essentially the same in the atmosphere and in the solar and planetary components identified in meteorites. The primordial $^{40}Ar/^{36}Ar$ ratio is observed to be nearly zero (in meteorites) and terrestrial ^{40}Ar is essentially of radiogenic origin. . . . Argon composition in the continental crust varies from nearly atmospheric (e. g., groundwaters) to "purely" radiogenic for old rocks devoid of fluid inclusions (Jambon 1994, p. 487).

A variety of terms are used to refer to argon which is not believed to have resulted from *in situ* ^{40}K decay in a given igneous body (Singer *et al.* 1998). "Inherited argon" refers to argon gas which is presumed to have accumulated radiogenically in a mineral during a history prior to its incorporation in the magma which subsequently congealed to form the igneous rock now being dated. "Excess argon" pertains to that argon which is believed to have been incorporated into a mineral by other processes than radioactive decay of ^{40}K (beyond that which has already been subtracted by the atmospheric-argon correction). "Extraneous argon" encompasses both "inherited" and "excess" argon.

It is interesting to note the widespread use of various K-Ar isochrons. Very often, they indicate a supposed initial $^{40}Ar/^{36}Ar$ ratio substantially different from 295.5 (e. g., Copeland *et al.* 1991; Hartz *et al.* 1998; Tegner *et al.* 1998), which means that, on its own terms, the uniformitarian assumption of atmospherically-equilibrated Ar isotopes is explicitly contradicted. Ironically, there are also times when the $^{40}Ar/^{36}Ar$ intercept does agree with the assumed atmospheric correction value of 295.5, yet the K-Ar date is unacceptably old (e. g., Singer *et al.* 1998). This is blamed on hidden xenocrystic contamination of the magma, with the extraneous argon being in the form of inherited argon rather than excess argon. This type of reasoning, of course, at least partly begs the question about the validity of the atmospheric correction.

In addition, there now are theoretical and empirical grounds to doubt this foundational assumption behind K-Ar dating:

> Later, K-Ar workers sought a justification for the use of the atmospheric Ar correction in the prevalent belief that Ar could not stay in molten magma. . . . Rocks solidifying rapidly at Earth's surface or plutonic rocks solidifying under far greater pressure could quite possibly retain greater amounts of Ar. The $^{40}Ar/^{36}Ar$ ratio of this Ar depends on the magma's history prior to its solidification and is unlikely to be identical to the present atmospheric value of 295.5. . . . It may be argued that in equilibrium the isotopic composition of Ar in a magma should be the same as that of the atmospheric Ar and hence the atmospheric Ar correction is still valid. *This may be true in some cases but in general it is questionable* (Hayatsu and Waboso 1985, pp. 100-101) [emphasis added].

At the same time, the tendency of magmatic argon gas to be trapped in a rapidly-forming and rapidly-congealing magma affords an explanation of multimillion-year K-Ar results in the context of a young earth (e. g., Snelling 1998). The vast amounts of magma which crystallized during the Flood year must have trapped considerable amounts of magmatic argon, and at ratios considerably different from that assumed by the standard atmospheric correction. This resulted in built-in ages of many millions of years for igneous rocks that are actually only thousands of years old (figure 13).

Myth: Most recent volcanics give essentially zero K-Ar ages, and this proves that excess argon phenomena are infrequent and unimportant.

Dalrymple (1984, pp. 81-82) would have us believe this.

Fact: To begin with, recent volcanics give nonzero K-Ar dates much more frequently than previously realized (see Austin 1996, and references cited therein; Austin and Snelling 1998;

Singer *et al.* 1998, and references cited therein; Snelling 1998). Moreover, use of modern volcanics as a guide to ancient ones begs the question about the validity of uniformitarianism and of the great antiquity of the earth! In other words, when the rates of magma emplacement are small (as at present), it is usually true that little non-atmospheric argon is trapped in them. Only K-decay can endow them with more Ar. However, if indeed most igneous bodies had been generated during the Creation and the Flood, conditions would have been much more favorable for them to have "built-in" K-Ar ages of millions and billions of years, caused by excess argon (Snelling 1998). Even from a uniformitarian viewpoint, the inheritance of argon comes down to a question of *rate*:

> We therefore suggest that rapid emplacement and cooling are important factors in the entrapment of extraneous argon in igneous minerals, because long cooling times or recharging of magma chambers would provide sufficient time for the loss of trapped argon by diffusion (Richards and McDougall 1990, p. 1412).

Myth: Excess argon is rare in ancient rocks, and geochronologists regard it as a curiosity.

Dalrymple (1991, p. 91-92) asserts that excess argon is "uncommon."

Reality Check: While there exists, to my knowledge, no systematic inventory which enumerates the frequency of K-Ar dates that are "too old" and have to be attributed to excess argon, there are a variety of indirect indicators that point to the commonness of its occurrence. For instance, Poths *et al.* (1993) titled their GSA abstract as follows: *Ubiquitous Excess Argon in Very Young Basalts*. Unless the apologists for isotopic dating have their own private dictionary which differs from that which everyone else uses, there is no escaping the fact that the word "ubiquitous" is opposite of "rare." What about presumably older rocks?

> Any component of ^{40}Ar, other than ^{40}Ar derived from atmosphere and radiogenic decay, is termed excess argon, and is *widely recognized in dated materials* [reference cited]. Large plutons are *particularly prone to contamination* by excess ^{40}Ar due to incomplete re-equilibration with atmosphere at the time of crystallization and assimilation of radiogenic ^{40}Ar from the adjacent country rocks during hydrothermal alteration (Tegner *et al.* 1998. p. 79) [emphasis added].

> One of the limitations of the K-Ar method for dating minerals is their excess ^{40}Ar, which is responsible for the anomalously old age determined for these minerals (Morozova *et al.* 1997, p. 716).

> A *significant problem* in K/Ar isotopic dating is the siting of "excess" ^{40}Ar acquired by minerals from their environment (that is, ^{40}Ar not produced by radiogenic

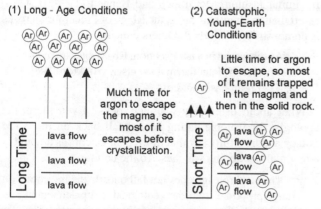

(1) Long - Age Conditions

(2) Catastrophic, Young-Earth Conditions

Much time for argon to escape the magma, so most of it escapes before crystallization.

Little time for argon to escape, so most of it remains trapped in the magma and then in the solid rock.

Long Time: lava flow / lava flow / lava flow

Short Time: lava flow / lava flow / lava flow

Figure 13: The K-Ar method tacitly presupposes an old earth by assuming that igneous bodies form slowly enough for any entrapped argon to leave prior to the solidification of the magma (1). Under Flood conditions (2), igneous bodies trap large amounts of argon and so acquire high "built-in" K-Ar "ages"—and without significant K-decay.

decay within the mineral) (Cumbest *et al.* 1994, p. 942) [emphasis added].

K-Ar dating is based on the decay of potassium to ^{40}Ar. *A major constraint* is the possibility that a mineral may contain excess radiogenic argon, which results in anomalously high ages (Morozova *et al.* 1996, p. 52) [emphasis added].

It is difficult to imagine how so-called excess argon could be described in terms of such things as "widely recognized," "particularly prone to contamination," "a limitation of the K-Ar method," "a significant problem," if it were infrequent in occurrence and/or just some kind of easily-recognized nuisance. Furthermore, in contrast to those apologists for isotopic dating who would have us believe that discrepantly-old excess argon phenomena are rare, other researchers are more forthright. Australian geochronologists McDougall and Harrison (1988, p. 11) consider it "not uncommon." Elsewhere, here is what they have to say about excess argon:

Potassium-argon ages much greater than are geologically plausible *often are observed*, and in some cases they are older than the age of the earth (McDougall and Harrison 1988, p. 106) [emphasis added].

Austin (1996) provides many examples, from the literature and from direct dating of recent Mount St. Helens volcanic rock, of the commonality of excess argon. Other authors affirm the fact that excess argon is not at all a rare phenomenon. This is notably the case for some of the commonly-used minerals in K-Ar dating, such as hornblende and biotite:

Indeed, the presence of excess argon in amphiboles appears to be *much more common than previously suspected* (McDougall and Harrison 1988, p. 28) [emphasis added].

There have been *numerous cases* reporting the presence of excess argon in biotite. . . (Hyodo and York 1993) [emphasis added].

Where present, this excess Ar yields an anomalously old age and, in certain environments, is a *common phenomenon in some minerals, especially biotite* (Smith *et al.* 1994b, p. 808) [emphasis added].

Clearly, then, "excess argon" is not some sort of freak occurrence. In fact, it commonly occurs in igneous rocks over a fairly large geographic area. For instance, a swarm of dikes in western Arizona yielded "too old" K-Ar results *as a rule* (Nakata 1991, p. 25). The same phenomenon is characteristic of the 1 x 2 quadrangle of west-central Colorado:

Nevertheless, many Proterozoic and Tertiary rocks have produced Paleozoic and Mesozoic dates. For the Tertiary rocks, all of which are plutonic, the abnormally

old K-Ar dates probably can be attributed to excess argon (Wallace 1995, p. 6).

Likewise, excess argon is common in the Kola Peninsula of Russia's Far East (Ivanenko and Karpenko 1988).

Several analytic techniques have been alleged to independently detect the presence of excess argon (e. g., K-Ar isochrons, potassium- vs. -age plots, and ^{40}Ar/^{39}Ar spectra). All of these, as we shall see, are used inconsistently, and have their own sets of assumptions and special pleadings. Furthermore, the majority of claims about the existence of excess argon arise on an *ad hoc*, after-the-fact basis:

Also, in most cases the explanation for the excess argon is given without any real proof, while the identification is usually based either on comparing the results with the precisely established geological age or by comparison with other isotopic methods (Rublev 1985, p. 73).

A rather obvious example of this is the following:

The K-Ar ages of hornblende and biotites from these rocks are, with two exceptions, older than crystallization ages and the explanation for this must be excess argon. It is difficult to ascribe any significance to the dates because of this (Hunt and Roddick 1992, p. 217).

Currently, uniformitarians are unsure whether to blame "excess argon" on K-decay in the mantle, or on an external source (Phillips *et al.* 1998).

Myth: Rb-Sr isochrons not indicative of the correct date for a rock seldom occur.

Fact: To the contrary: they are actually believed to be common:

The literature on Archean geology is cluttered with dubious age determinations — particularly whole-rock Rb-Sr pseudochrons — of minimal validity, and I do not generally here cite such ages nor discuss the confusion produced by them (Hamilton 1998, p. 2).

In similar fashion, McCulloch and Bennett (1994, p. 4726) assert that, in almost all cases, the Rb-Sr of Precambrian rocks is demonstrably disturbed. Others concur:

As discussed in a later section, Rb-Sr ages are *commonly* reset by later thermal events. . . (Bickford 1988, p. 419) [emphasis added].

What about ostensibly-younger rocks? Even there, the apologist for isotopic dating cannot fall back on the **ATM** fallacy and truthfully say that discrepant isochrons amount to a few malfunctioning watches. To the contrary:

The isochron age does not fall outside the injection range proposed from the geological and paleobotanical data, so there is no increase in the apparent injection age as is *fairly common* for acid magmatites (Bubnov and Goltsman 1993, p. 48) [emphasis added].

Rubidium-Sr geochronology, particularly in high-grade metamorphic terranes, often yields ages that are inconsistent with other geochronological techniques (Gazis *et al.* 1998, p. 694).

The phenomenon of Rb-Sr whole-rock ages significantly younger than Rb-Sr mineral ages or in other words rotation of isochrons is found to be a *common feature* for acid igneous rocks. . . (Baumann *et al.* 1991, p. 686) [emphasis added].

Perhaps the best proof of the fact that the Rb-Sr isochron method is fundamentally unreliable is that geochronologists do not recommend that its results be *ipso facto* trusted:

Unfortunately, the parent radionuclide, ^{87}Rb, is a volatile and mobile alkali element, characteristics which lead to open-system behaviour and anomalous ages. *The current practice is not to rely on the Rb-Sr system to give the only absolute age information* on the crystallization age of a suite of rocks but to use it in concert with other decay schemes (Shirey 1991, p. 11) [emphasis added].

Note how different this is from a true "malfunctioning watch" situation. A person trusts his/her watch to indicate the correct time and does not normally feel the need to routinely verify the accuracy of one's watch by comparing it with other timepieces!

Myth: Discrepant U-Pb whole rock isochrons are infrequent.

Fact: They are actually so common that the use of U-Pb dating on whole rocks is rarely trusted:

Unfortunately, the U-Pb and Th-Pb systems *rarely stay closed* in silicate rocks, due to the mobility of Pb, Th, and especially U, under conditions of low-grade metamorphism and superficial weathering (Dickin 1997, p. 105) [emphasis added].

Much the same can be said about Pb-Pb whole-rock isochrons. Keeping in mind that no part of the ocean is supposed to be older than Mesozoic, $^{207}Pb/^{204}Pb$ vs. $^{206}Pb/^{204}Pb$ plots on oceanic basalts nevertheless keep turning up which define considerably older ages. For instance, Pb-Pb dates of 1.8–2.0 Ga (Allegre and Lewin 1995) are supposed to either date the "stirring time" in the upper mantle, or are thought to be mixing lines with no geochronometric significance. In a comparable situation on land, Austin (1994, p. 126) reports a Pb-Pb isochron of 2.6 Ga on young basalts in the Grand Canyon. Other absurd "dates" have also been obtained from them (Vardiman 1998).

Myth: Inherited (xenocrystic) zircons, a source of U-Pb results which are "too old," are a rare occurrence.

Reality Check: The following statements speak for themselves:

There are *many examples* of intrusive granitoids containing old inherited radiogenic Pb in zircons which show an incomplete resetting of the U-Pb systems during melting event (Hong *et al.* 1990, p. 133) [emphasis added].

Granitic rocks *commonly* contain multiple zircon populations with variable ages (Laicheng *et al.* 1997, p. 363) [emphasis added].

U-Pb geochronology of zircon is widely recognized as one of the most precise and reliable methods for dating the crystallization ages of igneous rocks. A *major complication limiting the technique* is the presence of xenocrystic zircon either incorporated from wall rocks during magma emplacement, or entrained in magma as a residual unmelted phase from its source region (Roddick and Bevier 1995, p. 307) [emphasis added].

It is difficult to imagine that the xenocrystic-zircon rationalization for discrepantly-old U-Pb zircon results would be characterized as a "major complication limiting the technique" if it could be likened to a tiny number of malfunctioning watches in a world of functioning watches! In fact, some form of alleged xenocrystic contamination is not only routinely common, but virtually universal:

The dating of granitoid rocks used to be a relatively simple matter when Rb-Sr whole-rock and U-Pb multigrain analysis were used and when errors were in the order of several tens of millions of years. Single zircon analysis has changed this belief by documenting *the presence of variable amounts of inherited xenocrysts in virtually every granitoid rock*, thus making it difficult to obtain the precise age of magmatic emplacement (Kroner and Jaeckel 1994, p. 181) [emphasis added].

Myth: Discrepantly old U-Pb zircon dates from tuffs and bentonites, blamed on inherited (contaminant) zircons, seldom occur.

Fact: Once again, the following statement speaks for itself:

Zircon inheritance is *such a major problem* in the dating of continental ashes that efforts should be directed instead at searching for monazite as a preferential alternative (Roden *et al.* 1990, pp. 284-285).

(Apropos to this suggestion, monazite is discussed in the section on U-Pb dating, and is shown to be no panacea for the problems inherent in the U-Pb dating of zircon).

B. "Rigorous Testing" of Geochronometric Systems: Past and Present

Myth: Historically speaking, the overall validity of the isotopic dating methods had been very rigorously established prior to their recognition as such.

Reality Check: Whatever the degree of critical experimentation that had in fact pre-existed their general use, one could make a case that, in actuality, isotopic dating methods and their results had been accepted rather uncritically because the results seemed to fit in with uniformitarian ideas about the great antiquity of the earth. Far from being rigorously tested, the unspoken attitude in uniformitarian geochronology seemed (and still seems) to be as follows: "Use whatever dating method you have that seems to substantiate the belief that rocks are millions to billions of years old, until some better dating method comes along. Then use that method."

There are several lines of evidence which support this premise. One of these is the fact that, historically, several methods were widely used despite the fact that they confessedly gave poor results. For instance, the U-Th-He method usually gave unreasonably young results, but was used until K-Ar and other methods became available in the 1950's (Zeitler *et al.* 1987, p. 2865). Such was also the case with the now-abandoned lead-alpha method, which was used until the late 1950's, even though some geochronologists left nothing to the imagination when they were quoted as saying: ". . . the lead-alpha dates stunk" (Glen 1982, p. 88).

Subsequently, as new dating methods were being evaluated, the results were often evaluated according to what the researchers felt were reasonable, and not according to some mythical high standard of rigorous testing:

> With Cormier's first Rb-Sr determinates on "glauconite" (1956) began the study of authigenic minerals that were enriched in Rb and depleted in Sr. The results were encouraging, as the ages were *reasonable* compared to the suggested time scale (Clauer 1982, p. 245) [emphasis in original].

As K-Ar and Rb-Sr methods came into widespread use in the 1950's, the attitude of investigators towards them was not exactly one of cautious skepticism. Far from it. As I had pointed out in my earlier paper (Woodmorappe 1979, 1993), isochrons were then believed to be virtually foolproof indicators of age in the early days of isotopic dating. In fact, as shown below, *in almost every instance, opinions about the presumed reliability of geochronometers had proved to be far too optimistic.* This retreat from earlier expectations is also mute testimony to the fact that isotopic dating methods had *not* in fact been rigorously tested prior to their general use.

Consider, first of all, the retreat from the earlier belief that K-Ar dates are highly reliable indicators of the age of the rock:

> By the mid-1960's, ideas of closure temperatures began to develop and it was realized that at high temperatures Ar readily diffused out of minerals. K-Ar

dates began to be *correctly viewed as cooling dates, rather than some vague age of the rock system* (Armstrong 1991b, p. 14) [emphasis added].

The following concerns some K-Ar dates obtained in the mid and late 1960's:

> The K-Ar ages . . . were determined when phenomena such as excess ^{40}Ar were not fully understood, and instrumentation was not as precise as it is today (Nelson *et al.* 1992, p. 1547).

Apologists for isotopic dating can spin these as examples of the "progress" of geochronometry if they so like, but it does not change the fact that phenomena such as so-called excess argon and so-called cooling ages had *not in fact been rigorously tested prior to the widespread use of (in this case) the K-Ar method*. In like manner, the limitations of the fission-track (FT) method evidently had come *after* attempts had been made to use it on a fairly widespread basis:

> Two decades ago, the early attempts to date apatite from crystalline basement rocks by means of fission tracks at first produced bewildering results: The ages turned out to be consistently younger than any known major geological event such as rock formation or metamorphism (Wagner 1988, p. 145).

And, in spite of the fact that some minerals (e.g., zircon) are believed to retain nuclear tracks at relatively high temperatures, there is no escape from the following fact: there has been a conspicuous retreat from the prior belief that the FT (fission-track) method can generally provide acceptable (to uniformitarians, that is) dates for the crystallization of a host rock:

> For many in geochronology and isotope geology, the FT method was viewed as a Cinderella because of its inadequacy as a numerical dating method. A singular exception was the application of the method to volcanic and volcaniclastic problems where rapid cooling and near surface temperature often resulted in minimal annealing and *acceptable formation ages*. Solution to this apparent impasse came in the early to mid-1980's in two ways. Firstly the importance of track length in interpreting FT was re-evaluated leading to a re-orientation of the method as a source primarily of thermochronological information rather than formation ages (Hurford 1998, p. 25) [emphasis added].

In uniformitarian parlance, "thermochronological information" is a euphemistic cover-phrase for the fact that the method does not usually give the expected age of the rock, but instead may supposedly provide the date of the most recent heating event on the rock.

Like apples falling off a tree, the isotopic dating methods have fallen in credibility, one by one. It had been widely, and successively, believed that first Rb-Sr isochrons, then U-Pb

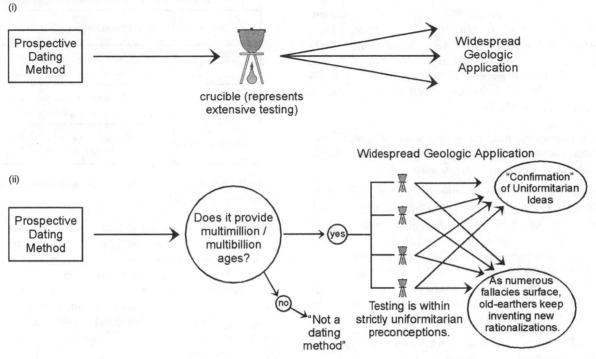

Figure 14: "Testing" of prospective dating methods had less to do with value-free empirical analysis (i) and more to do with its "fit" with *local* geology as viewed through uniformitarian spectacles (ii).

(on zircon), and finally Sm-Nd isochrons were too chemically robust to become open systems, and were therefore virtually foolproof indicators of the age of the rock. In all three instances, geochronologists have been forced to back down from these rosy beliefs:

> Each of the above dating systems had at some stage of its development been alleged to be immune from isotopic resetting under sub-solidus conditions. Examples to the contrary have been found. . . (Black 1986, pp. 156-157) [emphasis added].

There is likewise no question about the fact that the expectations for the presumed capabilities of the K-Ar, Rb-Sr, FT, and U-Pb methods had proved to be extravagantly optimistic:

> These methods have remained important, but often in more specialized applications than originally conceived. For example, Ar-Ar and fission track for cooling ages (Dickin 1997, p. xiv).

> The Rb-Sr whole-rock method was widely used as a dating tool for igneous crystallisation during the 1960's and 1970's, but lost credibility during the 1980's as evidence of whole-rock open-system behaviour mounted (Dickin 1997, p. 51).

Since all these serious problems had been discovered long *after* the dating methods in question had enjoyed widespread use, it can hardly be claimed that they had been rigorously checked *before* this widespread use! And what about the practical use of isotopic dating methods in everyday geologic applications? Even under such circumstances, the attitude of

geologists continues to be one of uncritical acceptance rather than cautious skepticism:

> The quantitative nature of geochronology, in contrast to the more descriptive nature of biostratigraphy, has led a number of earth scientists to place unquestioned faith in the published works of many geochronologists (Obradovich and Cobban 1975, pp. 32-3).

> "Absolute dates" are appealing if only for reasons of simplicity and universal comprehension. Because there is a tendency for those who use these dates to accept them at face value, a few cautionary remarks are in order (Woodburne 1987, p. 3).

When confronted with this evidence, apologists for isotopic dating change their tune. Having been exposed in their earlier-made blustery claims about the wonderful reliability of isotopic dating, they now give us a song and dance about the fact that they are the ones who had discovered the flaws in these dating methods. To give a hyperbolic example, this is like an arsonist who sets a building on fire, calls the fire department to report the fire he set, and then has the audacity to proclaim himself a hero for having reported the fire!

Furthermore, this progressive backpedaling away from earlier rosy expectations for the dating methods fulfills a prophecy of sorts in early-modern creationist research. Whitcomb and Morris (1961, p. 335) had noted that dogmatic claims had been made for *every* set of dates, from the early 20th-century ones all the way to the then-current crop of dates (late 1950's). However, the early dates eventually had to be rejected in spite of these once-voiced dogmatic claims about their impeccable factuality and accuracy. Hence Whitcomb and Morris had surmised that the same fate may befall the late-1950's ones. From the vantage point of thirty-eight years in the future (1999), and with the greatly diminished expectations for K-Ar and Rb-Sr dating (as demonstrated in this section), we can now appreciate the fact that the words of Whitcomb and Morris have proved to be prophetic.

Myth: An overwhelming preponderance of "good" over "bad" dates is necessary for the acceptance of the reliability of a dating method on a given material.

Reality Check: We can easily demonstrate the utter falsehood of this variation of the "malfunctioning watch" argument by examining how geochronologists actually reason when it comes to accepting the reliability of a given dating method. Consider the controversy as to the reliability or otherwise of the Rb-Sr system on acid volcanics. One group of geochronologists had discussed instances where Rb-Sr isochrons had been clearly "too young." In response to this group, we have the following comments:

> McKerrow *et al.* conclude that Rb-Sr whole-rock isochron ages for acid volcanics are always too young and that this radiometric clock has always been reset by some process or event post-dating extrusion. In contrast, we have concluded [2] that it should not be assumed that resetting has occurred in every acid volcanic system although it is well known that any Rb-Sr whole-rock system can be reset, regardless of rock type. There are examples of Rb-Sr whole-rock isochron ages for acid volcanics which are concordant with ages derived from other decay schemes (Gale *et al.* 1980, p. 9).

After listing *two* instances of K-Ar/Rb-Sr isochron concordances on acid volcanics, they continue:

> In view of such evidence, it is clear that Rb-Sr whole-rock isochrons should not be regarded as yielding ages which are inevitably too young relative to those derived using other radiometric methods (Gale *et al.* 1980, p. 10).

From this example, we can clearly see that the uniformitarian geochronologist does not need hundreds or thousands of examples of "good" results before accepting the provisional value of a dating method on a given material. All he needs is a few examples [in this case only 2(!)] in which the results seem to fit in with other evidence that he considers to be

Date	What Geochronologists Said Then:
1950's/1960's	Pre-1950 dates are not too reliable, but current ones are very reliable
1970's	Pre-1970 dates are not too reliable, but current ones are very reliable
1980's/1990's	Pre-1980 dates are not too reliable, but current ones are very reliable

Table 2: Every decade sees dogmatic claims about the finality of the dates obtained.

reliable. Nor does he feel the need to wait for the development of a situation where ostensibly "good" results outnumber the "bad" ones by an overwhelming margin (the way functioning watches outnumber malfunctioning ones). In fact, from the example above, the "good" results don't even have to be demonstrated to be in the majority! And all this is taking place in the very context wherein reliability criteria are supposed to be the most stringent—the development of the quantitative Phanerozoic time scale.

Further evidence that *the uniformitarian does not even need a simple majority of results being "good" before he accepts some method/material combination as a geologic "timepiece"* is obvious from the following chain of reasoning related to the direct use of U-Pb and Pb-Pb methods on carbonate rocks:

> The above "aberrant" ages were mainly obtained from samples collected from the Jixian Section. These "negative" results should not be the reason to discourage further U-Pb and Pb-Pb chronological studies. In fact, carbonate samples collected . . . near Beijing [have] yielded a Pb-Pb isochron age . . . [which] is very coherent with the assumed stratigraphic position, and thus may represent its depositional or early diagenetic age. We conclude that like the other classic elemental pairs used in geochronology (Rb-Sr, Sm-Nd) an open-system behavior observed in one locality may not have occurred elsewhere (Jahn and Cuvellier 1994, p. 141).

Ironically, therefore, the bogus "malfunctioning watch" argument can be turned around. That is, the uniformitarian geochronologist may need only a few instances where something seems to be a watch (according, of course, to his reckoning) before he accepts (or at least seriously contemplates) it a valid dating method!

Chapter 5

"Reliability Criteria:" Are Isotopic Systems Truly Self-Checking?

A. "Self-Checking:" Proved or Assumed?

Myth: Assessing the reliability of isotopic dates is a rigorous, scientific procedure.

Reality Check: To the contrary: The credibility or otherwise of dates is a matter of opinion, and the distinction between "reliable" and "unreliable" data is not at all clear-cut. This fact is proved by this comment on a compendium of isotopic results derived from British Columbia, Canada:

> It is very difficult to separate the K/Ar effects of intrusive (plus hydrothermal) events versus simple uplift events (Magaritz and Taylor 1986, p. 2194).

Presumably, the most stringent criteria for reliability are devoted to dates used to calibrate the Phanerozoic time scale. Even here, however, notions of reliability are subjective:

> There is no radiometric date yet reported which has been proved to be so completely reliable that it can be used as an anchor point in calibrating the Palaeozoic time scale. Such a calibration must instead be based on all available reliable data. . . (Gale and Beckinsale 1983).

Furthermore, despite the passage of many decades, the agreed-upon "absolute" values for parts of the Phanerozoic geologic column are still very much in flux, despite the large numbers of presumably reliable dates:

> However, correlation between the biostratigraphic time scale and absolute ages is continuously modified, and new but controversial data should always be considered (Hartz et al. 1998, p. 285).

This is true in specific instances no less so than in the general case. Consider, for instance, the dating of the Cretaceous-Tertiary boundary. There existed a three-way agreement between dating methods, and Obradovich (1984, p. 11, elaborated below) called this "an extremely impressive array of analytical data" despite showing some independent evidence of open-system behavior. This shows that even the "best" data can be tainted with doubts about its reliability. Thus, if geochronologists were to apply "reliability" criteria to the utmost, there would hardly be any dates left to accept as reliable! Conversely, a uniformitarian geochronologist can always use a particular date as a trial balloon, and if it later

turns out to be geologically unacceptable, he can always fall back on some flaw in the date and conclude that "Oh well, it wasn't a totally reliable date anyway." This is just a variant of the **ATT** (**A**ppeal **T**o **T**echnicality) fallacy.

Finally, the presumed reliability of specific dates, in the eyes of the uniformitarian, clearly is a subjective matter of *degree* (according to his assumptions, of course). Consider, for instance, U-Pb dates on zircons when contrasted with other dating methods:

> U-Pb zircon ages have long been considered to be the most reliable radiometric age from which to determine the time of crystallization of an intrusive igneous rock. . . (Wooden et al. 1996, p. 126).

Similar equivocations on "reliability" hold for other dates:

> The average age of the six dates *that we consider reliable* is 27.1 Ma, our best estimate of the age of the member (Rowley et al. 1994, p. 11) [emphasis added].

In the K-Ar method, there is also a supposed "degree of reliability." It is believed to be directly proportional to the K-content and also directly proportional to the amount of the presumed radiogenic content (e. g., Chevallier et al. 1992, p. 6). More on this later, including the inconsistency of its application.

Myth: Only after rigorous analysis do geochronologists disregard particular results as unreliable.

Reality Check: This may be true sometimes, but not usually. To begin with, there is always the temptation to challenge dating results which are out of step with other results. For instance, consider the attitude towards an Rb-Sr isochron date of 3.5 Ga which was not corroborated by the ostensibly more isotope-retentive U-Pb dates on zircons:

> Our inability to find zircon older than 2.7 Ga in another gneissic phase collected from this area points towards the need for reassessing the Rb-Sr data (Mondal et al. 1998, p. 74).

In fact, even under the best of circumstances, the selection and rejection of results is clearly based on posterioritic reasoning, and by no stretch of the imagination does it amount to a hard science:

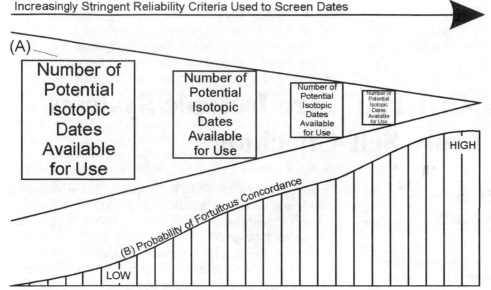

Figure 15. Use of ever-more stringent reliability criteria comes at a double price: A) fewer and fewer usable dates are obtained, and B) the few dates which pass the reliability criteria are more likely to owe their status to chance. Finally, use of the most stringent presumed reliability criteria fails to prevent the appearance of discrepant dates, which then have to be explained away on an after-the-fact basis.

In the following analysis, several criteria are used for interpreting the reliability of K-Ar dates. First, any date with a high error (i. e., the ±) is treated permissive, but not diagnostic of age. Second, the geologic context and/or study of mineral separates may indicate the possibility of an older detrital component which *could* correspond to anomalous results. . . . Third, the overall interpretation of a suite of dates is made by comparing all the dates, taking into consideration their stratigraphic relations, analytical quality, and their internal consistency on dates for different minerals. *This process inevitably remains somewhat subjective* and it is therefore important to have, whenever possible, multiple dates for each mineral and to date as many phases per sample as possible. The multiple dates presented in this study thus establish a more objective basis for rejection of some dates, particularly *if* suspect dates correlate with observable problems such as alteration and/or contamination (Marshall *et al.* 1986, p. 451) [emphasis added].

When it comes to the development of the "absolute" time scale and the ostensibly high standards which are supposed to govern the acceptance and rejection of isotopic dates, the somewhat loose approach used to reject certain dates is clearly in evidence:

It is commonly accepted by geochronologists that diverse processes of alteration usually lead to a preferential loss of radiogenic isotopes relative to the radioactive ones. Consequently, when such an opening of the system is suspected it is customary to accept the oldest apparent age measured as the best or minimum estimate of the actual time of closure of the system. The systematic application of this rule, when in reality the system has not been open during its history, may lead one to overestimate the actual age of the dated formation. Several factors can also result in measured apparent ages being *older* than the age of formation of the system under investigation. . . (Odin 1985, p. 43) [emphasis in original].

This same essentially-arbitrary rejection of data is taking place in conjunction with the dating of the global Triassic/Jurassic boundary:

The estimates are further skewed to older values by selective exclusion of younger dates. This apparently reflects a bias in favor of ^{40}Ar loss as a cause of scattered or conflicting data. Even though this conclusion is sometimes justified, it cannot be assumed automatically given the possibility that the younger dates may be more accurate (that is, if the anomalies are the result of the presence of excess ^{40}Ar). The selective exclusion of any data (younger or older) can not be justified in the absence of supporting evidence. As new information from the Hartford basin and other regions is used to revise the time scale, it is evident from this review of previously published time scales that care must be taken to avoid the unwarranted exclusion of data (Seidemann 1989, p. 561).

Lest we hear, from some apologist of isotopic dating, that old line about all this being just a tiny number of malfunctioning watches (or some other version of the old **ATM** fallacy), let us substantiate the fact that such arbitrary exclusion of dating results is far from rare:

It is common geochronological practice to regard the oldest age obtained from a suite of geologically contemporaneous rocks as a best estimate of the true age, radiogenic Ar loss implicitly being assumed to be the only perturbing mechanism (Mitchell *et al.* 1989, p. 56) [emphasis added].

Without doubt, isotopic dates which don't agree with then-current ideas as to "correct" age are summarily rejected. This occurs not as a result of the date having failed to pass some sort of rigorous reliability criteria, but solely at the discretion of the uniformitarian geologist. The following are just a few obvious examples of this:

One of these dates, 29.4 ± 2.2, on hornblende, is rejected because it is considered too old due to excess argon: the other, 26.4 ± 3.2 on plagioclase from the same sample, is geologically reasonable and is similar to a new date on the Spry intrusion (Rowley *et al.* 1994, p. 16).

The present K-Ar date of 102.0 ± 3.3 Ma is significantly older than the U-Pb date from the same sample and inconsistent with the previously-determined K-Ar dates. This date may reflect a serious problem with excess Ar in this sample and should be discounted in favour of the previously determined dates (Hunt and Roddick 1993, p. 131).

. . . there was a wide range of glauconite dates from the same bed, and Odin and Curry (1985) arbitrarily picked certain ones and ignored others that tended to give older ages. In other cases, they selectively ignored dates that did not agree with their preconceptions, even though these came from areas with well-established stratigraphy (Prothero and Schwab 1996, p. 455).

. . . it appears that four of the five samples yield an isochron age of 31 Ma. This is not in agreement with a K-Ar biotite age of the body of 55 Ma [reference cited]. We therefore interpret the Rb-Sr whole rock isochron age of 31 Ma as a pseudo-isochron because the Rb-Sr whole rock isochron age is younger than the K-Ar biotite age for the same body [references cited]. In this case, the pseudo-isochron may represent a mixing line between the source magma and upper crustal material (Kawano and Kagami 1993, p. 174).

. . . they dismissed this age as anomalous because their K-Ar age for this body (232 ± 5 Ma) agreed so well with the K-Ar ges of the adjacent Cockscomb pluton and the HMR pluton to the north. The Silurian Rb-Sr age also was rejected because no other Silurian-Ordovician rock ages were known in Belize (Steiner and Walker 1996, pp. 17,728-17,729).

Pertaining to the lattermost case, once some older U-Pb results were obtained, lo, and behold, the older dates were suddenly esteemed as credible.

Myth: Assessing the reliability of isotopic dates is so self-consistent and rigorous that geochronologists all agree on the reliability or otherwise of particular dates.

Reality Check: The fallacy of this premise is proved by the many instances when geochronologists had accepted particular ostensibly-reliable dating results as indicative of the true ages of the rocks, only to have to backpedal and abandon these claims when some new but contrary body of information became available. Examples of this have already been provided. Now let us consider situations where different geochronologists cannot even agree which body of conflicting isotopic dates to accept as reliable age-indicators of the rock. Consider, for instance, the interpretation of isotopic results from the central Brooks Range (Alaska, USA). A set of geologic field studies (cited by Aleinikoff *et al.* 1993, p. 59) had suggested that these bodies are either Devonian or Cretaceous. Isotopic results only fueled the conflict, with U-Pb and Rb-Sr results supporting the former age and the K-Ar results suggesting the latter. This led to a further disagreement as to which results to accept as valid indicators of age, and which to explain away. One group of geologists supposed that the Devonian results were correct, and that the Cretaceous ones were "rejuvenated." Another group contended that the Cretaceous results are the ones that give the correct age of the rock, while the Devonian results are artificially-old inherited ages from zircon crystals of xenocrystic origin.

Another example is provided by a situation where an Rb-Sr isochron result had been accepted as indicative of the age of the rock, until some U-Pb zircon results indicated a supposed older age. All of a sudden, this ostensibly-reliable Rb-Sr isochron was demoted from the realm of "age-indicative" isochrons to the realm of "rejuvenated" isochrons:

Eight of the ten grains yield $^{206}Pb/^{238}U$ dates between 428 and 478 Ma; two are within 5% of concordia at 444 and 477 Ma. These dates imply an Ordovician igneous crystallization age for the granite, which conflicts with a previously reported 369 Ma Rb-Sr date interpreted as the time of synkinematic intrusion. The Devonian Rb-Sr date and other geologic information are compatible with Devonian metamorphism of this Ordovician intrusion (Grimes *et al.* 1997, p. 20).

This clearly demonstrates that the interpretation of isotopic results is not only theory-driven, but is essentially arbitrary in the sense of being *a set of opinions* that are ultimately unverifiable. So much for the myth, propounded by apologists for isotopic dating, that "reliability criteria" are rigorous and objective.

Disagreements as to the reliability or otherwise of particular isotopic dates are most likely to occur in situations when none of the dating results obtained are so far "out of line" with uniformitarian geologic interpretations as to be immediately rejected out of hand as potentially-reliable age-indicators. And, of course, all this occurs in spite of any so-called reliability criteria connected with the dating results. Consider, for example, the question of whether to believe an $^{40}Ar/^{39}Ar$ plateau date (Eocene age: 52 Ma), or a series of Rb-Sr isochron dates (Late Cretaceous: 84-91 Ma), as indicative of the true age of a volcanic rock:

The isochrons are largely two-point fits between Rb-rich biotites and clusters of low-Rb phases. Slight variations in the initial $^{87}Rb/^{87}Sr$ ratios, or changes in the Rb/Sr ratios caused by, for example, deuteric alteration or weathering, *could* significantly affect the calculated ages. Alternatively, the Late Creta- ceous Rb-Sr mineral dates *could* record emplacement of the Independence intrusions, whereas the Eocene $^{40}Ar/^{39}Ar$ dates and characteristic remnant magneti- zation *may* record systematic resetting of the isoto- pic and magnetic systems due to thermal effects associated with emplacement of younger, overlying AVS rocks. This interpretation *seems* unreasonable. . . . We *argue that* complete resetting of the $^{40}Ar/^{39}Ar$ system would significantly perturb the Rb-Sr system, with the result that the Rb-Sr isochrons *should* give dates consistent with our $^{40}Ar/^{39}Ar$ re- sults. . . . It *seems* improbable that an Eocene ther- mal event could completely reset the biotite and hornblende $^{40}Ar/^{39}Ar$ dates and completely overprint an older Cretaceous magnetization in these rocks, yet still preserve Late Cretaceous Rb-Sr mineral emplacement ages (Harlan *et al.* 1996, pp. 1652- 1653) [emphasis added].

From the above statements, one can easily see the guess- work and assumptions involved in attempting to decide which results are more reliable. Of course, if we are in fact to reject the quoted Rb-Sr isochron whose points tend to cluster in only two locations, we would also have to do the same to *all* of the other Rb-Sr isochrons in the literature which exhibit similar characteristics.

Another example of the subjectivity (and even conflict) inherent in deciding which isotopic-dating results are "reli- able" comes from East Greenland. A $^{40}Ar/^{39}Ar$ plateau result was considered to be a cooling age and not an extrusion age by Stemmerik *et al.* (1998). This owed to the fact that the date was "too young" to be an extrusion date, with a con- straint imposed by faunally-dated sedimentary rocks. Hartz *et al.* (1998) disputed this interpretation, pointing to the sub- jectivity involved in the correlation of the time-constraining subjacent strata, as well as the possibility that the isotopic date in question could still be reconciled with its biostrati- graphic constraints even if these strata had been correctly correlated. In either case, it is obvious that the presumed re- liability of isotopic dates is a matter of interpretation, not rigorous methodology. Still another example of conflict be- tween geochronologists not being able to agree whether or not a particular result is reliable is provided by Rb-Sr glau- conite dates from the U.S. mid-continent [compare Seidemann (1992) with Stein and Kish (1992)].

Myth: "Further, scientists are routinely able to detect open- system behavior and to correct or ignore data from open systems (Leveson and Seidemann 1996, p. 429)."

Fact: Richard Milton, a British science journalist and ama- teur geologist who is neither a creationist nor a religious be- liever, has written an excellent popular-level critique of

isotopic dating and its apologists (Milton 1997, pp. 15-56). Not surprisingly, he has been subject to the same bogus ar- guments (e. g., Leveson and Seidemann 1996) that have been leveled at scientific creationists.

Apart from everything else that has been discussed in this section of the paper, the fallacy of the claims advanced by Leveson and Seidemann is proven by the many cases of dates which are recognized as reliable, only to be later discarded in favor of some other presumably-reliable dates which contra- dict the first set of erstwhile-reliable dates. Many such ex- amples are given in this paper. Let me give another: Some U-Pb zircon dates from the Adirondack Mountain region of New York (McLelland *et al.* 1997, p. A-466), based on bulk- zircon dating, yielded values up to 1416 million years old. These had been accepted as reliable—that is, until single-grain dates yielded results some 250 million years younger. All of a sudden, the earlier ostensibly-reliable dates had to be rejected.

And, by any standard, reliability criteria are *not* thought of by uniformitarians (except, of course, the apologists for iso- topic dating) as having eliminated the problem of spurious dates:

> Although these situations have caused much grief, over the years geochronologists have developed methods and standards to double-check and mini- mize problems. Nevertheless, there is always the possibility that undetected problems have caused er- roneous dates, even with flawless lab procedure (Prothero 1994, p. 47).

To pile proof upon proof that open-system behavior can- not be objectively ascertained in an isotopic system, let us examine some situations where presumably "self-checked" conventional K-Ar dates were later shown to be flawed—by the presumably self-checking $^{40}Ar/^{39}Ar$ method. These include a series of dates from the mid-to late-Tertiary dated volcanics of Africa:

> Some of the measurements done a long time ago using the K-Ar age method are proving to be less reliable than had been hoped. In cases where new $^{40}Ar/^{39}Ar$ age determinations are being made on the same rocks, there are sometimes significant differ- ences (Burke 1996, p. 352).

Lest some apologists for isotopic dating resort to the **ATM** (**A**ppeal **T**o **M**arginalization) fallacy by objecting that these dates from Africa had not necessarily been subject to strin- gent reliability criteria, let us now consider the highly-re- garded work of the "Berkeley team" in the early-mid 1960's. This group of geochronologists had employed every known reliability criteria to ensure the accuracy of their dates for the western US. If any set of dating results had become a show- case of self-checking *par excellence*, these dates did. Con- sider, however, what took place some 25 years later:

> When Carl Swisher of the Institute of Human Ori- gins in Berkeley began to redate the Flagstaff Rim ashes in 1989, he discovered something shocking.

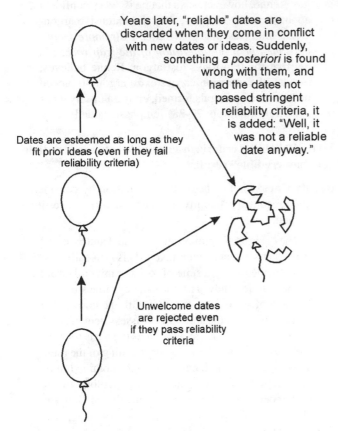

Figure 16. All isotopic dates are trial balloons which can be rejected *a posteriori* (sooner or much later). Reliability criteria are always subordinate to geologic interpretation in evaluations of the "reliability" of dates.

Many of the K-Ar dates first run by Jack Evernden and Garniss Curtis in 1963 were drawn from contaminated samples. These dates (Evernden *et al.* 1964) had served as the basis for dating the North American mammalian chronology for over a quarter century, and everyone relied on them. . . (Prothero 1994, p. 60).

Consider the following specific example of this:

> The same unit was most likely the one dated by Evernden *et al.* (1964) at 66.4 Ma. These ages are most likely too old, owing to the inclusion of detrital grains in the mineral separates (Swisher *et al.* 1993, p. 1994).

We can clearly see that, once again, the uniformitarians had cried wolf about the "self-checking" properties of dates, and had made unwarranted dogmatic claims about their reliability. As for the newest set of dates and their self-checking properties, how many times have we heard that one before?

Why should we *now* believe that the uniformitarians see a genuine wolf?

Myth: All in all, conventional K-Ar dates are self-checking for validity and accuracy.

Fact: The fallacy of this premise should be vividly obvious from the facts presented in both my earlier paper (Woodmorappe 1979, 1993) and this one. Finally, the development and widespread use of the $^{40}Ar/^{39}Ar$ method (discussed also in my 1979 paper and in much more detail later in this book) is a tacit admission that conventional K-Ar results are *not* actually self-checking at all:

> It is difficult to evaluate the internal argon systematics of a sample (i. e., alteration, contamination, excess argon) using the K-Ar method. Many laboratories have been involved, with differing methodologies and different approaches to calculation of analytical uncertainties (Tauxe *et al.* 1992, p. 563).

> Exclusive reliance in the past on K/Ar ages, in which complications related to extraneous argon, partial argon loss, or K alteration *may not have been recognized*, may impart systematic bias to estimates of hydrothermal longevity (Marsh *et al.* 1997, p. 802) [emphasis added].

> Either way, $^{40}Ar/^{39}Ar$ provided something that K-Ar dating could not—a method of measuring individual crystals, so that contamination could be detected, and error estimates reduced (Prothero 1994, p. 60).

> Excess ^{40}Ar contamination cannot be conclusively proven by conventional K-Ar dating techniques. . . (Richards and McDougall 1990, p. 1401).

Myth: We can conclude that C-14 dates are self-checking for validity and accuracy.

Fact: Even though the C-14 method is beyond the scope of this study, it is worth mentioning that it, too, is not self-checking in any objective sense of the word. As with the other dating methods, results are selectively interpreted on an after-the-fact basis:

> It is self-evident that a contaminated sample will give an erroneous date, but it is frequently impossible to ascertain if a sample has indeed been contaminated (Bradley 1985, p. 54).

> Relative ages are always subject to interpretation, and radiocarbon dates are often ignored or dismissed as a "bad date" if they do not fit an *a priori* hypothesis (Thompson *et al.* 1988, p. 392).

B. Credible/Non-Credible Dates: A Real or Contrived Dichotomy?

Myth: Isotopic dates are unambiguously divisible into "credible" and "non-credible" dating results.

This has been claimed by numerous apologists for isotopic dating.

Reality Check. In this entire section, I discuss various presumed reliability criteria for isotopic dates, and why even these are not true reliability criteria—if only because they are used inconsistently and selectively by uniformitarian geochronologists. For now, let it be clear that there is no such simple dichotomy between "credible" and "non-credible" dates! This is obvious from the following study, which has categorized thousands of isotopic dates from the Canadian Cordillera according to their ostensible significance:

> Each date is categorized as to its reliability and probable significance—if analytically accurate, reasonably precise, and on suitable material, then whether it represents a volcanic or intrusive event, is from a metamorphic rock, or is partially or totally reset by a younger metamorphic, uplift and erosion, or alteration event. *This is a somewhat subjective exercise* but if there is any error, it is on the side of giving significant event status to partially reset dates (Armstrong 1988, p. 59) [emphasis added].

Thus, on its own terms and even when using uniformitarian geologic interpretation *in addition to* analytic criteria, there is no such thing as an innately credible date. Further proof of this is the fact that uniformitarian geochronologists often cannot agree which particular dates to accept as reliable, and which to explain away. Consider, for example, the following situation pertaining to the dating of the subdivisions of the Ordovician Period:

> Palmer (1983) and Ross *et al.* (1982a) accept the 436 Ma date and reject the 454 Ma data, whereas Shaver (1985) rejected the 436 Ma date and accepted the 454 Ma date. If both the 436 and 454 Ma dates are accepted, the Blackriveran Stage is expanded to 14 my. . . (Heidlauf *et al.* 1986, p. 790).

Elsewhere, Harland (1983, p. 397) called attention to the ironic situation of geochronologists on one hand claiming that they can discriminate "good" from "bad" dates for timescale purposes while, on the other hand, they cannot agree which ones to identify as "good."

In view of Dalrymple's (1984) claims of isotopic dates being inherently "self-checking," it is interesting to note that neither he nor another geochronologist can agree as to which date is real and which is spurious when it comes to the Siberian traps and an intrusion which cuts the basalts:

> Over time, Dalrymple concludes, some of the argon-40 had leaked out of the trap's rocks, making them look 1 or 2 million years younger than they

are. Renne, however, says that he is "very confident about the new data" . . . they did extensive argon-argon analyses that *contradict Dalrymple's conclusions about the alteration of the trap rock.* It's not that the trap rocks lost argon, Renne believes; instead, the intrusion carries extra argon-40 picked up before the minerals formed, giving a falsely older age (Kerr 1995, pp. 27-28) [emphasis added].

Myth: Reliability criteria discriminate between "credible" and "not credible" results.

Reality Check: Let us begin this discussion by considering how the presumed reliability or otherwise of K-Ar results is ascertained:

> The basic assumptions must be tested and assessed in each study that is undertaken. This is usually best done by measuring a suite of rocks or minerals from the area under study. The consistency or lack of consistency of the results, together with the knowledge of the geology of the area, allows assessment of some of these assumptions, and provides the basis for conclusions as to the reliability and meaning of the measured ages. . . . In all cases, the ages obtained must be interpreted in the context of the geology of the region being investigated (McDougall and Harrison 1988, p. 12, 22).

While there is no doubt that results which are inconsistent cannot be factual (e. g., a rock cannot be 300 million and 600 million years old at the same time), the converse does not necessarily follow. If dates consistently give a result of 300 million years for a rock, it does not necessarily follow that the rock is actually 300 million years old, or, for that matter, that its age is necessarily in the millions of years at all. Clearly, internally-consistent results are *assumed* to be credible:

> K-Ar systems may be disturbed by diffusive argon losses or by extraneous (inherited or excess) argon. Therefore, ages are determined for reliable K-Ar chronometers such as separated minerals. Age concordance of different minerals and/or the WR [whole rock] is an example of an internal control and is taken as confirmation for the geological significance of ages (Muller-Sohnius and Horn 1994, p. 605).

> The general consistency of the age pattern, bearing in mind the range in bulk composition and diverse localities (see Figure 3) *argues* for the K-Ar results to record the emplacement of the False Bay Dolerites at 132 ± 6 Ma (Reid *et al.* 1991, p. 157) [emphasis added].

The assumption about concordant results being reliable, of course, begs the question about the large numbers of dates which are internally inconsistent and therefore rejected out of hand. Those who make self-serving assumptions about "all the good results" are engaging in the **CDMBN** fallacy *flagrante delicto*. As final proof that there is no such thing as a simple dichotomy between reliable and unreliable results, let us ponder the following criticism of the way that dates are being evaluated for inclusion or exclusion in the construction of the "absolute" Phanerozoic time scale:

> Finally, it is rarely a good solution to eliminate many apparently inferior results just because one date or one formation appears to be highly reliable. These remarks would appear to be somewhat obvious, but experience shows that these rules are frequently rejected (Odin 1985, pp. 42-43).

Moreover, this rejection of results also extends to dates which are ostensibly credible on analytic grounds:

> The uncritical use of such dates is a good illustration of why one should not nail down chronostratigraphic schemes with singular dates, no matter how "excellent," while ignoring other, analytically sound, and equally acceptable data that may not agree with our preconceptions (Haq *et al.* 1988, p. 602).

> It is of fundamental importance that analytically acceptable measurements are not suppressed or rejected, nor groups of data manipulated, simply because they cannot be understood at present or do not conform with the current wisdom as represented in this case by terrane-accretion models (Tanner and Dempster 1988, p. 763).

Of course, the more stringent the presumed reliability criteria, the fewer dates will be found that meet these criteria, and this will only make greater the chance that the "reliable" dates are fortuitous. In fact, this is recognized, as discussed below under U-Pb dating of individual zircons.

Let us consider the consequence of stringent selectivity of data points when it comes to the calibration of the Phanerozoic time scale:

> In their review of the geochronology of the Carboniferous, Permian, and Triassic Periods, Forster and Warrington (1985) accepted only forty-five dated items from five hundred separate articles. . . (Kamo *et al.* 1996, p. 3505).

And, finally, as is obvious from all of the material discussed in my 1979 work, and also updated below, all judgments about the "credibility" or otherwise, of isotopic dates, are always subordinate to uniformitarian geologic interpretations of what they presumably indicate. And, of course, as extensively discussed, severely deviant results are rejected out of hand. This continues to the present:

> Many items that have at one time or another been proposed as time-scale constraints have been excluded. The criteria for exclusion include rejection by the original authors and excessive uncertainty in date or stratigraphic position; i. e., generally those

that exceed 3% to 4% one-sigma errors or that lie more than 2 to 5 time-scale subdivisions from any likely time scale. *Items that are clearly anomalous with respect to the main body of data have also been excluded* (Craig *et al.* 1989, p. 830; Harland *et al.* 1990, p. 79) [emphasis added].

Myth: The reliability of isotopic dates can be assessed objectively from analytic data, and independently of any uniformitarian geologic interpretations.

Fact: To make it even more obvious that this is not the case, consider the following examples:

> Technological advances have made possible routine K-Ar dating of Tertiary and younger rocks, including silicic volcanic rocks bearing feldspar and biotite phenocrysts. For these rocks, dates from sanidine, anorthoclase, and plagioclase generally appear reliable *based on tests of stratigraphic consistency* and agreement with coexisting biotite ages. This contrast in reliability for K-Ar dating between volcanic feldspars and those in plutonic and metamorphic rocks has not been adequately explained (McDowell 1983, pp. 119-120) [emphasis added].

As for analytic consistency of dates, consider the following analysis of K-Ar dates on biotite from tonalites and granodiorites:

> Although most of them are within error of the mean, in the absence of field data it is not possible to say whether they represent pulses of the same plutonic unit, or different plutons with different cooling histories (Suarez *et al.* 1986, p. 583).

Further proof that K-Ar dating is not inherently self-checking stems not only from its reliance on extraneous (that is, uniformitarian, of course) information to verify the dating results, but also from the fact that internal consistency of results is *not* proof for their accuracy:

> With conventional K-Ar dating, the only tests for anomalously high ages are stratigraphic control and the reproducibility of the age measurements. Unfortunately, stratigraphic control is frequently lacking or inadequate, and *anomalously high ages can be very reproducible* (LoBello *et al.* 1987, p. 61) [emphasis added].

Further evidence that the ostensible reliability of K-Ar results *cannot* be deduced from analytic criteria, but *must* rely on geologic tests of presumed accuracy, is obvious from the following:

> We have dated a large phlogopite crystal (ca. 4 cm across) from the main Kholloaqui dike at 97.7 ± 2.8 Ma. In the absence of other data we assume that the crystal does not contain excess ^{40}Ar and that this date represents the age of intrusion (Kennan *et al.* 1995, p. 182).

Perhaps the most conclusive proof that there is no such thing as innately credible results occurs when there is back-pedaling over the significance of isotopic dating results. Indeed, there are times when isotopic dates are at first accepted as valid but, when the geology of the area is further studied, it then becomes obvious that they cannot possibly be correct. For example:

> Prior to this study, geochronological data from Eastern Nigeria lacked proper structural control which has led to geological inconsistencies. For example, in the Toro area, a granite-diorite pluton previously dated at 600 ± 20 Ma [reference cited] and migmatites dated at 550 ± 13 Ma and 499 ± 11 Ma [reference cited] are now known to be coeval (Ferre *et al.* 1996, p. 719).

> These studies demonstrate the importance of the Silurian "Salinic" orogeny in these areas, and also the unreliability of previous Rb-Sr and K-Ar dates. . . . Rb-Sr isochron ages of 360-320 Ma previously reported from several other intrusions [references cited] do not reliably indicate continuation of magmatism into the Carboniferous (Kerr *et al.* 1993, p. 2328, 2331).

Clearly, then, analytic criteria alone cannot decide which dates are reliable and which are not, and so isotopic-dating results most definitely are *not* in themselves self-checking!

Let us now verify the fact, once again, that the presumed reliability of isotopic dates is not in fact determined primarily from some sort of presumed reliability criteria, but from the agreement of the dates with biostratigraphic constraints upon the igneous body in question:

> Resetting of whole-rock Rb-Sr isotope systems in extrusive acid volcanic rocks is recognized wherever it can be demonstrated that isotopic ages are too young for the stratigraphic position of the extrusives. . . . In contrast, isotope resetting in intrusive rocks is generally much more difficult to distinguish because of the lack of detailed stratigraphic control (Evans 1989, p. 675).

> . . . Finster pluton whole rocks (Rb-Sr) give an isochron at 497 My. This age is too high stratigraphically and the limit is probably 450 My. This age is *thus inherited* (Poty 1989, p. 40) [emphasis added].

It should be added that even Rb-Sr isochrons with excellent analytic criteria (such as a low MSWD) still have to be checked against biostratigraphic information for presumed validity (e. g., Graham and Mortimer 1992, p. 397). Clearly, then, if the "self-checking" properties of isotopic dating systems were actually as powerful as apologists for isotopic dating make them out to be, it is difficult to imagine that geochronologists would have to resort to stratigraphic methods to "check" the validity of the isotopic-dating results! Indeed, the falsely-claimed self-checking properties of isochrons are discussed below under a separate chapter.

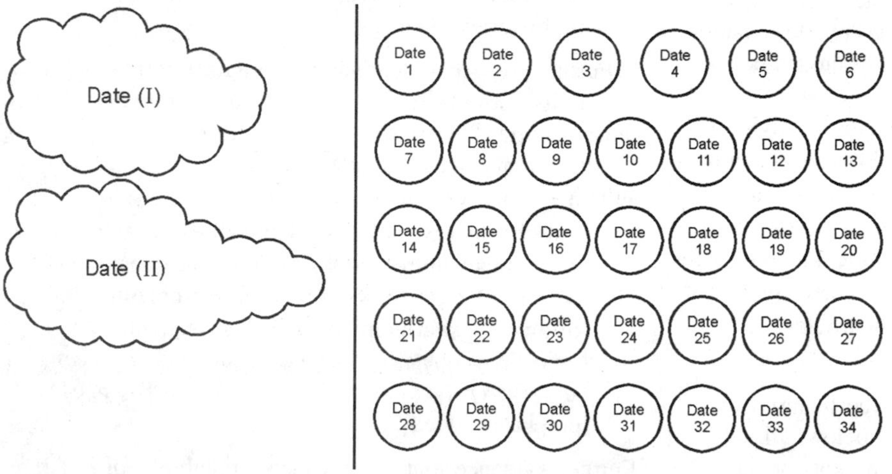

Myth: Particular isotopic dating results are carefully tested according to analytic standards before being subject to geologic interpretations.

Reality Check: While there is no doubt that many researchers do in fact carefully analyze their results (within the context of their uniformitarian preconceptions, of course), this has not been the case in perhaps the majority of instances. The following describes a situation from the Appalachian orogen (eastern USA):

> Unfortunately, geochronologic data is not always of uniform quality or reliability. Furthermore, lack of rigor in interpreting geochronologic data has led in many cases to inaccurate, or overly simplistic, tectonic models. . . . Although many of these problematic cases involve Rb-Sr whole-rock dates, improper interpretation of U-Pb zircon dates has also pro-

Previously, the only K-Ar and U-Pb dating options required *amalgamations* of mineral separates (usually micas for K-Ar, and zircons for U-Pb).

The current ^{40}Ar/^{39}Ar and U-Pb SHRIMP methods allow for the dating of *individual mineral grains* (depicted by circles), and even *parts* of individual grains.

Figure 17. The ability to date individual mineral grains is said to make isotopic dating more "self-checking," because many individual dates can now be checked for internal consistency. In the schematic example above, thirty-four individual dates can be compared against each other instead of just two. But this procedure begs the question about the numerous new inconsistencies uncovered. Also, the proliferation of individual dates makes it more likely for fortuitous patterns to arise, and generates a larger variety of numerical values from which the geochronologist can "shop around" for a preferred result.

duced erroneous tectonic interpretations. Considerable caution must be used in evaluating reported U-Pb dates based on large multi-grain fractions that have not been abraded (Samson 1997, p. 66).

(Of course, as discussed in the section on zircon dating, abrasion of zircons often does not remove discordancy. It merely adds a new layer of special pleading to the uniformitarian interpretation of U-Pb zircon dates).

Let us consider the K-Ar method and its use. The identical conclusion applies:

> Within the last decade or so, significant technical improvements in isotopic dating by solid source mass spectrometry have regrettably disparaged the reputation of the K-Ar method among some earth scientists, who now like to consider it only as a "historical stage" in the development of isotopic dating. Perhaps this misjudgment is due to the fact that a basic rule for any determination, namely that chronological data need internal controls before geological interpretations are possible, *was so often neglected* (Muller-Sohnius and Horn 1994, p. 604) [emphasis added].

Yet one keeps hearing about the analytic criteria for "self-checking," from apologists for isotopic dating. If these criteria are really so important, and so useful for the screening out of unreliable dates, why do so many geologists neglect them?

Myth: Different reliability criteria agree with each other in predicting which rock samples will yield reliable dates and which will not.

Reality Check: An instructive line of evidence against "reliability criteria" is the fact that one criterion often fails to corroborate another. Consider, for instance, analytic reproducibility versus the reliability of materials selected for dating. Vandamme *et al.* (1991), in order to improve the reliability of conventional K-Ar dates from ancient lava flows, opted to date magnetically-separated mineral fractions of plagioclase. When coming from unaltered samples, dates from these separates were considered to be more reliable than whole-rock dates, a conclusion partly based on the fact that the former often showed reduced analytic scatter over the latter. However, even a cursory look at table 1 of Vandamme *et al.* (1991, p. 162) shows a considerable overlap between the size of the 1-alpha uncertainties (68% confidence limit) of the K-Ar dates from both the "less reliable" whole-rock samples and "more reliable" magnetically-separated plagioclase fractions. Moreover, in other situations involving the use of plagioclase separates from crushed basalts, $^{36}Ar/^{40}Ar$ vs. $^{39}Ar/^{40}Ar$ isochrons, if taken at face value, nevertheless indicated the presence of some excess argon (Sinton *et al.* 1998, p. 164). The use of plagioclase separates in $^{40}Ar/^{39}Ar$ dating also did not forestall the appearance of discordant age spectra, which was, as is customary, interpreted as evidence of open-system behavior. Other examples of conflicts between

Is This Date Reliable?
Reliability Criterion 1 ------- "Yes"
Reliability Criterion 2 -------- "No"
Reliability Criterion 3 -------- "No"
Reliability Criterion 4 ------- "Yes"
Reliability Criterion 5 ------- "Yes"

Figure 18. Different presumed reliability criteria contradict each other in predicting the reliability or otherwise of a given isotopic date.

"reliability criteria" used in conjunction with $^{40}Ar/^{39}Ar$ dating are discussed in the section on that particular dating method.

There are other cases where the reproducibility of K-Ar dates, as a presumed reliability criterion, contradicts other presumed reliability criteria (such as potassium content and ^{36}Ar content). Consider a series of samples [numbered (1), (2), and (5)] from the Mageroy dolerite (Roberts *et al.* 1991). Samples (2) and (5) were concordant at the 1-alpha level, while all three samples were concordant only at the 2-alpha level. Therefore, based on reproducibility as a criterion, the latter two results should be accepted as the most reliable. However, an inverse relationship between potassium content and age was observed (often considered to be an indicator of excess argon). On that basis, sample (1), having the highest potassium content of the three, should be considered the most reliable. However, reliability of K-Ar results has also been supposed to vary inversely with ^{36}Ar content (e. g., Baksi 1987). Thus, on the basis of ^{36}Ar content, sample (1) should be considered the least reliable of the three. So, which one of these contradictory "reliability criteria" should have been believed? This question was not resolved (Roberts *et al.* 1991, p. 292).

Further evidence of the fact that reproducibility is not proof of validity is provided by certain uniformitarian geologic field practices themselves. That is, ostensibly "self-checked," reproducible dates can initially be accepted as valid age-indicators, only to suffer rejection when supposedly "more reliable" data become available:

> They fitted a line to all four points to determine an age of 452 + 51/-13 Ma, noting that three of four fractions give similar $^{207}Pb/^{206}Pb$ ages of 448 to 455 Ma (each ± 7 Ma) as additional justification for their age. However, the mixed-age zircon population of the sample was not recognized (Dunning *et al.* 1990, p. 899).

Thus, even within a uniformitarian context, inherited isotopes can produce spurious yet internally-consistent results. In another situation, a set of regionally-concordant K-Ar dates from a suite of plutons had been accepted as a "self-checked" indicator of the age of their emplacement. Subsequently, however, geochronologists have had to backpedal from this "self-checked" cluster of concordant dates when much older U-Pb results became available from these intrusive bodies:

> All K-Ar ages are *remarkably uniform* (table 1), clustering around an age of 230 Ma (new decay constant). The uniformity of K-Ar ages from all of the plutonic rocks of the Maya Mountains is *notable . . .* considered *the uniformity as "prima facie evidence" of a Triassic intrusive age for the two eastern plutons. . . .* Although very uniform ages of about 230 Ma amongst all plutons, derived from abundant earlier dating by the K-Ar system, led to the conclusion that intrusion mostly had occurred in the Late Triassic, the U-Pb ages (obtained from the same sites as the K-Ar dates) demonstrate that the K-Ar ages do not derive from a Late Triassic intrusive episode (Steiner and Walker 1996, p. 17,728; 17,733) [emphasis added].

Instead, the much-older U-Pb ages were accepted as indicative of the correct age of the rock. The now-unwelcome, erstwhile "self-checked" K-Ar dates were rationalized away as due to a later reheating event on the rocks. Thus, even within a uniformitarian context, consistent results are not *ipso facto* self-checked!

Now let us consider the work of Swisher *et al.* (1993). They had tested the lack of a preparatory NaOH bath on $^{40}Ar/^{39}Ar$ dating results on bentonites. If the experiment performed by them has produced valid results, then this constitutes further evidence that internally-consistent results are *not* "self-checked" as to their validity. After all, the new results are internally consistent, but so were the significantly-older NaOH-leached ones! Both sets of dates can be incorrect, but they cannot both be correct.

Arguments about reproducibility of results can also be made on a regional-geologic scale. Yet here, also, this "reliability criterion" is waived whenever the date comes in conflict with other information. This occurred, for instance, when a new Sm-Nd date contradicted, and was allowed to supersede, an earlier apparently-reliable Sm-Nd date. Let us consider why the earlier date had been accepted as reliable in the first place:

> This result seemed reasonable at the time because it agreed with other published ages for Kambalda and the surrounding greenstone belts (Chauvel *et al.* 1985, p. 315).

In conclusion, arguments about "reproducibility" and "consistency" of isotopic dating results are clearly special pleading. After all, uniformitarian geochronologists do not themselves accept reproducibility of results as *ipso facto* proof of their validity if it does not agree with their geologic conclusions. Most certainly diluvialists have every right to remain unimpressed with all of these claims of "self-checking" properties of isotopic dates.

Myth: A prognosis of reliable results can be made for unaltered samples of rock.

Fact: As extensively documented in my previous paper (Woodmorappe 1979, 1993), there are many instances of unaltered rock samples yielding "bad" dates, and vice-versa. This continues to the present. For instance, FT dating results that are "too young" have been reported from fresh zircons and sphenes by Wallace (1995, pp. 26-27). Likewise, discrepant K-Ar results continue to be derived from fresh basalts (e. g., Chevallier *et al.* 1992, p. 7; Fitch *et al.* 1985, p. 619; Sundeen 1989, p. 142; Vandamme *et al.* 1991, p. 161). Also, when it comes to K-Ar dating, the presumed suitability or non-suitability of material for isotopic dating, and interpretation of the results obtained, is obviously a matter of opinion:

> Clearly, decisions as to which rocks can be accepted for age measurements remain somewhat subjective. . . . The question of reliability of ages on fresh or slightly altered samples can best be evaluated by measuring a suite of samples in known stratigraphic relationship to one another. From the consistency or lack of consistency of the results it is often possible to assess the reliability of ages (McDougall and Harrison 1988, pp. 29-30).

Furthermore, efforts to correlate the presumed unreliability of K-Ar results, and the extent of a rock's alteration, have proved to be a clear-cut failure:

> It has been proposed that the degree of alteration of basic rocks, as quantified by alteration indices based on H_2O + contents or X-ray diffraction methods, can be used as a predictor of Ar loss. These hypotheses were tested using a sample of 36 zeolite facies metavolcanic basic rocks from Skye, Scotland, U. K., and found to be wanting. Hence, no independent criteria of Ar loss can be determined using these indicators (Higgins 1984, p. 175).

Not surprisingly, discrepant dates occur in rocks and minerals which appear to be unaltered, and therefore suitable for dating:

> . . . we suggest the younger dates in the earlier study . . . reflect partial loss of ^{40}Ar from some specimens. Since all specimens in the earlier K-Ar study passed detailed petrographic examination, it is apparent that rigorous thin-section examination cannot *unequivocally* eliminate whole-rock basalts that have suffered partial post-crystallization loss of ^{40}Ar (Baksi *et al.* 1993, p. 142) [emphasis added].

> The anomalously older date is petrographically, geochemically, and structurally the same as any other sample of this segment of SCPS [San Christoval plutonic suite]. The Early Jurassic date is not

meaningful and may indicate excess Ar in the hornblende (Hunt and Roddick 1991, p. 119).

Intrusive rocks are not immune and petrographic criteria alone may be inadequate to screen out all altered rocks (Harland *et al.* 1990, p. 76).

In addition, fresh magmatic biotites and unaltered hornblendes have given seemingly-reliable conventional K-Ar dates, only to show $^{40}Ar/^{39}Ar$ age-spectra indicative of disturbance (Clark *et al.* 1990, p. 1657). In like manner, discrepant but analytically-sound Rb-Sr isochrons appear not only in igneous rocks with petrographic evidence for subsequent alteration, but also in apparently-unaltered rock as well:

Plutonic rocks for which there is little independent evidence for a subsequent metamorphism are more difficult to explain. . . . There is no petrographic evidence for a post-crystallization metamorphic event that could have rotated the isochron and the isochron age has no apparent simple geological interpretation (Beakhouse *et al.* 1988, p. 346, 343).

Myth: Potassium content is a good reliability criterion to screen out unreliable K-Ar results.

Fact: It is suggested that minerals must have a K-content of at least 6% to be considered reliable (Drake *et al.* 1988; Obradovich and Cobban 1975; Odin *et al.* 1991). To begin with, the "correct" value for potassium content of an ostensibly-unaltered bentonitic biotite is an *assumption*:

Both biotite samples have been leached of potassium from a *presumed* volcanic composition of 7-8% K (Goodwin and Deino 1989, p. 1388) [emphasis added].

Minerals with low-K contents often show only slight independent evidence of having in fact experienced alteration sometime in the past:

Routine K-analyses determined that the K-content was anomalously low (4.43 wt.%) despite the fact that the mineral separate appeared to be of excellent quality. It is a golden brown biotite made up of subhedral laths with no apparent alteration of colour variation which might suggest chlorite is present. XRD analysis showed a possible serpentine alteration (Roddick *et al.* 1992, p. 175).

Clearly, assessing the value of an unaltered biotite is an exercise in circular reasoning. Secondly, while indeed it appears to be correct that "bad" results are more likely to come from materials which have low potassium contents, there are plenty of exceptions:

Detailed knowledge of the stratigraphical sequence (R.T.W) has enabled recognition of cases of gross K-Ar age discrepancy (occurring *especially* in the whole-rock dating of basalts containing low

concentrations of potassium) (Fitch *et al.* 1985, p. 610) [emphasis added].

Indeed, K-Ar results have at times seemed reliable based on replicability, and high K-content, only to have to be discarded because they could not be replicated again a year later (Odin *et al.* 1991, p. 207-208). Conversely, there are many instances of stratigraphically "good" dates from samples which have a K-content much below 6% (Odin *et al.* 1986, 1991; Obradovich 1993). There have been times when geochronologists have preferred the dating results of K-deficient biotites to those of K-rich sanidines (Odin *et al.* 1986, p. 130). Finally, drawing conclusions on the reliability of, say, biotites, for K-Ar dating, based on K-content, is limited by the fact that there is significant natural variability in the chemistry of comagmatic minerals (Odin *et al.* 1991, p. 212). In addition, other factors, such as presumed radiogenic Ar yields, come into play as supposed reliability criteria, and different geochronologists often disagree as to which set of conflicting K-Ar dates is thereby presumably more reliable (for discussion, see Kappelman *et al.* 1992).

When it comes to "excess argon," low potassium content in hornblende is often associated with the former. But this "self-checking criterion" is also used inconsistently. Low-potassium hornblende K-Ar dates have, in fact, been accepted as reliable when they have agreed with other evidence (Leitch *et al.* 1991, p. 201).

Just how diagnostic of open-system behavior is a relationship (direct or inverse) between K-content and K-Ar age? The evidence is equivocal. Biotites plotted on a $^{40}Ar/^{36}Ar$ isochron exhibited excellent collinearity (MSWD = 0.45), and defined an essentially-atmospheric initial $^{40}Ar/^{36}Ar$ ratio, all in spite of the fact that they contained "excess argon" (Sole *et al.* 1998, pp. 143-144), as deduced largely from an inverse relationship between K-Ar age and potassium content.

On the other hand, some studies (Hess and Lippolt 1986; Hess, Lipolt, and Wirth 1987) have suggested such a relationship. In doing so, however, they have also exploded the myth that apparent sample unalteration and high K-content are near-guarantees of closed system behavior over the (assumed) millions of years.

TEM investigations reveal that high-K biotites, though microscopically appearing homogenous, may contain considerable amounts of submicroscopical alteration products. . . . Summarizing, we maintain that low-temperature increase of biotite age spectra may often be the result of ^{39}Ar displacement into K-poor alteration phases within the biotite even if evidence of such phases are missing and high K concentrations and optical properties of the sample give the impression of proper biotite (Hess *et al.* 1987, pp. 137, 147).

Of course, when minerals do show such minute amounts of alteration under very close examination, yet nevertheless yield "good" K-Ar dates (e.g., Roddick *et al.* 1992, p. 176), it is conveniently supposed that the tiny low-K inclusions had somehow managed to remain closed systems.

Finally, if, as a reliability criterion, one were to add absence of the tiny amount of secondary minerals (to the samples already previously screened for unalteration at the microscopic level, as well as high-K content), this would only create a new problem. The number of datable materials, under this new standard, would become quite small, thereby greatly exacerbating the trend illustrated in figure 15.

Myth: Whenever there are xenocrystic crystals (in lavas, tuffs, and bentonites), such contaminants can be identified and removed before the host rock is dated.

Reality Check: Let us consider lavas first. Often, minerals are alleged to be of xenocrystic origin only on a *posterioritic basis*, that is, when a rationalization is needed because K-Ar dates from certain crystals have turned out to be "too old:"

Most of the xenocrysts are difficult to distinguish optically or chemically from feldspar phenocrysts, illustrating the necessity of single-crystal analysis to date many young volcanic rocks accurately (Gansecki *et al.* 1996, p. 91).

In volcanically active regions where tens of hundreds of eruptions can occur over geologically short time intervals, entrainment of older volcanic material in younger flows can be problematic. *Identification of those contaminant (xenocrystic) populations can be extremely difficult* (Karner and Renne 1998, p. 740) [emphasis added].

Contamination by older material is a major problem in the isotopic dating of both effusive and explosive young volcanic rocks, especially in distal ashes reworked by wind or water . . . many of the problems may be related to the presence of sanidine xenocrysts that are chemically and visually indistinguishable from phenocrysts (Gansecki *et al.* 1998, pp. 343-344).

The xenocrysts are impossible to identify from petrography or chemical parameters such as their K/Ca ratios (Singer *et al.* 1998, p. 427).

When it comes to tuffs and bentonites, some xenocrystic crystals can indeed be visually identified and discarded. But others can only be *assumed* to be in existence on an *after-the-fact* basis when dates turn out to be "too old," and a rationalization for them is needed:

Because feldspar is a common constituent of sedimentary rocks, the chances of detrital contamination of a sanidine concentrate are fairly high. The risk of biotite contamination is lower because of the less frequent occurrence of biotite in igneous rock, and the relative instability of biotite in the weathering cycle. In some cases, weathering of biotite may give anomalously old or young ages. *Criteria for detrital contamination are not well established* (Forsman 1983, p. 324) [emphasis added].

We suspect that the discordant age spectra are the result of a two-component K-feldspar mixture: an endogenous K-feldspar and an older disturbed K-feldspar, which were *indistinguishable in a hand-picked analytical sample of apparently clear and clean grains. . . .* Older ages that were determined by the K-Ar method on both biotite and sanidine separates indicate that *contaminant minerals included both biotite and K-feldspar* (Nielson *et al.* 1990, p. 577) [emphasis added].

. . . removing the altered, opaque, and clearly detrital grains by hand-picking . . . bentonites from the *Watinoceras devonense* and *Collignoniceras woolgari* zones have yielded anomalously old ages despite containing sanidine displaying good optical properties. Unfortunately, the sanidine crystals were too small to permit dating single crystals and thus to evaluate the possibility of multiple populations (i. e., primary plus detrital volcanic component) (Obradovich 1993, p. 382, 391).

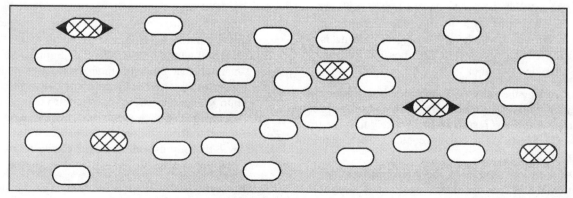

Figure 19: Special pleading on "xenocrystic contamination." Mineral crystals with a distinctive color and/or shape are suspected to be xenocrysts, and are removed before dating. Yet any of the remaining "normal-looking" crystals can still give an unacceptably old date, and thus be labeled a xenocryst, on a posterioritic basis.

[The claim (e. g., Gansecki *et al.* 1998) that the ^{40}Ar/^{39}Ar method invariably distinguishes between magmatic and contaminant mineral grains in tuffs and bentonites is considered in the section on ^{40}Ar/^{39}Ar dating].

Myth: Unrecognized xenocrysts are unlikely to have a significant effect on K-Ar dates.

Fact: Simple computations show that K-Ar dates in the few tens of millions of years are, in fact, extremely sensitive to any appreciable contribution of argon derived from known or hypothetically-imputed xenocrysts:

> Mixing calculations indicate that only 1%–4% contamination may be required to increase K-Ar ages by 10–15 Ma, for xenocrysts outgassed as much as 75% (Nelson *et al.* 1992, p. 1547).

Of course, other combinations of ^{40}K content, percent degassing, etc., can produce substantially greater inflation of K-Ar "ages." It also means that it is easy for the uniformitarian geochronologist to fall back on the **CDMBN** fallacy. He can freely invoke either a "xenocryst contamination" or "excess argon" rationalization whenever K-Ar dates are "too old." As noted in the previous entry, he can invent "hidden xenocrysts" at will.

The converse is also true. If petrographic examination unambiguously reveals the existence of xenocrysts or xenoliths, and yet they and/or the groundmass produces acceptable ages, the uniformitarian geochronologist can simply assume that the argon of these inherited materials had been degassed at the time of their inclusion in the host magma:

> Minerals from xenolithic inclusions in igneous rocks can be used when their K-Ar systems have been reset upon inclusions in the host melt (Muller-Sohnius and Horn 1994, p. 605).

Once again, heads, I win; tails, you lose. And this shows the logical inconsistency of Dalrymple's (1984, pp. 81-82) argument about the xenolithic contaminants in the 1801 Hualalai volcano. He had belittled creationist citations of the anomalously-old dates with the following remark:

> Quite simply, xenoliths are one of the types of rocks that cannot be dated by the K-Ar technique (Dalrymple 1984, p. 81).

Well then, based on the statements of Muller-Sohnius and Horn (1994, p. 605), it evidently *is* possible to date xenoliths by K-Ar—that is, whenever the results do agree with uniformitarian preconceptions, and it is therefore assumed that the xenoliths have been degassed. Of course, it can also simply be assumed that the xenoliths are penecontemporaneous with the host magma. This occurred, for instance, when large boulders of gabbros, suspected of being Precambrian xenoliths residing within a Cretaceous-Tertiary boundary basalt, instead produced ^{40}Ar/^{39}Ar results consistent with the age of the host basalt (Sheth *et al.* 1997).

All things considered, xenocrysts and xenoliths are true friends of the uniformitarian geochronologist. They show up in a visible-yet-degassed state as well as invisible-yet-nondegassed state, whenever and wherever the uniformitarian wants them.

C. Arguments Based on Consistency and Concordance of Dating Results

Myth: "Excess argon" can independently be ruled out if the K-Ar results are homogenous over a wide geographic area.

Reality Check: There have been times when "excess argon" has been invoked despite considerable geographic homogeneity of the K-Ar or even ^{40}Ar/^{39}Ar results (Ruffet *et al.* 1997). Thus, on uniformitarians' own terms, claims about "excess argon" being only a very local phenomenon are clearly an appeal to the **ATM** fallacy.

Myth: Reproducibility and consistency of isotopic dates is proof for their geochronometric validity.

Fact: It is not, as documented in my 1979 paper (Woodmorappe 1993, 1999). To begin with, reproducibility is often *assumed* to be an indicator of validity, as is the converse:

> The young U-Pb columbite ages represent either emplacement ages of the pegmatites, prolonged cooling ages following emplacement, or thermally reset ages. . . . *We consider it* highly unlikely, however, that pegmatite samples from three widely separated (up to 3.5 km apart) localities would yield identical regional, postmetamorphic cooling ages (Mauthner *et al.* 1995, p. 2094) [emphasis added].

Such suppositions are also applied to newer dating methods, such as Re-Os:

> Disagreement between Re-Os ages obtained by replicate analyses for each molybdenite sample indicates that the sample underwent alteration and the obtained Re-Os ages do not show their formation ages (Suzuki *et al.* 1996, p. 3155).

Secondly, it is recognized that various laboratory procedures can cause systematic errors, and these can hide under seemingly-impressive statistics:

> Although the average K-Ar date of 63.1±0.5 for these dates is precise, it is not necessarily accurate. . . . Statistical error treatment can therefore sometimes lend a spurious respectability to average values, especially if constant errors have crept into the measurements (Baadsgaard *et al.* 1988, p. 1094).

Thirdly, the fact that internally-consistent results are not proof of age-indicative validity is, if nothing else, proven by the fact that uniformitarians *themselves* do not invariably accept them as such. This is demonstrated by the following conflict in groupings of K-Ar dates:

Two explanations were considered possible to explain the results. First, that the spread of apparent ages of the hornblende samples might be due to a metamorphic overprint at approximately 6 Ma which variably reset the K-Ar system in igneous rocks which were emplaced at 14 Ma or earlier. In this case, the *concordant grouping of biotite ages* at 6 Ma might reflect the greater susceptibility of this mineral to resetting, compared with amphiboles. The second possibility is that the discordant ages are due to the presence of variable amounts of excess ^{40}Ar in hornblende, and that the apparent ages for this mineral are too high. In this case, the biotite ages may approximate the true age of intrusion (Richards and McDougall 1990, p. 1401) [emphasis added].

With the application of the ^{40}Ar/^{39}Ar technique, the authors resolved this in favor of the younger ages. However, the fact remains that the internal consistency of the younger K-Ar biotite ages had not been taken as an *ipso facto* indicator of their validity.

Fourthly, there is no doubt about the fact that internally-consistent results are rejected by the uniformitarian geochronologist whenever the need arises to do so. This, in fact, happened to one of the monitor minerals used for the ^{40}Ar/^{39}Ar method:

> For whatever reason, this biotite sample has a *consistent but anomalously old age* when compared to the age of the original FCT sanidine and the sanidine from the latest preparation (Obradovich 1993, p. 389) [emphasis added].

A fifth line of evidence against reproducibility being evidence of validity also occurs under uniformitarians' own terms. That is, internally-consistent conventional K-Ar dates, which should thereby *ipso facto* have been closed systems since crystallization, do in fact exhibit open-system behavior when subject to ^{40}Ar/^{39}Ar analysis:

> Within the limits of analytical uncertainty, the ages are indistinguishable from one another. . . . The age of sample 86Acr019 is concordant with the other ages, but ^{40}Ar/^{39}Ar data (described later) suggest that this sample may have undergone some argon loss (Conrad *et al.* 1992, p. C4).

Myth: Mineral-pair concordances, by a single method but from minerals with different isotope-retentive closure temperatures, reliably indicate the correct age of the rock.

Reality Check: Support for this premise is derived from the following line of argumentation: some minerals (e. g., micas in K-Ar dating) have closure temperatures to argon loss that are much lower than other minerals (e. g., amphiboles in K-Ar dating). Hence, one would not expect a reheating event to affect both sets of minerals equally. Therefore, if a rock has been reheated since crystallization, the dates from the different minerals will be discordant, and this will warn the geochronologist about the nonreliability of the results for establishing a date for the crystallization of the rock. Conversely, if a pair of minerals with different argon-retentive properties give concordant results, this indicates that both were undisturbed since crystallization.

To begin with, this "self-checking" property of K-Ar dates on mineral separates is not used consistently by uniformitarian geochronologists. We thus have many situations where there are concordant results from mineral pairs, yet the date indicated is "too young" to be acceptable as the correct age of the rock:

> All the rocks in the thoroughly reset area surrounded by the zone of discordant ages yield anomalous potassium-argon cooling ages even though most mineral pairs from this anomalous area are concordant or nearly concordant. . . . Many of these concordant ages are on rocks known to be much older than the measured potassium-argon age on the basis of lithologic correlation with rocks outside the reset area (Miller and Morton 1980, p. 2, 19).

Whenever such a situation occurs, the rationalization for it is as follows: the rocks were so thoroughly reheated that all of the minerals lost their original radiogenic argon. Subsequently, the area cooled rapidly enough so that all of the minerals, despite their widely divergent argon-retentive temperatures, became closed systems to new radiogenic argon at about the same time. Obviously, such storytelling makes sense only to someone who already believes in the validity of the dating methods, and in the validity of mineral pairs as "self-checking" devices for K-Ar dating. And it certainly begs the question about the validity of concordant mineral pairs for reliably indicating the correct age of rock emplacement, even on uniformitarian terms. Finally, mineral-pair concordance cannot stand on its own as a presumed reliability criterion, but must always be subordinate to geological interpretation:

> Reliability criteria are provided by age agreement of the paragenetic nepheline and mica and the absence of conflicts with the sedimentary stratigraphy (Ivanenko and Karpenko 1988, p. 77).

Myth: If a U-Pb dating result on a zircon grain is reproducible, it is thereby self-checked, and therefore gives a reliable crystallization age for the host rock.

Fact: This "reliability criterion" is also subject to special pleading, as it is not used consistently by uniformitarians. Thus, for instance, a zircon crystal can give a reproducible age that is clearly "too old" biostratigraphically, and which must therefore be explained away as being xenocrystic in origin (Compston and Williams 1992, p. 61), all despite the fact that it has no morphological difference from ostensibly-magmatic zircons. More on this in the section on U-Pb zircon dating.

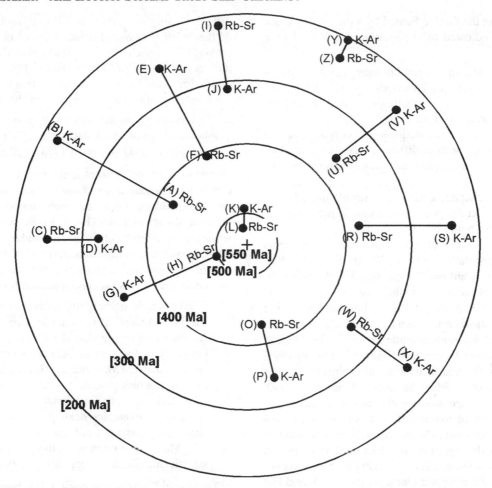

Figure 20. One could throw darts at a target and "explain" *a posteriori* any pattern of dates from pairs of isotopic-dating systems. Concordant pairs (KL) which coincide with geologically-acceptable values (in this example, the "bulls eye" of 500-550 Ma) are assumed to correctly date the rock. When, however, one date in a pair (H) falls-in with acceptable dates but the result of the other dating method (G) is discordant, the former (H) is assumed to date the rock, and the latter (G) is assumed to have lost and/or gained isotopes. Most pairs (AB, CD, EF, IJ, RS, UV, WX) are discordant and "too young." We are told that both systems have become open, and the discordancy stems from the fact that we should not expect different isotopic dating systems to gain and/or lose isotopes in a concerted manner. However, when a pair of results is concordant (YZ) yet unacceptably young, this is blamed on a "complete resetting" of both "clocks" to zero at that time (~240 Ma years ago for YZ). Alternatively, the YZ concordance can be considered fortuitous.

The above "target" relates to dates which are either "correct" or "too young." A similar "target" could be made in order to illustrate dates which are either "correct" or "too old." In such an instance, concordant pairs of "too old" dates would be regarded as fortuitous, or they would be blamed on inheritance of validly-dated source effects.

Myth: Concordant results by different dating methods are reliable on the following ground: one would not expect gains and/or losses of isotopes to be concerted.

Reality Check: Again, this premise, while perhaps intuitively appealing, has never been proven to be fact. Furthermore, such reasoning is used inconsistently by geochronologists. That is, they are prepared to accept the existence of concerted gains and losses of isotopes if it fits with their other ideas:

Although such K-Ar ages ranging between 1701 and 1740 could represent a reasonable formation age for the Mooirivier Complex, they probably ought to be interpreted as geologically meaningless, because the analyzed biotites not only suffered from a severe loss of ⁴⁰Ar which would have had to be proportional in all samples, but also from a certain loss of potassium which is discussed above (Ziegler and Stoessel 1993, p. 21).

Remarkably, pairs of zircons analyzed from each of three differently abraded batches of zircons yielded very similar, discordant U-Pb ages. This unusual replication suggests either a constant proportion of core to overgrowth or a very uniform degree of lead loss (Wastenys, Wardle, and Krogh 1996, p. 1311).

Myth: On theoretical grounds, concordant results by different dating methods are virtually conclusive proof for the accuracy of the dates obtained.

Dalrymple (1991, p. 124) had called concordance between different dating methods "powerful evidence for correctness," similar to checking the time indicated by a mainspring clock against the time indicated by a pendulum clock or electric clock.

Reality Check: While this argument may sound intuitively appealing, no one has, to my knowledge, ever computed the probability of different dating methods coming up with the same "date" by chance. Such an analysis would have to measure, among other things, the frequency of concordance and discordance between results of different dating methods. Obviously, for this to be attempted, all results would have to be published.

In a subsequent chapter, I perform a simple quasi Monte Carlo analysis of fortuitous concordances. It turns out that chance agreements should be fairly common.

It is interesting to note that most if not all of the elements involved in isotopic dating (Rb, Sr, K, Ar, U, Th, Pb, Sm, and Nd) show an upward enrichment factor in the range 30-150 going from depleted mantle to the crust (Armstrong 1981, p. 451; DePaulo 1988, p. 107). In fact, all the isotopic-dating systems appear to show enrichment trends which, going from mantle to crust, form parent-daughter regression lines whose slopes are parallel to each other (see figure 4.1 of Shirey 1991, p. 112). Thus, Nd, Pb, and Sr isotopes are subject to similar fractionation processes within the earth (Meijer *et al.* 1990, and citations). There are also geochemical similarities between the behaviors of many different isotopes on a sub-crustal scale. For instance, the elements K and Rb tend to behave similarly during granulite-facies metamorphism (Bridgwater *et al.* 1989, p. 281). It is also interesting to consider the fact that the daughter elements (at least Sr and Pb) are much less mobile than the parent elements (Rb, U, and Th) (Moorbath *et al.* 1986, p. 76). All of these facts add up to a pattern of concerted behavior among the isotopes used in isotopic dating. Concordance of results of different dating methods, therefore, may be the result of chance superimposed on comparable geochemical behavior of the relevant isotopes. This possibility should be investigated thoroughly by someone with a strong background in geochemistry as well as statistics.

Myth: On practical grounds, concordant results by different dating methods are proven indicators of the correct age of the rock.

Reality Check. They are not. Instead, they are, at most, *assumed* to be reliable indicators of the correctness of the derived age. And, as we shall see in this section, even this "reliability criterion" is not used consistently by uniformitarians. As a start, it is interesting to note that some authors appear to have equivocated somewhat on concordance as a virtually conclusive proof of a rock's age:

> The reliability of results is obviously strengthened when a rock unit yields the same age by several different methods (Zartman and Naylor 1984, p. 523).

It is also interesting to discover the fact that uniformitarian geochronologists themselves do not use concordance of different dating methods as conclusive proof for the accuracy of the result obtained. For instance, in contrast to a cited author, Obradovich (1993, p. 388) rejected a 3-way concordant result (by K-Ar, Rb-Sr, and U-Pb), and reckoned it anomalous, all because of the fact that the rocks were obviously altered, and also because of the following:

> It is surprising that a linear trend still exists at all; however, some of the data were rejected to achieve this linearity (Obradovich 1993, p. 388).

Therefore, even on uniformitarian terms, concordant results cannot be accepted as *ipso facto* evidence for the validity of the dates obtained. Let us now consider concordances based on three dating methods (K-Ar, Rb-Sr, and U-Pb) on bentonites believed to be at the K-T boundary. Despite the fact that the results are concordant, they do in fact contradict, outside of experimental error, ostensibly equally-reliable dates from elsewhere. This fact prompted the following remarks:

> This is an extremely impressive array of analytical data. Accepting the data at face value one is forced to conclude that the Cretaceous/Tertiary boundary is diachronous between southern Alberta and northeastern Montana and Golden, Colorado . . . or there is a bias of some 4 percent between the two laboratories. . . . I believe that this is one of the most complex of examples dealing with analytical precision and accuracy, but that the overall result of 63.5 Ma is 2.5 million years too young, a small but significant difference (Obradovich 1984, pp. 23-24).

To "resolve" this discrepancy, it has been alleged that, in addition to laboratory bias, there was a slight amount of open-system behavior in these isotopic systems despite the close concordance between the results. Let us now consider more recent examples of contradictory data sets for "highly reliable" datings of the K-T boundary (Swisher *et al.* 1993). They concluded that leaching the parent bentonites in NaOH during earlier lab procedures had caused open-system behavior. Finally, instances of such conflicting data have evidently become so numerous that rationalizations based on "elastic biostratigraphy" have come into vogue:

> Comparison of the absolute radiometric dates with biostratigraphic determinations yields discrepancies of between 2-5 Ma. For both the Cenomanian-Turonian and the Campanian-Maastrichtian boundaries radiometric dates appear to be older than biostratigraphic determinations . . . biotic heterochroneity. . . . Paleofloral provincialism of some of the Late Cretaceous age-diagnostic pollen genera may explain their earlier appearance at higher latitudes (Muecke *et al.* 1994, p. 229).

A comparable set of problems has arisen from concordant U-Pb dates on zircons:

> Traditionally, concordant U-Pb zircon data are considered to be reliable while non-concordant data

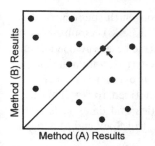 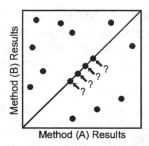

Figure 21: Traditionally concordance between dating methods has been taken as evidence of closed-system behavior since the rock formed (left). However, U-Pb results can produce a *chain* of concordant results from the same rock, of which only one, at most, can be correct (right).

are unreliable because of a disturbance to the U-Pb systematics (high- and low-T Pb loss, new zircon growth, U movement, etc.) or preservation of inherited grains or both. U-Pb studies of single zircon grains by both conventional and ion microprobe techniques, however, show that individual grains from the same sample can have a range of concordant ages that exceed the analytical precisions of the methods used . . . this result is common. . . . *The conclusion is that U-Pb zircon ages do not necessarily define a more reliable time of crystallization than other radiometric ages from intrusive rocks even when the U-Pb age is older, concordant, and has a very small analytical precision* (Wooden *et al.* 1996, p. 126) [emphasis added].

Reznitskiy *et al.* (1994, p. 42) also report composite concordances of zircon dates. Another example of sets of concordant U-Pb results, which conflict with each other at least potentially outside of experimental error, is provided by Maboko, Williams, and Compston (1991). In this case, an isotopic lead loss was invoked. In still another instance, there were found *two distinct clusters* of concordant [207]Pb/[206]Pb zircon dates (Beyth and Reischmann 1996). The older cluster (near 600 Ma) was taken as indicative of the age of the rock, and the younger cluster (near 570 Ma) was blamed on an *ad hoc* secondary event that was supposed to have caused Pb loss at the latter time.

There are even more dramatic situations wherein *several* pairs of concordant U-Pb dates give rise to a self-contradictory range of values from the same rock:

> The 93 m.y. spread of concordant titanite ages within a 20x20 km area demonstrates that cooling through isotopic closure is only one of several possibilities to be considered when interpreting metamorphic titanite ages in high-grade orogenic terranes (Ketchum *et al.* 1998, p. 25).

> We suggest that the ~82 m.y. spread in concordant U-Pb ages in this sample is indicative of high-temperature Pb-loss during one or more protracted periods of granulite-facies metamorphism with only minor episodic or continuous metamorphic zircon growth. . . . Our results suggest a note of caution for the interpretation of concordant zircon ages in

metaigneous rocks affected by high-grade metamorphism of long duration (Tucker *et al.* 1998).

The "protracted duration" of the metamorphism, of course, begs the question about the validity of the dating methods and the spans of time they purportedly measure.

Clearly, then, when it comes to concordant U-Pb results from zircons, the uniformitarian has "too much of a good thing:" not just a concordancy of dates but a contradictory *array* of *several* concordant U-Pb dates which, of course, cannot simultaneously be correct. Furthermore, this phenomenon is not limited to zircon, but is also true of U-Pb dating of monazite:

> In the absence of physical evidence for inheritance, the range of single grain ages remains problematic. However, the discordance behavior can be explained if single monazite grains comprise complex mixtures of domains which have exhibited open system behavior with respect to U, Th, and Pb, including excess [206]Pb, during cooling. *Concordant analyses of single grains may represent fortuitous mixtures of these domains* (Hawkins and Bowring 1994, p. 131) [emphasis added].

We are told that, originally, the points were located above the concordia. Subsequent open-system behavior, however, put them *on* the concordia by chance:

> Therefore, the concordant analysis may be a fortuitous mixture of inheritance and Th-disequilibrium, and if the analyses were free of inheritance, they would plot above concordia. . . . The monazite results for MC-94-36 suggest instead that each fraction represents a mixed population that may overlap fortuitously on concordia (Coleman 1998), pp. 560, 567).

Other "meaningless" open-system concordant U-Pb dates, albeit from zircon, are noted by Lawlor *et al.* (1999, p. 89). Of course, as discussed in the previous paper (Woodmorappe 1979, 1993), situations where dates are concordant by two or more methods, yet unacceptably young or old, are hardly limited to situations where the results are discrepant by only a few to several percentage points! An isotopic date which is supported by two or more dating methods (most commonly K-Ar with Rb-Sr isochron), but nowhere close to the accepted age of the rock, is blamed on a later reheating event on the rock (e. g., Evans 1989). Thus, both dating methods are believed to be "mutually rejuvenated" (see bottom of figure 4), which, of course, begs the question about the validity of dates indicated by concordant results of different dating methods. And what if the concordant set of results on a mineral is "too old" for the host igneous rock? It is then assumed that the mineral has remained a closed system since its earlier origin in an older rock:

> Analysis of one pink, rounded zircon from the Tai Mo Shan Formation (HK11837), which was clearly a xenocryst, gave a concordant datum point with an

age of 1872 ± 3 Ma. Its concordancy indicates that it was isotopically undisturbed by the emplacement of its much younger host rock (Davis *et al.* 1997, p. 1073).

For another example of "inherited" concordant zircons, see Gamble *et al.* (1999, p. 293).

An "impossible" concordance, one which violates the law of superposition, is shown by lithologies of the Barberton Greenstone Belt of South Africa. Silicified carbonates, sandwiched between volcanics dated at 3.2–3.4 Ga, have yielded a concordant set of Rb-Sr, Pb-Pb, and Sm-Nd results with the following unexpected value:

> All three isotopic systems of whole rocks indicate ages of ~2.7 Ga, much younger than the depositional age of the successions (Toulkeridis *et al.* 1998, p. 129).

The rationalization? All three systems were completely rejuvenated 2.7 Ga years ago. However, the event was—quite conveniently—supposedly not strong enough to have also rejuvenated either the underlying *or* the overlying volcanics!

Still other concordances by different dating methods are summarily dismissed if they cannot be pigeonholed into existing geologic interpretations. For instance, a concordance between $^{40}Ar/^{39}Ar$ plateau and Rb-Sr isochron results was rejected as having any geologic meaning (Ruffet *et al.* 1997). Similar backpedaling on "mutually-corroborated" results occurred elsewhere:

> Previously, the Early Carboniferous Rb-Sr age for the MPR pluton [reference cited] had appeared to be supported by a similar U-Pb date from the Rabinal granite in adjacent Guatemala. . . . However, the Late Silurian U-Pb dates for the MPR from the present study indicate that the similarity of ages was fortuitous and a function of a disturbed Rb-Sr system in the MPR granite. . . (Steiner and Walker 1996, pp. 17, 733).

In still another situation, Sm-Nd and Pb/Pb dates agreed at 3.3 Ga. But this was geologically unacceptable, so the concordance was believed to be fortuitous, and partly the result of the generation of so-called transposed palaeoisochrons (Whitehouse *et al.* 1996).

D. "Mutually Corroborated" Biostratigraphic, Magnetostratigraphic, and Geochronometric Systems

Myth: Geochronometric results are corroborated by the geomagnetic polarity time-scale (GPTS).

Reality Check: They are not. There are, in fact, many contradictions between paleomagnetic data and the Pleistocene Magnetic Polarity Scale, and they are explained away in various ways. To begin with, a certain amount of contradiction is built into the system solely as a result of the analytic

uncertainty which is common among such young K-Ar dates (Armstrong and Ward 1991, p. 13,208), combined with uncertainties as to which material is to be accepted as reliable. For instance, there is a large overlap (i. e., within the 1-alpha error bars) of dating results which overlap *both* reversely-magnetized and normally-magnetized rocks. This self-contradictory overlap of polarities and dates falls in the interval of 0.8-1.2 Ma (see figure 1 of Spell and McDougall 1992, p. 1182).

It is interesting to note the varying standards of what presumably constitutes reliable material for use in construction of the magnetic polarity scale. For instance, in their database of 354 presumably-reliable data points, Mankinen and Dalrymple (1979, p. 623) included 54 points whose dates were based on material which "contains glass, cryptocrystalline, very fine grained interstitial material, or slight ground-mass alteration." More recently, Spell and McDougall (1992, p. 1182) discuss some earlier-used results, relevant to the placement of the Brunhes-Matuyama boundary, which they believe are "too young" owing to argon loss. They point out the fact that this material shows evidence of alteration. The question this raises is as follows: If alteration is an issue, why was the date ever taken into consideration for the calibration of the polarity scale? And if alteration was not an issue *then*, why is it an issue *now*, with the date being discrepant? Looks like another use of dates, and "reliability criteria," as trial balloons.

Whenever a conflict arises between the two systems, one or both data sets are discarded. This applies as well to the $^{40}Ar/^{39}Ar$ results. For instance, dates which are "too old" for the magnetic polarity of the rock are often blamed on xenocrystic contamination (e. g., Spell and McDougall 1992, pp. 1181-1182).

In another situation, an "excess argon" rationalization came in handy when the dated basalt failed to agree with the magnetic-polarity scale:

> The age of this rock is much greater than expected. The basalt flow lies at the bottom of the present valley and is therefore later than the most recent episode of uplift and erosion. Quaternary sediments which are thought to predate the basalts are reversely magnetized. This indicates that they are older than the Bunhes/Matuyama reversal (about 790 ka). After the sample was dated, paleomagnetic work indicated the basalt is normally magnetized. Hence it appears that the basalt should give an age younger than 790 ka. The older calculated age [3.69 million years] is probably related to considerable excess Ar in the wholerock sample (Hunt and Roddick 1991, p. 116).

How many contradictions actually exist between the two systems, and which never see the light of day of publication, is impossible to ascertain. There are also times when the uniformitarians themselves cannot agree on which rationalization to invoke for a discrepant result. Thus, one discrepancy blamed on excess argon by one set of investigators was instead attributed to incorrect stratigraphic placement by Singer and Pringle (1996, p. 48).

In still other instances of disagreement between isotopic-dating and paleomagnetic results, some form of geologic gymnastics is performed in order to impose a conformity between them. For instance, at the height of the famous KBS Tuff controversy, the then-believed dates were forced to conform to the Pleistocene Magnetic Polarity Scale:

> . . . many of the specimens apparently had a normal overprint that was not removed during demagnetization. This, compounded with the fact that Bock and Isaac were trying to calibrate their magnetostratigraphy with the erroneous dates of the KBS Tuff, meant that the magnetostratigraphy had to be reinterpreted. . . . Because of the anomalously old date on the KBS Tuff, they placed a disconformity above it to account for the "missing" lower Matuyama and upper Gauss intervals. . . . Clearly, the paleomagnetic interpretation is susceptible to the revisions in radiometric dating and does not reveal the disconformities by itself (Prothero and Schwab 1996, p. 445).

This is not an isolated instance by any means. A less spectacular example of a comparable situation is discussed by Diehl *et al.* (1987). His team came to a very different conclusion, from another research team, as to the validity of isotopically-dated tuffs and their correct placement relative to the Brunhes and Matuyama Polarity Chrons. However, the isotopic dating results, and magnetic-polarity data, as gathered by the earlier research team, had seemed to corroborate each other.

Fission-track (FT) dating is often used on tephras. It is therefore interesting to note that apparent corroboration of magnetic polarity scales by FT dates may, at least in some instances, be illusory:

> However, the reliability of some fission-track ages determined by older techniques in the 1970's and early 1980's has been questioned . . . and thus this concordance may be fortuitous (Shane 1998, p. 112).

Another example of backpedaling on once-accepted FT dates is provided by Oard (1998), who evaluated the dating of the Davis Creek silt (Alberta-Saskatchewan). Moreover, dates were not the only unknowns manipulated in order to force agreement between tephrochronology and the Magnetic Polarity Scale. There were some *ad hoc* revisions in the correlation of similar-appearing tuffaceous beds, and, as had been the case with the previously-discussed KBS Tuff, there was an invention of unseen hiatuses in deposition.

Clearly, then, on uniformitarians' own terms, if the Pleistocene Magnetic Polarity Scale has at times been "corroborated" by erroneous dates, it can hardly now be claimed that it is also "corroborated" by very different "correct" dates! In actuality, this situation shows that both systems are plastic enough that each can accommodate whatever the rationalizations that are

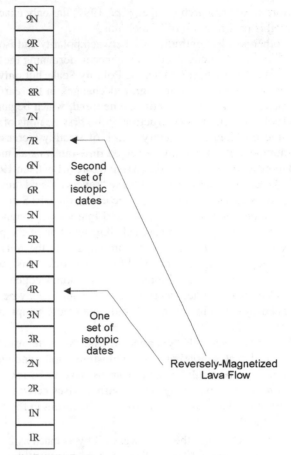

Magnetic-Polarity Scale

Figure 22. Magnetostratigraphy does not corroborate isotopic dating because it does not produce unique constraints. Whenever one set of dates (and resulting placement in the Magnetic-Polarity Scale) fall out of favor, the new results simply pigeonhole the igneous body into a new location on the Magnetic-Polarity Scale.

necessary in order to enforce conformity between the two systems.

We have examined those contradictions between isotopic age-data and the Pleistocene Magnetic Polarity Scale, and which were rationalized away as open-system dates and/or inadequately-removed secondary magnetization. In addition, there exists another set of contradictions between the two systems. Unlike the first set, these contradictions are themselves too consistent in occurrence to be so easily dismissed as "open systems" or "secondary magnetization." For this reason, they have been blamed on short magnetic reversals (within a longer interval of either reversed or normal geomagnetic polarity), or on regional "excursions" of the earth's magnetic field:

> A review of the status of short polarity events within the Brunhes and Matuyama Chrons indicates that the data base documenting them is quite extensive, and the data suggest that there may be more subchrons than were generally believed . . . all these events to be *directionally fully opposite in polarity to the chron that they are within* (Champion *et al.* 1988, p. 11,677) [emphasis added].

More recent research (Singer *et al.* 1999) has only exacerbated this proliferation of "subchrons."

In other words, contradictions between polarity and isotopic dates are not recognized as evidence undermining the validity of the Pleistocene Magnetic Polarity Scale, but only as indicators of hitherto-unrecognized changes in the earth's magnetic polarity. This continues the trend, which began in the 1960's during the construction of the first versions of the Pleistocene Magnetic Polarity Scale, of steadily increasing the numbers of normal and reversed time-intervals as more and more data were accumulated (see figure 6.1 of Glen 1982, p. 224). Of course, the more of these "reversals" and "reversals within reversals" are found, the closer the GPTS comes to a random assortment of dates and intervals of magnetic polarity! In view of the presumed short duration of the presumed short polarity reversals, combined with the relative inaccuracy of dates on presumably-young rocks, this takes on further significance. Moreover, it is acknowledged that the choice of presumed short periods of polarity may be influenced by the reinforcement syndrome (see Champion *et al.* 1988, p. 11,677).

As is the case with "younger" rocks, the correlation of magnetochrons is largely based on biostratigraphy, and identifications of particular magnetochrons have to be revised, on an *ad hoc* basis, whenever a conflict arises between the two systems. The same occurs to magnetochrons in the face of isotopic dates:

> In some cases, the dates were off by as much as 2 million years. Flagstaff Rim Ash J., for example, had been K-Ar dated at 32.5 million years, but laser-fusion ^{40}Ar/^{39}Ar methods gave a date of 34.4. . . . There was no way the reversed interval could represent Chron C12R; we now think it represents Chron C15R (Prothero 1994, p. 60).

As can be vividly seen, a backpedaling took place, as to identification and correlation of particular magnetochrons, when "reliable" K-Ar results (which had presumably passed some sort of reliability criteria) had been replaced by "more reliable" ^{40}Ar/^{39}Ar results. It should be added that pre-Pleistocene geomagnetic polarity scales are fraught with large contradictions even when only "good" dates are used. Thus, for instance, the age of magnetochrons in the range of 15-17 Ma has recently been revised by 0.9 million years (Baksi and Farrar 1990, p. 1119).

Myth: Overall, the geochronometric, biostratigraphic, and magnetostratigraphic chronologies all agree, thereby producing a strongly self-checking system.

Reality Check: It should be clear, by now, that the three systems are *forced* to agree, one way or another. Now, let us reconsider the implications of "mutually corroborated" lines of evidence. Earlier, I had discussed the example of the dating of plutons in the Yucatan Peninsula (Steiner and Walker 1996). Several ostensibly independent lines of geologic evidence had to be set aside to accommodate some discrepantly-old U-Pb dates. Hence, even on uniformitarians' own terms, one has to be a bit skeptical even about "several independent lines of geologic evidence" which appear to form a mutually-corroborating network with isotopic dates (see figure 3).

What about three-way agreements between isotopic, biostratigraphic, and paleomagnetic chronologies? Even this is not conclusive proof for their accuracy, even with the context of uniformitarian assumptions, as is acknowledged with respect to the dating of the Jurassic of the US Atlantic states:

> In fact, of the pair-wise combinations possible, the fish-zone data prove consistent with each of the other classes of data. In addition, the basalt geochemical data and the paleomagnetic data are compatible, and together consistent with the fish data. The K/Ar data, while consistent with the fish data, do not agree with either the basalt geochemical or the paleomagnetic data. While this could be taken as support for the fish-zone correlation, we lack confidence that any one class of data is to be preferred over any other. No relevant geophysical or paleontological data are free of compromising assumptions and technical difficulties. *Agreement among three independent lines of data does not add reliability to the correlation if the data are equivocal* (Olsen *et al.* 1982, p. 26) [emphasis added].

Of course, whether or not evidences are equivocal is a matter of opinion and subject, of course, to uniformitarian assumptions. What about other instances of correlating isotopic/ biostratigraphic/ magnetostratigraphic information? In each case, there is "massaging" of one, two, or all three lines of evidence in order to get them to fit with each other. This had been shown when it came to the revision of magnetochrons as discussed above, and is shown to be a general practice, as evidenced by the following:

> Geologic time scales are the result of iterative processes, and as new definitive data becomes available, either geochronometric, biostratigraphic, or magnetostratigraphic adjustments will have to be made (Obradovich 1988, p. 767).

Myth: Isotopic dates confirm the relative age of fossil-bearing sediment.

This has widely been claimed by apologists for isotopic dating. Perhaps the most recent of these claims, and the one most likely to be read by the general public, includes the following:

> . . . the rarity of locations where rocks with well-controlled fossils dates are closely associated with proper mineral material for very precise radiometric dates. A few hundred of these well-dated localities represent the primary control points on which the entire dating system of the geologic column is based. Where such ideal conditions exist, the same

horizons yield the same precise dates even if the locations are continents apart (Wise 1998, p. 165).

Reality Check: To begin with, when Wise (1998) cites the study by Obradovich (1993) on the dating of Cretaceous bentonites, there are a variety of facts from the latter's study which Wise conveniently fails to mention to his readers. These include such problems as interlaboratory bias (Obradovich 1993, p. 382), the common rejection of $^{40}Ar/^{39}Ar$-dated biotites which are "too old" (p. 382), subjectivities and inconsistencies of using different monitors for the $^{40}Ar/^{39}Ar$ method (p. 389), the existence of internally-consistent yet anomalous dates (p. 389), backpedaling on Cretaceous biozonal stratigraphy (p. 388), and attribution of pristine sanidine crystals to contamination on a posterioritic basis (p. 391), etc.

Of course, Wise (1998) does not stand alone in his rosy portrayal of isotopic dating to unsuspecting readers. Statements about the "amazing agreement between geochronometers and biostratigraphy" are made all the time, and are disingenuous in the extreme. As demonstrated in detail in the previous paper (Woodmorappe, 1979, 1993), and in an earlier section of this book, biostratigraphic methods are actually used to *check* whether or not a given isotopic dating result should be accepted as a valid age of the rock! And, as documented, isotopic results which disagree with biostratigraphic order are automatically disregarded as incorrect. This process continues today, as demonstrated by the following examples:

> Taken together, the data for the Bridge River Group plot in a band about 0.002 wide in $^{87}Sr/^{86}Sr$, with an initial ratio of about 0.7050 and a 152 Ma (Late Jurassic) slope. This must represent a reset age, as it is younger than the youngest known (Lower to Middle Jurassic) fossils in the Bridge River cherts . . . (Leitch *et al.* 1991, p. 201, 203).

> Fossil palynomorphs from the lowermost nonmarine rocks indicate an early Maastrichtian age. . . . A fission-track age of 50.0 ± 7.7 Ma (Eocene) was obtained on a thick, waterlain tephra that crops out stratigraphically below the measured sections. . . . This isotopic date provides an extreme minimum age, obviously representing alteration, because the tephra occurs well below dinosaur-bearing horizons. Preliminary $^{40}Ar/^{39}Ar$ analysis . . . indicate an age range between 68 and 71 Ma (late Maastrichtian). . . (Brouwers and DeDeckker 1996, pp. 208-209).

Note how the result which agreed with the biostratigraphically-determined age was assumed to be correct, and how the isotopic date which disagreed with this was assumed to be altered. And, when it comes to the construction of the Phanerozoic time scale, an isotopic date must meet *both* the conditions of tight biostratigraphic control *and agreement with presumably-correct dates* before it is considered to be a reliable calibration point:

> Lack of biostratigraphic control has necessitated exclusion of many radiometric age determinations even though the age is within the range of dates for the Silurian-Early Devonian (Jones *et al.* 1981, pp. 199-200).

Sometimes, however, it is intercontinental biostratigraphic correlations that are held to be in error as a result of conflicts with isotopic dates (Hess *et al.* 1999).

E. Do High "Closure Temperatures" Accredit Prolonged Closed Systems?

Myth: The closed-system behavior of K-Ar and Rb-Sr systems, over millions or billions of years, is a robust scientific assumption.

Fact: Even on its own uniformitarian terms, it most certainly is not:

> Of the various methods of radiometric age determination that of U-Pb on zircons is one of the most reliable. The U-Pb system in zircons is very insensitive to metamorphic or tectonic events and alteration generally has no detectable effect. In contrast, other systems such as K-Ar and Rb-Sr are *very sensitive* to these external sources of disturbance (Cocherie *et al.* 1992, p. 131) [emphasis added].

(In the section on U-Pb zircon dating, I show that, to the contrary, U-Pb zircon results have their own large body of rationalizations to cope with discrepant and unwanted results).

Myth: (Re: Closure Temperatures) The tested high temperatures necessary to cause open-system behavior in rocks and minerals substantiates the premise that isotopic dating systems must have remained undisturbed for millions and billions of years.

Fact: They do no such thing. Let us examine first the issue of so-called closure temperatures for different minerals and rocks, and as presumably applicable to different dating methods. To begin with, the conditions leading to presumed closure temperatures are, by any standard, much more complex than earlier believed. Consider K-Ar dating. The argon-retentive temperature is now believed to depend not only upon the kind of mineral, but also its physical size, structural state, precise chemical composition, and presumed cooling rate (Snee *et al.* 1995, pp. 366-367). Since the latter can only be deduced from the pattern of discordantly-young "cooling ages" obtained from a given pluton, the circularity in reasoning is obvious. It is also recognized that, if a rock were to cool through a series of pulsative changes in temperature, it would be impossible to recognize this having taken place in any sort of a presumed dataset of "cooling ages" (Cumming and Krstic 1991).

Furthermore, the range of presumed closure temperatures is, by any standard, much greater than earlier believed. Snee *et al.* (1995, p. 367) have summarized the closure temperatures to argon diffusion based on studies conducted in the

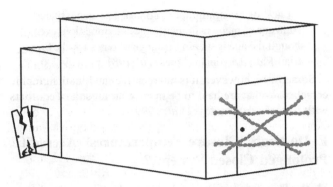

Figure 23. What good is it that the prisoner cannot readily break down the heavily-chained front door when he can easily open the flimsy rear door and escape? Analogously, what good are the high closure temperatures of minerals to isotope diffusion when in fact the "imprisoned," "radiogenic" isotopes can easily be leached out by comparatively low-temperature, fluid-dominated processes?

1980's. These are: 580°C-480°C for hornblende, 325°C-270°C for muscovite, 300°C-260°C for biotite, and 160°C-100°C for microcline. Other estimates for closure temperature of biotite, the most common mineral used in K-Ar dating, range up to 345°C (Harrison *et al.* 1985) and even 450°C (Villa and Puxeddu 1994). Conventionally-interpreted geologic evidence has some mica (notably muscovite) remaining at least partly closed to Ar loss at temperatures as high as 500°C (Villa and Puxeddu 1994). It is also now suggested that there is no simple "closure temperature" for Ar-loss in metamorphic amphiboles (Blanckenburg and Villa 1988), whereas that of igneous hornblende may be as low as 450°-500°C (Cumming and Krstic 1991), in contrast to the 480°-580°C quoted above. As for the other dating methods (Sm-Nd, U-Pb, Lu-Hf), the range of possible closure temperatures, for commonly-used minerals, also spans an uncertainty ranging from a few hundred to several hundred degrees Celsius (Cherniak *et al.* 1997).

It is hardly surprising that "closure temperatures" for isotopic systems are highly contradictory—especially when one dating method is used to gauge the presumed closure temperature of another. This is particularly evident in the case of Sm-Nd dating of garnet, for which closure temperatures spanning the range of 500°C-900°C have been entertained (Wang *et al.* 1998b, pp. 334-335). In fact, in this cited study, the interested reader can see a virtual comedy of pick-and-choose when it comes to deciding which isotopic dates to select in order to constrain the closure temperature of the Sm-Nd "clock."

As if all this were not enough, there now is evidence that the closure temperature is also affected by the petrographic composition of the rock. Thus, for instance, the closure temperature of biotite to Sr will vary solely as a result of the proportions of certain other minerals (Jenkin 1997).

Overall, the huge range of values for closure temperature greatly undercuts the claim that "cooling ages" and "rejuvenated" ages have a solid rational foundation, even within the uniformitarian paradigm. Thus, the range of uncertainty for the closure temperature of a given mineral is considerable under actual geologic conditions. This creates an over-

lap with a similar broad range of closure temperatures applicable to classes of "more retentive" and "less retentive" minerals. On top of that, there is the inherent uncertainty of how rapidly a pluton or suite of plutons is supposed to have been uplifted above these poorly-defined closure temperatures. This removes the issue of "cooling ages" and "rejuvenated ages" away from any form of quasi-rigorous methodology, and places it squarely in the realms of speculation and rationalization.

It is also interesting to note instances where geologic evidence *explicitly contravenes* "closure temperatures." This occurs whenever an isotopic system with a relatively low closure temperature yields an *older* date than one with a higher closure temperature. Among these are occurrences of K-Ar dates older than Rb-Sr whole-rock isochrons from the same rock (Baumann 1991, Kawano and Kagami 1993, Kwan *et al.* 1992, Siebel 1995). A comparable situation occurs, within K-Ar dating itself, whenever a less retentive mineral produces older ages than a more retentive one. This is often called reverse discordancy or inverse discordancy. In the previous paper (Woodmorappe 1979, 1993), I had pointed out this phenomenon in the form of some studies on dates from biotite/hornblende pairs. More recent examples are provided by Anderson (1988) and Miller *et al.* (1991). In fact, in addition to the usual claim about dates which are "too old," such "anomalous pairs" are *assumed* to be evidence of excess argon contamination:

> It is well known that argon can be added during heating to many minerals [reference cited] as shown by: 1. dates that are far too old to be reasonable cooling ages for any known heating event in the vicinity; 2. dates that are in "anomalous pairs" [reference cited] from a single sample, in which the mineral that usually has the lower argon diffusion temperature gives the older date (in contrast with "normal pairs") (Anderson 1988, p. 714).

In a similar situation, a reverse discordancy (K-Ar biotite dates older than FT dates on zircon, sphene, and apatite) was likewise blamed on excess argon (Bryant *et al.* 1981, p. 22). In the other situation (Miller *et al.* 1991), the reverse (or inverse) discordance between micas and hornblende has been attributed to the action of hydrothermal fluids. More on this shortly.

Myth: Isotopic dating systems are robust "clocks" by virtue of the fact that only a significant thermal event (one which heats a rock above a closure temperature of a particular isotope) is capable of causing a rock or mineral to become an open system.

Fact: In addition to the internally-inconsistent information about thermal closure temperatures, discussed above, it is of utmost importance to recognize that high temperatures are not the sole means by which rocks and minerals can become open systems. To the contrary, many low-temperature events can demonstrably cause open-system behavior in rocks and minerals. Let us begin by considering lab procedures. Consider, for instance, the effects of an acid bath on K-Ar results:

> Our major concern in breaking down the bulk rock and separating the biotite was to avoid the possible leaching of potassium and loss of argon that might have occurred if the carbonate matrix had simply been dissolved in HCl. It has been found that prolonged immersion in concentrated HCl causes nonproportional removal of argon and potassium from the biotite (unpub. data, U.C. Berkeley K/Ar Laboratory), which would invalidate radiometric age determinations. However, short immersions in diluted HCl do not have any deleterious effects on biotite. With this cautious assumption, we have bathed our biotite separates in dilute 10% HCl for 30 s or less, just enough to eliminate unwanted residual calcite (Montanari *et al.* 1985, p. 596).

> To break apart the organic-rich bentonite clays, the samples were treated in a 1M solution of NaOH at approximately 100°C. Was it possible that this procedure set up an ion exchange of Na for K in the feldspars during preparation, resulting in apparently old ages? To address this hypothesis, new sanidine separates were prepared from two untreated bentonite samples using only water and dilute (7%) hydrofluoric acid. The results of the present study are approximately 2.0% younger than previous replicate $^{40}Ar/^{39}Ar$ analyses on the IrZ and Z sanidines using NaOH. . . . These new results support the ion exchange hypothesis (Swisher *et al.* 1993, p. 1993).

Despite the obvious vulnerability of the K-Ar system to low-temperature chemical effects, on a time scale measured (in this instance) in seconds, minutes, or perhaps hours, we are asked to believe that K-Ar isotopic systems have actually been closed for millions of years! And, of course, no one is suggesting that HCl and NaOH are the *only* low-temperature reagents capable of adding or removing isotopes from a rock or mineral.

What about the K-Ar "clock" under actual geologic conditions? It is recognized that hornblende can become an open system, as a result of the action of hydrothermal fluids, at temperatures far below the traditionally-accepted range for closure temperature of 490°-578°C (Miller *et al.* 1991). An analogous line of evidence applies to the ostensible closure temperatures of the other "clocks," such as Rb-Sr, Sm-Nd, and U-Pb. It has long been supposed that the Rb-Sr whole-rock isochron can remain a closed system at far higher temperatures (some several hundred degrees C) than the K-Ar "clock." However, this premise tacitly assumes that the only way the Rb-Sr system can be open is under the conditions of high-temperature controlled diffusion, which could theoretically be true if there existed some miraculous guarantee that the Rb-Sr whole-rock system would remain strictly under anhydrous conditions for the millions or billions of years of

its existence. In actuality, the Achilles' heel of the Rb-Sr system is not the degree of its resistance to temperature, but its considerable vulnerability to hydrothermal alteration under relatively low temperatures. Thus, if a fluid phase exists, transport of chemical species is greatly facilitated, and an Rb-Sr whole-rock isochron can be "reset" or "rejuvenated" at temperatures as low as 350°C or below (Evans 1989, p. 678). Other authors have underscored the unexpected and unappreciated vulnerability of the Rb-Sr system to hydrothermal processes (Kwan *et al.* 1992, Siebel 1995). This is also true of the Sm-Nd "clock" no less so than the Rb-Sr one:

> We conclude that the Rb-Sr and Sm-Nd isotopic systems are much more sensitive to metasomatic processes than is commonly believed (Frost and Frost 1995, p. 283).

Moreover, various open-system arrays will often retain the characteristic of well-defined isochrons, but:

> . . . meaningless linear arrays of Rb-Sr isotope data can result from incomplete isotopic re-equilibration in an open system. These mixing arrays can record apparent ages older or younger than the age of the shear zone (Hickman and Glassley 1984, p. 280).

This fact nullifies the premise that there exists a rigorously-predictable temperature (and a high one at that) below which the Rb-Sr system will ostensibly remain closed. It also relegates the invocation of "rejuvenated" Rb-Sr whole rock isochrons into an *ad hoc* rationalization, to be freely invoked whenever an Rb-Sr whole-rock isochron yields an age that is either "too young" or "too old."

Despite the fact that the Sm-Nd and U-Pb systems are believed to be even more resistant to thermal effects than the Rb-Sr system, fluid-transport at relatively low temperatures can also cause open-system behavior, at relatively low temperatures, in the Sm-Nd and U-Pb "clocks." This fact is discussed and documented in the respective places in this book where these dating methods are examined in detail.

Myth: The study of patterns of "rejuvenation" at contact metamorphic aureoles accredits the premise that isotopic dating systems are likely to have remained closed systems over millions to billions of years.

Reality Check: It does no such thing. At most, it tells us that the heat of contact metamorphism causes an imbalance between presumed-parent and presumed-daughter products, and in favor of the former. Otherwise, it tells us nothing about the validity or otherwise of the dating method itself. For example, the "rejuvenation" of presumed Proterozoic rocks in southern Arizona, by Meso-Cenozoic plutons, is hardly limited to the immediate vicinities of the so-dated Meso-Cenozoic plutons. To the contrary: Proterozoic "basement" can display Meso-Cenozoic K-Ar and FT dates even though it is many tens of kilometers from the nearest known so-dated Meso-Cenozoic intrusion (see figure 18-3 of Reynolds *et al.* 1988). Conversely, so-called primary Proterozoic dates (>1.0 Ga) can be found

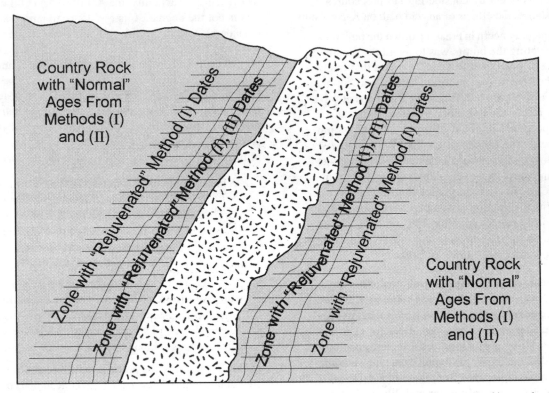

Figure 24: It is sometimes claimed that the pattern of reheated isotopic dates found around contact-metamorphic aureoles accredits the dating methods. It does no such thing. At best, such patterns indicate to what extent isotopic-dating systems are vulnerable to *localized, secondary* geologic effects. They tell us nothing about initial conditions related to the crystallization of the host rock.

in the immediate vicinity of strongly-"rejuvenated" (e. g., 40-80 Ma) Proterozoic lithologies.

In the previous paper (Woodmorappe 1979, 1993), I had provided several examples where dates were supposed to have remained closed systems despite their proximity to more-recent intrusions. Conversely, I had also documented *ad hoc* claims of "rejuvenated" systems where there had been little or no independent geologic evidence of a reheating event.

Moreover, presumed closure-temperature estimates, based on contact-metamorphic aureole studies, are widely contradictory. For example, the Frost and Frost (1995) study, discussed above, which indicated the unexpected and heretofore-unappreciated sensitivity of Rb-Sr and Sm-Nd systems to the leaching effects of circulating fluids, was based on a study of rocks surrounding a contact-metamorphic aureole. In the end, biostratigraphy must be used to determine the presumed extent of "rejuvenation" caused by contact-metamorphism of nearby intrusions:

> Glenorchy samples . . . yield a possibly younger Rb-Sr age (161 ± 28 Ma) and younger K-Ar age (150 ± 2 Ma). However, in the absence of good stratigraphic/paleontological data, it is not possible to unequivocally determine whether the younger Rb-Sr age is due to a difference in burial metamorphic age, or resetting owing to the emplacement of scheelite-bearing quartz veins, or to a later uplift from deeper metamorphic levels (Graham and Mortimer 1992, p. 397).

Finally, the limited utility of contact-metamorphic aureole datings, for purposes of constraining isotopic-dating systems generally, is proved by the widely unpredictable effects of intrusions upon such systems in the country rock. Thus, the effects of an intrusion's heat and/or hydrothermal fluids are not diagnostic, on the isotope-dating systems of country rock, even in clear-cut instances:

> With large-scale igneous activity taking place just a few kilometers west, one would expect newer titanite crystals and growths over the older ones in the central Ramagiri Complex. However, no newer titanites have been observed, and the $^{207}Pb/^{206}Pb$ and concordant ages of various titanite fractions are identical to that of zircons. It is indeed surprising that such a widespread intrusive episode of the western granitic terrane has neither reset the U-Pb systematics nor resulted in newer growth of titanites in the central Ramagiri Complex (Balakrishnan *et al.* 1999, p. 81).

To those who make much of "testable predictions" in uniformitarian geology in general and isotopic-dating in particular, here is yet another example of an obviously failed prediction. Incidentally, one wonders if anyone is "keeping score" over the frequencies of successful versus failed specific predictions in uniformitarian geology. Someone definitely should.

Chapter 6

Isochron Methods (Rb-Sr, Sm-Nd, Lu-Hf, Re-Os, Pb-Pb, and Some K-Ar)

A. Analytic Data and the Collinearity of Points on Isochron Plots

Myth: The initial isotopic homogeneity of consanguineous magmas, a foundation of all isochron-based dating methods, is a robust assumption.

Fact: This is increasingly being questioned:

> Whole-rock Rb-Sr dating is extensively used to date times of differentiation, because of its resistance to resetting, but is not without numerous pitfalls. Identical $^{87}Sr/^{86}Sr$ initial ratios for all samples of a cogenetic suite are assumed but this is rarely true in detail and sometimes spectacularly false (Harland *et al.* 1990, p. 76).

> Rb-Sr and U-Pb dating of plutonic or metamorphic rock relies on rather tight constraints, which, if not obeyed, put limitations on the use of age and isotopic data. For the Rb-Sr chronometer, it is commonly assumed that, upon cooling by either conduction or heat-driven convection, the pluton to be dated passed through a stage of strontium isotopic homogeneity.

The isochron age is supposed to provide the time at which this event took place. *Evidence that rock units are isotopically heterogeneous is, however, rather common* (Juteau *et al.* 1984, p. 532) [emphasis added].

There has also been a series of studies of the Sm-Nd system in a metamorphic environment (e. g., Grau *et al.* 1990; Thoni and Jagoutz 1992), wherein unacceptable dates from isochrons were blamed on the isochrons having been based on samples which had isotopic heterogeneities. Of course, these "isotopic heterogeneities" also occur frequently in igneous rocks:

> If a rock suite has variable initial ratio, and especially if the Sm/Nd ratios and the initial ratios are correlated, *as is often the case*, both the determined age and the initial ratio may be seriously in error. . . . As an example, rocks of very nearly the same age (± 15 m. y.) from the Peninsular Ranges batholith of southern California exhibit variations in initial $^{143}Nd/^{144}Nd$ of some 0.14%, equal in magnitude to the total range of $^{143}Nd/^{144}Nd$ expected along

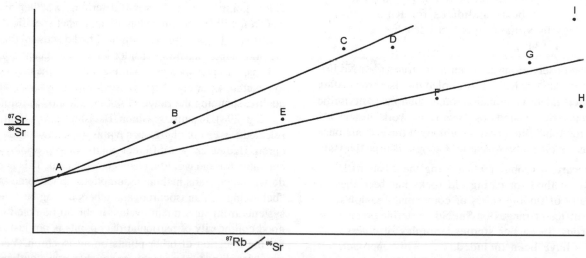

Figure 25. Fudging isochrons for every occasion. In the above example, points (H) and (I) have been disregarded because they are not collinear with any other array of points. The remaining points are forced to define two candidate isochrons. Which to accept, which to reject? Does isochron AEFG give the correct age of the rock, and is isochron ABCD an inherited isochron? Or is perhaps isochron ABCD the one which dates the crystallization of the rock, and isochron AEFG the one that defines the age of some later heating event on the host rock? Then again, maybe either or both isochrons are mixing lines. Finally, the uniformitarian may well conclude that "none of the above" is applicable, and that either or both isochrons are meaningless but collinear arrays of points that have resulted from complex open-system behavior. As always, geologic interpretations will dictate the conclusions.

a typical isochron [reference cited]. Furthermore, the $^{143}Nd/^{144}Nd$ initial ratios are roughly correlated with $^{147}Sm/^{144}Nd$ in the rock, so that the data scatter about an apparent "isochron" of 1.7 b. y., even though the crystallization age is about 0.1 b. y.! (DePaulo 1988, p. 21) [emphasis added].

Myth: The consanguinity of magmas, a requirement which must be met by all isochron-based dating methods, is readily determined.

Fact: On uniformitarians' own terms, this is increasingly seen not to be the case. As noted earlier, plutons which were geographically close and similar to each other in chemistry and/or mineralogy, and had in fact been correlated together as one igneous body, later turned out to have very divergent isotopic "ages," which were then accepted as evidence of heterochroneity (Braddock and Peterman 1989, p. 97; Bryant et al. 1981, p. 23).

Moreover, the need for points to spread out sufficiently on an Rb-Sr isochron diagram has admittedly caused a relaxation of the assumption that all of its constituents had been co-magmatic (and therefore, according to the assumption behind Rb-Sr isochrons, had necessarily shared the same $^{87}Sr/^{86}Sr$ ratio):

> . . . selection of samples for isochron-age analysis should not be made solely on the basis of seeking the maximum possible spread in the $^{87}Rb/^{86}Sr$ ratios (Field and Råheim 1979, p. 499).

> It has been common practice in Rb-Sr geochronology to regress all analyses from such rocks together in order to enhance the range of Rb/Sr ratios. . . . The rocks that are most susceptible to disturbances of their Rb-Sr isotope systematics are those with high Rb/Sr ratios. . . . These units typically have a large range of Rb/Sr ratios and are often considered to be the best candidates for Rb-Sr geochronology by virtue of this fact (Beakhouse et al. 1988, p. 344, 349).

The above observations are even more true of Sm-Nd isochrons, where data are habitually pooled into isochrons, often without independent justification, other than the posterioritic conclusion that the methodology seems to "work" (ostensibly according to "reliability criteria" which, in the end, are once again forced to take a back seat to geologic interpretations):

> A recurrent problem when using the whole rock Sm-Nd method for dating old rocks has been the difficulty of finding suites of comagmatic samples with sufficient ranges of Sm/Nd to define precise isochrons. In earlier studies, samples of diverse origins have been included. . . . This approach neglects one of the basic precepts of geochronology; namely that analyzed samples should have formed simultaneously from sources with identical isotopic compositions. Samples from different locations or of different rock types are unlikely to have had the

same initial isotopic ratios, leading to the possibility of incorrect ages. Nevertheless, the method continues to be used, partly with the justification that ages so far reported have been consistent with those obtained using other methods (Cattell et al. 1984, p. 280).

As we shall see in the following entries, posterioritic reasoning in geochronometry (Williams 1992) is once again vividly evident. The choice of samples used to construct the Rb-Sr and Sm-Nd isochrons places them in the role of trial balloons. Thus, if the resulting isochron seems to fit in with other dating methods, or with conventional geologic interpretations, it is then claimed that the samples had in fact been comagmatic and had been undisturbed since crystallization. On the other hand, if the points are not collinear (or if they are collinear but define an unacceptable date), then we are told that the samples had not been comagmatic in the first place (and/or had become open systems since crystallization). Heads, I win; tails, you lose. The following is an example of a Sm-Nd isochron which had been ostensibly self-checked, yet had to be rejected afterwards:

> Justification for such studies can come from the internal consistency of results so obtained, and indeed the previous interpretation of the komatiite-granite correlation as a real age for Kambalda was based on the tightness of the regression through all the samples used . . . the age derived from mixing the plutonic and volcanic samples is spurious (Claoue-Long et al. 1984, p. 699).

Myth: The isochrons themselves are rigorous and objective constructions, and yield unambiguous dates of crystallization of the host rock.

Reality Check: To begin with, there is actually room for fudging the isochron by selectively including or excluding individual points from it. This will determine whether or not an isochron will be recognized at all, and what specific date the isochron will ostensibly determine. I had discussed this in the previous paper, and now consider some more recent examples.

Thus, different choices of samples allowed the investigators to generate a variety of Rb-Sr isochrons, of varying analytic quality, spanning the range of 400-432 Ma (Compston et al. 1982, p. 298). In similar fashion, Balashov et al. (1994, p. 89) selected eleven out of eighteen points to generate a Rb-Sr isochron. Had he chosen different points, an appreciably different value for age would have been calculated. This is easy to do when one starts making assumptions about some samples "belonging" on an isochron, and others having become open systems from subsequent events. It should be noted that the good collinearity of particular data points is not justification for the rejection of other points on an isochron. Yet many geochronologists plot isochrons and then reject outliers on an *a posteriori* basis (Lutz and Srogi 1986; for an example of this, see Ziegler and Stoessel 1993, p. 47).

Furthermore, the practice of picking and choosing certain points to define an isochron is not limited to individual points, but is also applicable to sets of points. Such a procedure can go as far as causing conflicting interpretations among geochronologists as to whether or not the isochron is meaningful, or if it represents an *ad hoc* concoction [for instance, compare Moorbath and Whitehouse (1996) with Bowring and Housh (1996)]. In another situation, a team of researchers has come up with a diverse set of Rb-Sr isochrons, none of which reproduced the Rb-Sr isochron determined by an earlier investigator on the same suite of rocks:

> Our Rb-Sr date from these localities show no sign of the 375 Ma crystallization age recorded by the data of Adams (1987) and the SHRIMP analyses. Either the younger ages of circa 330 Ma are spurious or they reflect a cryptic response to a later phase of intrusion, identified below (Pankhurst *et al.* 1998, p. 2533).

Furthermore, Pankhurst *et al.* (1998, pp. 2532-2533) demonstrate the considerable malleability of Rb-Sr isochrons, not only in terms of age indicated, but also the precision of the date. Although all of the prospective isochrons he discusses have very low MSWD values, the choice of points on the isochron governs the spread of Rb/Sr values, and hence the precision of the date. For instance, the inclusion of a "possibly cogenetic aplite vein" converts an anomalously-young but imprecise 330 ± 20 Ma Rb-Sr isochron to a more-precise but more-anomalous Rb-Sr isochron of 319 ± 6 Ma. Perhaps the clearest statement about the malleability of Rb-Sr (and other) isochrons is the following:

> The data demonstrate the possibility of producing statistically distinct good-fit whole-rock isochrons from the *same body of rock* at the *same locality*. The secondary isochrons have only been detected in this case because sampling was on the scale of a few metres. . . (Smalley *et al.* 1983, p. 278) [emphasis in original].

Still other examples of two or more isochrons (whether "real" ones and/or reference isochrons) obtained from the same rock are described by Kroner (1982), MacIntyre and Berger (1982), Tanner *et al.* (1997), Wooden *et al.* (1988), and Ziegler and Stoessel (1993). In the first and fourth cited studies, one isochron is supposed to indicate the age of the rock, and the other is relegated to an "overprint" age of a reheating event. The second and fifth cited studies both involve the breakup of isochrons formed by previous authors. These are now believed to be a concoction of invalidly-commingled data points. In the case of Ziegler and Stoessel (1993, pp. 47-48), both new isochrons are believed to be geologically meaningless, despite the excellent collinearity of points (r = .999 and .995, respectively). In the third cited study (Tanner *et al.* 1997, and references cited therein), a wide variety of different interpretations had been proposed by different geologists to account for the occurrence of widely-divergent Rb-Sr isochron ages (ranging from 396 Ma to 528 Ma) from the same granitic body.

These included inherited isotope systematics, thermal "overprints," open-system behavior caused by metasomatism, etc.

As noted in the previous entry, it is common during isochron construction for a geologist to sample a large area for rocks having a sufficient spread in isotopic ratios. This can only increase the diversity of points which can be selectively lined up to create a tendentious isochron, which can just as easily be dissolved (as a trial balloon) if the geologic interpretation falls out of favor. On its ruins, one or more alternative isochrons can be constructed. For instance, a Rb-Sr isochron of 602 Ma was dissolved into two new isochrons, yielding ages of 581 and 685 Ma (Stern and Hedge 1985, pp. 114-115). A comparable example is discussed by Brookins (1983), wherein an isotopically-diverse array was collected from the Coldbrook volcanics. Depending upon which data points were selected from the array, a diverse series of Rb-Sr isochrons were constructed, ranging from 370 million to 1.15 billion years.

The Sm-Nd isochron method is especially vulnerable to the tendentiousness of selecting samples to define the isochron, as discussed below. This is aggravated by the need to sample large geographic areas to get an adequate spread of isotopes for the isochron, and thus stretching the assumption about the materials having all come from the same parent magma. And, as with the Rb-Sr isochron, the Sm-Nd isochron can be fudged according to the choice of points used to define it, particularly if the investigator is forced to work with a constricted range of Sm/Nd ratio when constructing it. For instance, Cliff and Rickard (1992, pp. 1124-1125) were able to vary a Sm-Nd isochron from 1.49 to 1.63 Ga depending upon the inclusion or exclusion of a point on it. Either choice, however, had little effect on the low MSWD value, which changed from 2.1 to 2.9. Elsewhere, a single Sm-Nd isochron of 2.225 Ga could easily be broken down into five different alternative isochrons (based on petrologic and geographic criteria) which would define ages ranging from 1.665 Ga to 2.574 Ga (Ziegler and Stoessel 1993, p. 67).

Myth: The fact that points are collinear on the isochron diagram validates the method, as well as the dating result obtained.

The following is a typical rendition of this mythology:

> As mentioned earlier, the methods of estimating ages are self-checking; if some of the particular minerals selected for analysis were not closed systems, then the isotopic abundances would not fall on a straight line (the "isochron") (Brush 1982, p. 49).

Hayward (1985) has made this argument even more dramatic by comparing this situation to the repeated accidental dropping of peas on a floor, and finding that the peas consistently form a collinear diagram.

Reality Check: As discussed below, Brush's claim has been shown to be inaccurate long ago. Hayward's argument is absurd in the extreme: no scientific creationist suggests that the earth's isotopes and their relative distributions in rock are governed by random processes which bear any resemblance to the spilling of peas on a floor. In fact, much has already been written about well-defined isochrons that cannot be accepted by uniformitarians as indicative of the age of the rock (e. g., Austin 1994; Helmick and Baumann 1986). Furthermore, a whole set of jargon has been developed about these confessedly non-chronometric isochron plots: inherited isochron, apparent isochron, mantle isochron, pseudoisochron, secondary isochron, source isochron, erupted isochron, mixing line, mixing isochron (Zheng 1989, p. 1), etc. There is no doubt about the fact that this consideration applies to *all* isochron-based methods:

> . . . mixing processes produce straight line arrays on bivariate plots of two ratios sharing a common denominator (e. g., A/X vs. B/X): well defined "isochrons" of no age significance will therefore result from mixing of two components having different X ($^{87}Rb/^{86}Sr$, $^{147}Sm/^{144}Nd$, $^{206}Pb/^{204}Pb$, etc.) and Y ($^{87}Sr/^{86}Sr$, $^{143}Nd/^{144}Nd$, $^{207}Pb/^{206}Pb$, etc.) compositions. Uncritical acceptance of an isochron date can, as a result, potentially be as misleading as accepting a data set where excess scatter has confidently been identified. A strong relationship between variables does not therefore prove, or necessarily imply, that the dependant ("Y") variables are age-controlled results of the ("X") independent variable. Additional information, in our case geological, is necessary before such causal inferences can be made (Harmer and Eglington 1990, p. 854).

Numerous authors (Kwan *et al.* 1992, Siebel 1995, Schliecher *et al.* 1983, and many others) have warned against assuming that a series of well-aligned points on an isochron diagram therefore make it valid. Moreover, not even "inheritance" nor "mixing lines" are actually necessary to produce an isochron which has no bearing on the actual age of a rock. It turns out that *simple* open-system behavior can "rotate" isochrons. Lutz and Srogi (1986) performed a computer simulation wherein a random amount of strontium was added to a Rb-Sr system. Various collinear arrays of points, readily (yet erroneously) interpreted as isochrons, were generated. Therefore, the tacit premise about open systems not being capable of producing a linear array of points is patently false.

All of the foregoing discussion must be put in perspective, however, in that there are many instances where sought-after isochrons cannot be formed because the prospective points are not collinear. This is commonly blamed on an isotopically heterogeneous magma and/or secondary disturbance of the isotopes in question (Britt *et al.* 1997, p. 47). Such rationalizations only beg the question about the validity of the assumptions behind the isochron methods in the first place. Ziegler and Stoessel (1993) discuss some Precambrian geochronology in southern Africa. Of thirty-five data points collected for

the purpose of erecting an Sm-Nd isochron, only eighteen could be thus aligned. The remainder had to be rejected.

Thus, to further expose the absurdity of Hayward's (1985) silly argument (about the collinear distribution of peas spilled accidentally on the floor), consider this: Not only can the collinearity of the "peas" be explained without radioactive decay of parent isotopes, but the "collinearity of peas on the floor" occurs only in particular instances. Even then the collinear pattern emerges only as a result of special pleading (i. e., the disregarding of those peas on the floor which do not fit the collinear pattern which the uniformitarian is looking for).

Myth: But if the points on an isochron diagram are strongly collinear, the isochron must have age-indicative validity.

Dalrymple (1991, p. 108-109) would have us believe that, whenever points on an isochron diagram are strongly collinear, such isochrons could only have come into existence by radioactive decay of the parent element over vast stretches of time.

Reality Check: In actuality, even on uniformitarians' own terms, analytically "good" isochrons need not have any meaning whatsoever:

> Inaccurate ages and initial ratios are expected even when the exchange process is purely stochastic, i. e., when the amount of exchange varies from sample to sample and is independent of the original Sr concentrations and Rb/Sr ratios of the samples. Furthermore, systematic errors are decoupled from random errors. *Thus, the fit of a regression is unrelated to the accuracy of age estimates.* We show that extensive alteration of the Rb-Sr chemistry is not required for significant systematic errors to occur (Lutz and Srogi 1986, p. 63) [emphasis added].

We therefore see how, once again, a "self-checking" aspect of isotopic dating (the construction of an isochron with excellent collinearity of points) has been demonstrated to be no such thing.

Furthermore, the fallacy of the "highly linear isochron" argument can perhaps best be demonstrated by pointing out the inconsistencies of its usage. For instance, a certain Rb-Sr isochron was once believed to offer a geologically-significant date because of the "reasonable linearity" of its points (Kroner and Willner 1998, pp. 5, 16-17), only to fall by the wayside when presumably-more reliable U-Pb zircon dates became available. In another situation, Kamber *et al.* (1998) argued for the validity of a certain Sm-Nd isochron largely on the basis of the "tight correlation" of the data points. However, Bennett and Nutman (1998) were unimpressed with this reasoning. They suggested instead that the Sm-Nd isochron is a mixing line, based on the physical distances of the samples gathered, petrologic characteristics of the samples, and the conflict of the Sm-Nd "age" with older and "better" U-Pb zircon dates.

Myth: A low MSWD value for points on an isochron indicates that, if not the correct age of the rock, it must have some other geologic meaning.

Reality Check: In both K-Ar and Rb-Sr dating by isochrons, a MSWD > 2.5 is usually taken to indicate that the points scatter to a larger extent than expected from experimental error alone (McDougall and Harrison 1988, p. 126), although, strictly speaking, an MSWD below 1.0 is required to satisfy this analytic criterion (Dickin 1997, p. 35). [Other investigators use the SUMS/(N-2) statistic (e. g., Sinton *et al.* 1998, and citations) to evaluate the scatter of points on an isochron diagram]. In spite of all this, however, geochronologists frequently treat Rb-Sr isochrons with MSWD's greater than 2.5 as putatively indicative or rocks' ages because of the comparative rarity of isochrons that satisfy the more stringent requirements. In fact, isochrons with MSWDs as large as 4.0 are commonly accepted as valid isochrons which ostensibly date the time since crystallization of the host igneous rock (Asmerom *et al.* 1991, p. 171).

Conversely, there are many situations where isochrons are completely disregarded as indicative of geologic meaning (e. g., Stern and Hedge 1985, Patton *et al.* 1987), all because they do not fit with conventional geologic interpretations—*in spite* of the fact that some of these isochrons have good statistical qualities (e. g., Stern and Hedge 1985, p. 115). It should be emphasized that an MSWD below (or even much below) 2.5 is not in itself proof for the validity of the isochron date. Uniformitarian geochronologists do assign Rb-Sr isochrons to a status of "complete rejuvenation" (Schaltegger 1990, p. 721), possibly-inherited systematics (Munksgaard 1984, p. 357) or even "geological meaninglessness" (Beakhouse *et al.* 1988, p. 344; Field and Raheim 1979, p. 498) despite each isochron in question having an MSWD below 2.5. Likewise, a Rb-Sr isochron with an MSWD of only 0.62 was rejected because the samples used to construct it came from different localities, thus raising doubts about the original magmatic consanguinity of the samples used to construct the isochron (Kroner *et al.* 1994, p. 366). In another instance, the presumed significance of an Rb-Sr isochron with an MSWD of only 0.69 was considered uncertain (Graham and Mortimer 1992, p. 397), as there existed no biostratigraphic information to evaluate the date obtained.

A serious if not fatal blow to the presumed significance of the MSWD value, as a reliability criterion for isochrons, is provided by a study conducted by Kalsbeek and Hansen (1989). Having noted that a standard isochron calculation assumes that the analytical errors scatter in a normal distribution about the "true" values, these researchers subjected previous isochrons to a "bootstrap analysis." This allowed the actual distribution of putative isochron ages to be determined. The MSWD value was found to *vary widely* dependant upon which alternative data points were used to repeatedly generate the isochron:

> The bootstrap method shows that the MSWD-value obtained for an isochron is a very poor estimator of

MSWD-values that could be obtained from other sample suites from the same rock (Kalsbeek and Hansen 1989, p. 289).

Myth: The value for initial $^{87}Sr/^{86}Sr$ ratio in a Rb-Sr isochron determines whether or not the isochron is indicating the correct age of the rock.

Fact: To begin with, this criterion is not proved. It is *assumed*:

> However, some plutons have unrealistically low (< 0.702) calculated $^{87}Sr/^{86}Sr$ ratios at 300 Ma, and thus *do not appear* to have remained closed with respect to the Rb-Sr system (Coler *et al.* 1997, pp. 267-268) [emphasis added].

> The initial $^{87}Sr/^{86}Sr$ ratio of the bentonite 2 parent material is high enough to *suggest* contamination by preexisting crustal materials (Baadsgaard *et al.* 1993, p. 774) [emphasis added].

Thus, deviations from the "undisturbed" ratio are *assumed* to indicate some sort of open-system behavior, or even complete "rejuvenation" or "resetting" of the isochron. Obviously, such a claim begs the question about open-system behavior. Ironically, the converse is also true. Experimental Rb-Sr isochrons, deliberately performed on obviously-altered material, demonstrate that bogus isochrons can pass the "initial ratio reliability test:"

> It is important to note that in our case, the erroneous character of the rhyolite isochron was recognized due to the unrealistically low value of the initial Sr isotopic composition. However, in the general case, the proposed interpretation does not require an obligatory unrealistic primary isotopic composition. This composition can incidentally be so reasonable that the whole-rock isochron can easily be mistaken for a true one in the absence of data on minerals (Shatagin and Volkov 1998, p. 133).

In like manner, Field and Råheim (1979, p. 499) warn that spurious isochrons can define plausibly-low initial $^{87}Sr/^{86}Sr$ ratios. Of course, the converse is also true. Rb-Sr isochrons with a good alignment of points can define absurd (i.e., negative) initial $^{87}Sr/^{86}Sr$ values (e.g., Negrey *et al.* 1996, p. 239).

B. The "Inherent Geologic Reliability" of Isochron Dates

Myth: Even though K-Ar dates can easily be rejuvenated, Rb-Sr isochron dates are very reliable owing to their resistance to open-system behavior.

Reality Check: At first, uniformitarians had made claims about the great reliability of K-Ar dates. Subsequently, they have been forced to take back this claim, and to relegate most K-Ar results on plutons to so-called cooling ages. Next, they claimed that Rb-Sr isochrons can be counted on to give the correct age of the rock. Now they are steadily backpedaling away even from this second premise.

> It is inferred that Rb-Sr isochron ages determined on samples of Precambrian age must be regarded with caution: a residual bias may somewhat alter the information from statistically acceptable isochrons (Juteau 1984, p. 532).

Furthermore, so-called "rejuvenated" isochrons are being invoked on an *ad hoc* basis, as high-grade metamorphic events are no longer believed to be necessary to disturb the Rb-Sr isochron system:

> This study lends further support to the hypothesis that whole-rock Rb-Sr systems can be disturbed and reset to give good-fit secondary isochrons by relatively low-grade events even when there may be little field evidence and only apparently relatively minor mineralogical alteration (Smalley *et al.* 1983, p. 278).

> The overprint caused partial or complete resetting of the isochrons by lowering the isochron slopes, increasing their "initial" Sr ratios and maintaining a linear point array. The overprint is assumed to be of hydrothermal nature, because any remnants of a Mesozoic thermal event (volcanics, Mesozoic mineral ages in the non-Alpine realm) are lacking throughout the Aar Massif. . . . This event (a) had only minor impact on microscopic textures. . . (Schaltegger 1990, p. 721, 722).

Myth: The discrepancies of Rb-Sr mineral isochrons are solved by whole-rock isochrons.

Fact: When mineral isochrons give younger results than whole-rock isochrons, this is taken to be evidence that the minerals had become open systems. But the rock itself has remained a closed system. For that reason, Rb-Sr whole-rock isochrons are believed to be more reliable age-indicators than Rb-Sr mineral isochrons:

> Mineral dating usually does not tell us whether these dates relate to magmatic cooling or to a subsequent metamorphic event (Schleicher *et al.* 1998, p. 1769).

Interestingly, however, the interpretation of isochrons also leads to the diametrically opposite conclusion (Baumann *et al.* 1991; Kostitsyn 1992), wherein it is supposed that individual minerals have been closed systems, and the rock itself has not! Once again, we can vividly see that, when it comes to isotopic dating, *any* observation can be "explained" *a posteriori*.

Myth: Whatever their etiology, Rb-Sr isochrons can be predicted and unambiguously reconciled with the local geology of their occurrence.

Reality Check: To begin with, even if this were true, it would, at best, only indicate that uniformitarian geologic concepts are plastic enough to accommodate *any* observation on an after-the-fact basis. As it is, uniformitarian geochronologists do acknowledge the great difficulty of providing scientifically-robust understandings of supposed open-system isochrons:

> . . . we regard the separate isochrons as fortuitous and the scatter of points in Fig. 6 as the product of an open isotopic system [references cited]. *Interpretation of open isotopic systems requires a framework of assumptions and a unique solution is rarely possible* (Holland and Lambert 1995, pp. 502-503) [emphasis added].

Furthermore, a backpedaling of interpretations on Rb-Sr isochrons takes place whenever such isochrons are first accepted as indicative of the age of the rock and then, when conflicting evidence emerges (such as from newly-acquired presumably-reliable U-Pb zircon dates), these "inherently self-checked" isochrons then suddenly become not so reliable after all. Instead, they now assume a new status: "rejuvenated" or even completely invalid isochrons:

> Previously reported Rb-Sr ages for metavolcanic rocks in the Stinkfontein and Gariep Groups . . . must be regarded as geologically meaningless and can be explained by partial resetting during the Gariepian metamorphism. . . (Frimmel *et al.* 1996, p. 467).

Myth: Owing to the resistance of REE's (rare earth elements) to mobility, Sm-Nd isochrons are very resistant to "resetting," and are therefore a very reliable indicator of a rock's age.

Reality Check: To begin with, this premise is largely an assumption, and one that is subject to an ever-increasing body of contrary evidence:

> The REE (and thus Sm and Nd) are commonly treated as immobile during metamorphism. This view has gained support from the frequent preservation of Sm-Nd whole rock isochrons which are in agreement with U-Pb ages on zircons from the same suites of polymetamorphic rock but in which the Rb-Sr or Pb-Pb whole rock systems are disturbed. However, fluid movement during the formation of new mineral assemblages has a potentially disturbing effect on the Sm-Nd system with changes in Sm/Nd ratios and $^{143}Nd/^{144}Nd$ isotopic compositions in response to changes in fluid/mineral distribution coefficients (Bridgwater *et al.* 1989, p. 283).

> . . . Sm-Nd ages could be highly susceptible to age shifts because the strong chemical coherence of the rare-earth elements (REE) causes strong positive correlations between Sm and Nd concentrations. On geochemical grounds it is expected that Nd is much less mobile than Sr in hydrothermal solutions. However, *the REE are known to be mobile under some conditions*. . . (Lutz and Srogi 1986, p. 71) [emphasis added].

A geologic example of the "resetting" of a Sm-Nd isochron is provided by Black (1986). It also bears repeating an earlier-quoted study which warned that:

> We conclude that the Rb-Sr and Sm-Nd isotopic systems are much more sensitive to metasomatic processes than is commonly believed (Frost and Frost 1995, p. 283).

An up-to-date summary of evidences for open-system behavior in the Sm-Nd isotopic system is provided by Brewer and Menuge (1998, and citations therein). They warn us as follows:

> . . . (REE), are usually believed to be immobile under greenschist and amphibolite facies metamorphic conditions. It has been shown however that these "immobile" elements can be mobilised by some hydrothermal and low-grade metamorphic fluids (Brewer and Menuge 1998, p. 2).

Myth: The Sm-Nd method turns out to be an extremely reliable dating method.

Reality Check: Let us consider the full implications of Sm-Nd dating. While "rejuvenation" or "resetting" of Sm-Nd isochrons appears to be seldom invoked (e. g., Shirey 1991, p. 110), this does not mean that Sm-Nd isochrons are straightforwardly accepted as a reliable indicator of the rock's age. To the contrary: the Sm-Nd system has its own Achilles' heel. Frequently, Sm-Nd isochrons turn out to be "too old" or "too young" for the "correct" age of the rock as envisioned by uniformitarians (for instance, Chauvel et al. 1985).

More recent examples of this are given by Grau et al. (1990) and Pukhtel et al. (1991). Such unwanted isochrons are explained away as the result of source-mixing effects and/or initial isotopic inhomogeneities. The invocation of the latter rationalization is encouraged by the long half-life of ^{147}Sm, which is thus incapable of producing sufficient radiogenic Nd, even over the presumed hundreds of millions of years, to "swamp out" the initial isotopic inhomogeneities in the host rock (Bowring and Housh 1996). Other grossly too-old Sm-Nd isochrons are supposed to "turn out" to date mantle-depletion events (e. g., Togashi et al. 1992) instead of the time since crystallization of the host rock. Such rationalizations, of course, beg the question about the age of the earth in general and the validity of the Sm-Nd method in particular.

Myth: Sm-Nd model ages date the time since formation of Earth's crust in different geographic areas of our planet.

Reality Check: It must be realized that models of Nd geochemical evolution rest heavily on both uniformitarian assumptions and selective usage of data:

> Nd model age curves . . . are, for time periods older than 3.0 Ga, based largely on linear extrapolations from chondritic compositions ($\in_{Nd}$=0) at 4.55 to modern mid-ocean ridge basalt compositions, rather

than empirical definition. . . . This also highlights the general tendency for Nd isotopic data from Precambrian rocks in general and most particularly for Archean rocks to be accepted uncritically if they "fall on the line." This approach leads to self-fulfilling conclusions; all Nd isotope data should be subject to equally rigorous scrutiny. . . . If this relationship is not seen in the initial isotopic compositions, then the end compositions are assumed to be wrong (Bennett and Nutman 1998, p. 216).

Others who have recently expressed doubts about the primary nature of $\in_{Nd}$ values include Nagler and Kramers (1998), as well as Vervoort and Patchett (1998). One of the tacit uniformitarian beliefs is the one that the earth has undergone geochemical evolution with reference to chondritic meteorites—the so-called CHUR (chondritic uniform reservoir). It also assumes no change in Sm/Nd ratios over the presumed interval of time (Bartlett et al. 1998, p. 188). Furthermore, even on uniformitarians' own terms, so-called Sm-Nd model ages can only be accepted as such when ostensibly confirmed by other dating methods:

> Nd model ages can be interpreted in two ways. If they coincide with U-Pb zircon ages or other independent evidence of an orogenic event, a case can be made that they date the time of crust-mantle differentiation. If, on the other hand, they lie between groups of U-Pb zircon ages and do not coincide with any specific orogenic event, they are better interpreted as giving an average age of a mixed source (Arndt and Goldstein 1987, p. 895).

More recently, use of Pb isotope systematics has been used to constrain and interpret the Nd model ages (e. g., Moller et al. 1998). So, instead of a questioning of the method, we get a new layer of special pleading. Once again, the **CDMBN** fallacy has been put to use.

Myth: The Re-Os (rhenium-osmium) method corroborates the fact that, as predicted, Sm-Nd and U-Th-Pb systems remain closed over eons of geologic time.

Fact: By way of introduction, the Re-Os Method has come into widespread use in the 1990's (Shirey and Walker 1998, p. 424), after a variety of earlier technical problems have been solved. As discussed elsewhere (see pages 34-35), the claim of "almost certain closed-system behavior" had once been claimed for nearly all the isotopic dating systems, notably the Sm-Nd whole-rock and U-Pb zircon, and has been observed by the following quotation, the application of the Re-Os method to the Precambrian rocks of Africa and other places. The Re-Os model ages turned out often older than the Sm-Nd and U-Pb dates, clearly demonstrating that the latter isotopic systems could not have remained closed systems. Moreover, the open-system behavior of Sm-Nd and U-Pb dating methods is evidently more common than believed earlier:

The resistance of the Re-Os system in SCLM samples to later processes that have clearly affected the Sm-Nd, Rb-Sr, and U-Th-Pb systems *illustrates the widespread effect of metasomatism and metamorphic reequilibration* in the SCLM (Shirey and Walker 1998, p. 471) [emphasis added].

Myth: The Re-Os method almost invariably exhibits closed-system behavior.

Reality Check: By no stretch of the imagination is this the case:

Mineral vs. whole-rock isochrons have strengths and weaknesses. . . . For silicate rocks, low-Re/Os resistant phases such as chromite offer the promise of highly-accurate initial Os isotopic compositions [reference cited], but these phases can be altered to give anomalous results on the small scale of individual grains [reference cited] in a manner that is difficult to test. Conversely, whole-rock isochrons offer the benefit of sampling on a larger scale, but they are more affected by the metamorphic reactions involving silicates (e. g., serpentization) and also may not allow attainment of Re/Os ratios low enough to precisely constrain the initial $^{187}Os/^{188}Os$ (Shirey and Walker 1998, p. 473).

Myth: The Re-Os method can reliably be used to date source-area effects.

Fact: This is yet another optimistic belief from which uniformitarian geochronologists have been forced to retreat:

A consequence of this is that the rhenium-osmium isotopic system should not be relied on to yield accurate mantle extraction ages for continental rocks (Saal *et al.* 1998, p. 58).

The Re-Os method has now also met the fate of all the other isochron-based methods which were once believed to yield isochrons that necessarily had geochronometric meaning:

Our data show that apparent whole-rock Re-Os isochrons with no age significance may be produced during AFC processes by depletion of Os through olivine-sulphide fractionation, coupled with assimilation of radiogenic crust (Saal *et al.* 1998, p. 61).

Myth: The new lutetium-hafnium (Lu-Hf) method is a powerful new dating method.

Fact: To the contrary, it immediately encounters severe problems:

The Lu-Hf system is demonstrably sensitive to the mineralogy of magma sources in the mantle and crust (Scherer *et al.* 1997, p. 63).

Myth: Pb/Pb isochrons are likely to have remained undisturbed for millions of years.

Reality Check: Again, uniformitarians want to have it both ways. They tell us that collinearity of points helps establish the reliability of a date, and then turn around and reject some isochrons at their convenience. To rationalize this procedure, they attribute the collinearity of points to fortuitous open-system or inheritance effects:

The widely used whole-rock Pb/Pb method of geochronology is *highly susceptible* to the generation of spurious isochrons, primarily the result of disturbance of U in a system in the absence of complete Pb-isotopic homogenization (Whitehouse 1989, p. 717) [emphasis added].

Bridgwater *et al.* (1989), Whitehouse (1989, 1990), and Whitehouse *et al.* (1996) also present several different ways that open-system behavior of the U-Pb system can cause a collinear set of points to arise, and thus create a spurious date. In fact, such false isochrons are commonly called TPI's (transposed palaeoisochrons).

Myth: The conventional K-Ar isochron technique undoubtedly yields reliable results.

Fact: This too is subject to special pleading (the selective acceptance of evidence):

A drawback of the conventional isochron plot is that, in general, the isotope measured with the poorest precision, ^{36}Ar, is common to both axes. A result is that the errors associated with both axes are highly correlated, and may give rise to misleading linear correlations (McDougall and Harrison 1988, p. 122).

Of course, K-Ar isochrons are not claimed to give accurate solutions for every confusing K-Ar age pattern affected by excess Ar. . . . Thus, the systematics of the data array in Fig. 4 may well be an effect of pure coincidence (Blanckenburg and Villa 1988, p. 6).

Furthermore, it should be noted that earlier flaws found in K-Ar isochrons had failed to include another mechanism by which bogus K-Ar isochrons could form:

None of these discussions of the K-Ar system considered the role of K exchange (concomitant with Ar exchange) as a determining factor in generating "isochrons" and defining their gradients and intercepts (Mitchell and Euwe 1988, p. 100).

On the other hand, the fact that potassium and argon can sometimes replace each other may provide a fertile field for creationist scholarship in the understanding of the K-Ar system in a non-geochronometric, young-earth context.

Myth: The $^{39}Ar/^{40}Ar-^{36}Ar/^{40}Ar$ isochrons detect excess argon.

Fact: On uniformitarians' own terms, the results of these inverse isotope correlation diagrams are equivocal:

> Excess argon, which would lead to spuriously old ages, can *sometimes* be identified from $^{39}Ar/^{40}Ar$ versus $^{36}Ar/^{40}Ar$ correlation plots. These can demonstrate a contribution of ^{40}Ar which is not accounted for by the air correction, and so does not result from radiogenic decay since the mineral was last closed to Ar loss (Inger *et al.* 1996, p. 158) [emphasis added].

> The results of this study have also demonstrated that *many geologically meaningless young $^{40}Ar/^{39}Ar$ dates* have, in part, resulted. . . . The effects of recrystallization, mixing, and excess argon may cause anomalously young or old K-Ar dates in minerals, and could potentially lead to a misinterpretation of thermal history (Lo and Onstott 1995, p. 95, 96) [emphasis added].

> Some of these samples yield very good isochrons yet give apparent ages which are significantly younger than the primary ages (Smith *et al.* 1994a, p. 297).

In other instances, the results of these types of isochrons are subject to widely divergent interpretations, any one of which would mean that it had failed to detect the occurrence of excess argon after all:

> In this case, possible explanations for the biotite having an age greater than the muscovite include (1) the possibility that the biotite is Mg rich and has a correspondingly high closure temperature [reference cited], (2) *the possibility that the biotite contains anomalous trapped Ar not resolved on the isochron diagram*, (3) the chance that the effective diffusion dimension of the muscovite is much smaller than that of the biotite, or (4) the possibility that some of the muscovite grew during a late stage metamorphic event which did not produce new biotite (Copeland *et al.* 1991, pp. 8480, 8486) [emphasis added].

Of course, such isochrons are typically used in conjunction with the $^{40}Ar/^{39}Ar$ dating method, wherein they frequently lead to conflicting interpretations as to which "reliability criteria" should be used, singly and/or in combination (Setterfield *et al.* 1992). More on this later.

Other isochrons used in conjunction with the K-Ar method include the $1/^{36}Ar$ vs. $^{40}Ar/^{36}Ar$ one. These, too, can be difficult to interpret. Moreover, despite the excellent collinearity of points, they can yield absurd (in this case negative) $^{40}Ar/^{36}Ar$ intercepts:

> However, the very low intercept of this line at $^{40}Ar/^{36}Ar = -3349$ shows that it not only represents an admixture of atmospheric argon but also indicates that

a combination of various processes must have affected the analyzed biotites. . . . These processes rotated and tilted the original isochron in a way that tthe resulting "isochron" of 576 now intercepts the y-axis at an unreal $^{40}Ar/^{36}Ar$ value of -2396 (Ziegler and Stoessel 1993, p. 21, 22).

C. "Distinctions" Between "True" and Non-Chronometric Isochrons

Myth: Inverse plots of isotopic ratios distinguish valid isochrons from mixing lines.

It is often claimed (e. g., Dalrymple 1984, p. 87) that inverse plots (such as $^{87}Sr/^{86}Sr$ as a function of $1/Sr$), if nonlinear, rule out that particular assemblage having resulted from a mixing line.

Fact: On uniformitarians' own terms, the situation is not so simple. To begin with, it is acknowledged (Graham 1985; Stein and Kish 1992; Ziegler and Stoessel 1993) that ostensibly valid, age-indicative isochrons can likewise form collinear inverse plots. Moreover, these inverse plots only "work" if the age of the rock is already known, which, of course, begs the question about the validity of all the dating methods:

> Such diagrams can only be used as a quantitative test for mixing if the probable age of isotopic closure for the system is established by an independent means (Stein and Kish 1992, p. 642).

Moreover, it is unclear how presumably crude the $^{87}Sr/^{86}Sr$ vs. $1/Sr$ plot has to be before a mixing-line origin for it is presumably precluded. Graham (1985) found that his data produced a crude linear inverse plot (N=30, PCC=.875) but was uncertain as to the status of the original Rb-Sr plots (whether to allow for a mixing-line interpretation or not) until they were independently corroborated as presumably valid, time-indicative isochrons by other lines of presumed evidence.

There are other studies in which uniformitarian geologists cannot agree if the points on an inverse plot are collinear enough for the original isochron to be explained as a simple mixing line of two end members. Thus, Roy and Sarkar (1997) argue for the affirmative; Dhar (1997) for the negative. Moreover, the latter points out that (as in the famed picture of the woman who sees her reflection in the mirror, and then a skull), the information can be looked at in more than one way (figure 26).

In an analogous manner to Rb-Sr, it has been claimed that Sm-Nd mixing lines can be distinguished from "true" Sm-Nd ages because, in the former case, a linear relationship will exist between $^{143}Nd/^{144}Nd$ as a function of $1/Nd$. But it is now understood that a nonlinear relationship between the two is not necessarily conclusive evidence against a mixing line:

> The trend *need not be linear* if the crustally contaminated primary magma underwent fractional crystallization at depth in a large magma chamber

before eruption to the surface (Kumar *et al.* 1996, p. 213) [emphasis added].

Most important of all, a nonlinear inverse pattern need not exclude a mixing process. Instead, it probably indicates *a more complex pattern of mixing* than one expected from a simple two-component admixture. For instance, there are models which predict nonlinear inverse plots as a result of episodic admixtures of contaminant isotopes (see figure 4 of Briqueu and Lancelot 1979, p. 391). Finally, even if a two-component mixing line is discounted on the presumed basis of an inverse plot, it does not, on uniformitarians' own terms, *ipso facto* mean that the original isochron has geochronometric validity. Instead, such a spurious isochron can be blamed on isotopic homogenization sometime in the past (Ziegler and Stoessel 1993, p. 48).

Let us now examine more closely the consequences of isochrons forming solely from mixing processes and not from radioactive decay of the relevant isotopies. It is sometimes argued that, if a simple mixing of two end members is contra-indicated by the evidence (such as collinear inverse plots—figure 26), it is very unlikely that any sort of mixing process could explain the existence of a good isochron. To begin with, a seemingly-unlikely coincidence must be placed in perspective by remembering the "tries" which geochemical processes have on earth. As expected from simple probability, the vast majority of "tries" are failures. As a start, many (if not most) rocks fail to form statistically-defined isochrons at all (figure 27)—something to be expected of a quasi-random complex mixing process. Second, most isochrons accepted by geologists are not particularly of high quality—so their origins by mixing processes should not be deemed particularly unlikely.

Thus, for instance, de Laeter *et al.* (1981, pp. 149-151) found that only 9 of the 69 isochrons they had considered (with three others lacking analytic data to make a judgment) passed certain criteria to qualify as "superior isochrons." To do this, they had to have a very small analytic error in both the initial ratio and the age, had to define an initial ratio of at least 0.70, and had to be composed of samples collected within a maximal transverse distance of 10 km, could not have been formed from both whole-rock and mineral phases, and their construction could not have been heavily reliant on a small number of samples having high Rb/Sr ratios. In view of the fact that such "superior isochrons" are so few and far between, it is not difficult to realize that chance mixing processes can "succeed" in making them (figure 27).

Myth: True (i. e., age-indicative) Rb-Sr isochrons can easily be distinguished from those resulting as an artifact of mixing effects.

Fact: Even on uniformitarians' own terms, this is certainly not the case:

> Whether or not a Rb/Sr isochron age represents a true intrusion or metamorphose age or is the result of mixing of two or more sources with no geological meaning cannot be decided in all cases (Wendt 1993, p. 305).

Other uniformitarian geochronologists are more pessimistic:

> . . . therefore it is generally difficult to prove that the whole-rock isochron is a mixing line. . . . Some of the rather old ages for those kinds of rocks in earlier works may include the pseudo-isochron ages

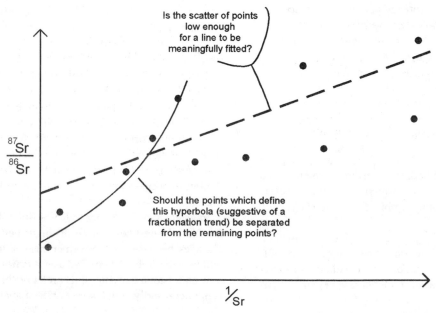

Figure 26: Inverse plots are subject to contradictory interpretations: 1) no agreement on how far points have to deviate from collinearity before a "linear hypothesis" is falsified; 2) disagreement about the propriety of alternative curve(s) for some or all of the data. Example shown above is modified from figure 1 of Dhar (1997, p. 467). Finally, lack of collinear relationship on the inverse plot does *not* prove that the isochron resulted from *in situ* radioactive decay, much less over millions to billions of years.

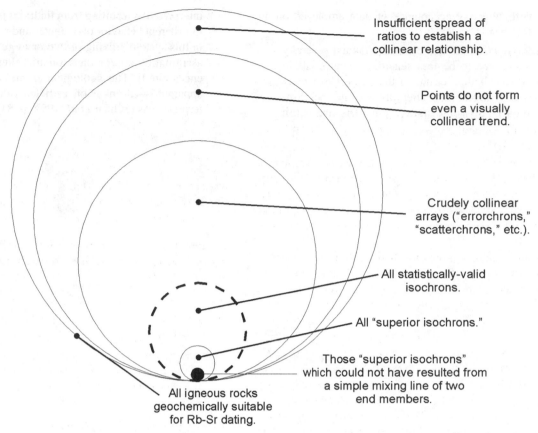

Insufficient spread of ratios to establish a collinear relationship.

Points do not form even a visually collinear trend.

Crudely collinear arrays ("errorchrons," "scatterchrons," etc.).

All statistically-valid isochrons.

All "superior isochrons."

Those "superior isochrons" which could not have resulted from a simple mixing line of two end members.

All igneous rocks geochemically suitable for Rb-Sr dating.

Figure 27: If all isochrons had to originate strictly from mixing processes, isn't it improbable that a series of complex-admixture events would give rise to highly-collinear "superior isochrons"? Yes, but it must be kept in mind that very unlikely coincidences (smaller circles) occur must less frequently than do more probable coincidences (larger circles).

caused by such mixing processes (Terekado and Nohda 1993, p. 76).

Myth: Mixing lines, as a cause of spurious Sm-Nd isochrons, are a rare and trivial problem.

Fact: They are actually considered common, and can in no sense be likened to a few malfunctioning watches:

> There is a *general problem* in Sm-Nd isotopc dating in the probability of obtaining linear relationships representing mixing lines between isotopically distinct members or mantle isochrons defining the separation times of the mantle sources (Bibikova *et al.* 1994, p. 45) [emphasis added].

Myth: Geochronologists can determine which Sm-Nd isochrons are fortuitous, which are mixing lines, and which are geochronologically meaningful.

Fact: Even on their own terms, they can not. This is proved by the fact that, when isochrons are derived, all three options have to be kept open (Di Vincenzo *et al.* 1997, p. 1408), and all the options have to be subject to uniformitarian geologic interpretation. Moreover, even after exhausting all of the presumed reliability criteria for "true" Sm-Nd isochrons, Kumar *et al.* (1996, p. 213) called the acceptance of their Sm-Nd

isochrons, as a valid age of rock crystallization, "our preferred interpretation of the Sm-Nd linear array."

The ambiguity inherent in isochron construction and interpretation, and the need for geologic interpretation (in the light of uniformitarian preconceptions, of course), should by now be almost a self-evident truth to the reader:

> Spurious isochrons (both whole-rock and mineral) should be expected when either or both of the critical isochron prerequisites of common initial ratio and subsequent closed-system evolution are not achieved. *Unfortunately, it is often difficult to confirm that the prerequisites have been satisfied on the basis of the isotopic data alone*, and even if they have been, unambiguous assignment of the ages to magmatic or metamorphic events may be difficult. . . . There is *no reliable objective way* to assess the validity of any given whole-rock (or mineral) isochron using the regressed data alone, or in combination with element concentration data. Isochron data should be assessed in the light of all available field, petrographic, geological, geochemical, and other geochronological evidence (Whitehouse *et al.* 1996, p. 3092, 3100) [emphasis added].

In like manner, special pleading is employed whenever source-area effects are presumed to be dated by the Sm-Nd method, with selective acceptance of data employed on an after-the-fact basis:

> Although the REE [rare earth elements] generally are considered to be less sensitive than the alkali metals and alkaline earths in the case of metamorphism or hydrothermal alteration, whole-rock Sm-Nd ages of lower-crustal xenoliths are often interpreted as resulting from fictitious isochrons, due to coherent behavior of daughter and parent isotopes in this system, mixing of two or more components, assimilation and/or metasomatic alteration [references cited]. The geological significance of such apparent isochrons is of restricted value for age interpretations (Schaaf *et al.* 1994, p. 81).

Chapter 7

The ^{40}Ar/^{39}Ar Method and its Imagined Diagnostic Properties

By way of introduction to this topic, useful summaries of the ^{40}Ar/^{39}Ar method are provided by Hanes (1991), Baksi (1999), McDougall and Harrison (1988), and Snee *et al.* (1995). In this entire section, I discuss the interpretation of results provided by this method. I also demonstrate how the uniformitarian geochronologists have had to beat a hasty retreat from their earlier beliefs about the diagnostic capabilities of this method.

Myth: The ^{40}Ar/^{39}Ar method dates rocks and minerals with pinpoint accuracy.

Reality Check: As we shall see, the exacting precision is not what determines the accuracy of the dating result itself. We can liken it to an artillery piece whose shells all impact within a very small circular area, but the artillery piece itself cannot be aimed with sufficient accuracy to take full advantage of the precision of its shots. This is analogous to what occurs with ^{40}Ar/^{39}Ar dating.

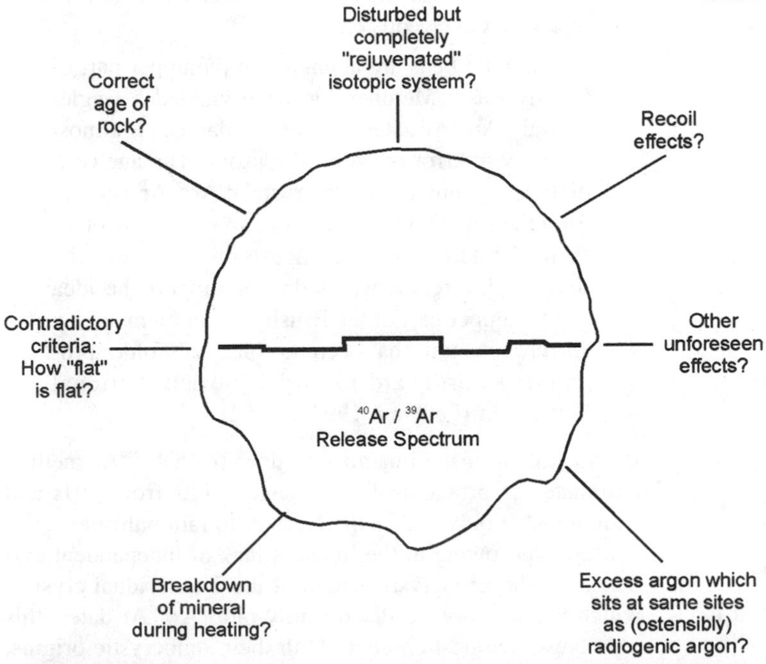

To begin with, the ^{40}Ar/^{39}Ar dating method is not really an independent one, and so cannot possibly be any more accurate than its foundation:

> The ^{40}Ar/^{39}Ar technique is a relative method that depends on the age of the monitor mineral being accurately known. It is, therefore, still dependent upon the conventional K-Ar technique being able to measure accurately the quantities of K and ^{40}Ar in the monitor mineral. Given a well-calibrated monitor, however, the ^{40}Ar/^{39}Ar approach is inherently more precise because only isotopic ratios and not isotopic abundances need to be measured (Obradovich 1993, p. 382).

A skeptic of isotopic dating is, of course, not exactly impressed about the validity of dates from presumed monitor minerals. Furthermore, a significant source of uncertainty in the interpretation of ^{40}Ar/^{39}Ar dates originates from the fact that they have to be calculated against the fluence monitor mineral of "known age" (Berggren *et al.* 1995; McWilliams 1994). The choice of monitors has in fact affected the outcome of ^{40}Ar/^{39}Ar results to a degree far beyond the pinpoint precision of the age determinations themselves (Berggren *et al.* 1995; Obradovich 1993; Vandamme *et al.* 1991), thereby fulfilling the analogy with the difficult-to-aim but extremely precise artillery piece. Moreover, despite recent alleged improvements in intercalibrations of internationally-used standards, the exaggerated precision of ^{40}Ar/^{39}Ar results remains a very real issue:

> The absolute ages of ^{40}Ar/^{39}Ar standards remains an unresolved issue and as a result, detailed comparison of data from the ^{40}Ar/^{39}Ar system with other geochronometers is not well founded unless appropriate (*though heretofore unpracticed*) error propagation is employed (Renne *et al.* 1998, p. 118) [emphasis added].

The belated appearance of error-propagation schemes in the calculation of Ar-Ar dates has resulted from the need to rectify the unrealistic claims of their precision:

Figure 28. A "flat" release spectrum in the Ar-Ar method is not nearly as diagnostic of "true" age as once claimed by geochronologists. In fact, the multifarious interpretation of even simple spectra greatly weaken, if not nullify, the presumed diagnostic capabilities of the Ar-Ar method.

Uncertainties in decay constants and the ages of standards have traditionally been ignored in estimating the errors associated with $^{40}Ar/^{39}Ar$ dates.... Systematic errors become particularly important when they are compounded by several standard intercalibrations. . . . *It is noteworthy that errors introduced by uncertainties in the values of decay constants and the age of the primary standard magnified by several intercalibration steps are significantly larger than those due to analytical uncertainties alone. The large magnitudes of these errors...* (Karner and Renne 1998, p. 743) [emphasis added].

In conclusion, therefore, it is pointless for the uniformitarian geochronologist to exult in the under-one-percent precision of the $^{40}Ar/^{39}Ar$ dates. After all, it merely takes a different monitor mineral to instantly change the date by at least 2% (e. g., see Obradovich 1993, p. 389). Furthermore, the question of correct monitor minerals can even lead to divergent geochronological conclusions about particular suites of dates (e. g., see Kamo *et al.* 1996, p. 3506; Vandamme *et al.* 1991, p. 163; and Venkatesan *et al.* 1996, p. 990). In addition, the age of a standard can be "tweaked" in order to create agreement between Ar-Ar dates and astronomical cycles (e. g., see Hilgren *et al.* 1997).

Myth: The $^{40}Ar/^{39}Ar$ method follows a rigorous, self-consistent methodology for the analysis and interpretation of spectra.

Reality Check: Leaving aside, for a moment, the question of what spectra mean or don't mean, let us begin by pointing out the lack of agreement on what a flat spectrum actually *is*:

Several different criteria have been published for deciding whether a set of age steps constitutes a reliable age plateau. . . . It is also implicit in these criteria that, since errors are assumed to be analytical and therefore random, successive steps of a plateau should not show a trend; in the literature, *this requirement is commonly ignored.* Discrepancies between sets of criteria are *inevitable because they are necessarily arbitrary to some extent*—for instance, no precise limit can be put on the length of a plateau, or its number of steps—but some criteria are needed to distinguish a slightly disturbed spectrum from a strongly disturbed one (Setterfield *et al.* 1992, p. 1135) [emphasis added].

Myth: The $^{40}Ar/^{39}Ar$ method solves the problem of xenocrystic contamination in lavas, tuffs, and bentonites.

When it comes to the dating of tuffs and bentonites, it is widely claimed (e. g., Gansecki *et al.* 1998) that the $^{40}Ar/^{39}Ar$ dating method unmasks the identity of unsuspected contaminant crystals as it allows a suite of dates to be made on individual crystal grains.

Reality Check: Let us first briefly discuss the use and interpretation of this method:

In $^{40}Ar/^{39}Ar$ dating, a single crystal is heated in a vacuum, and it gives off argon gas (both from the parent potassium and from the daughter decay product) first from its edge, and then from the less altered interior of the crystal. The stepwise heating $^{40}Ar/^{39}Ar$ method compares the age determined from the altered edge with the center, and thus screens out any alteration or contamination. Another method takes each individual crystal and zaps it with a laser, releasing its argon. In this laser-fusion method, the geochronologist can measure dozens of individual crystals and analyze their results to see if they cluster, or if they are so scattered that contamination or leakage must be a problem (Prothero 1994, p. 60).

Note that this method does not screen out bad dates *per se*. Instead, it allows for individual dating results to be rejected when they are inconsistent. But this *assumes* (not establishes) the premise that consistent results are reliable, and begs the question about the existence of numerous internally-inconsistent results. And, of course, since *individual* crystals are now dated instead of *assorted masses of crystals*, this increases the number of dates actually obtained. This, in turn, can only increase the chance that internal consistency will occur fortuitously. After all, the more dating tries are attempted, the better the chances of obtaining a fortuitously-consistent result.

The number and diversity of dates now made available also allows the geochronologist to "shop around" for individual results which he considers to be valid. Consider, for instance, the following Cretaceous example:

Bentonite beds are abundant in the upper part of Brushy Basin Member and have yielded 5 single-crystal $^{40}Ar/^{39}Ar$ dates.... A sixth date ... is almost certainly in error for several reasons. The age conflicts with another single-crystal $^{40}Ar/^{39}Ar$ age ... from the same unit, it does not agree with the other $^{40}Ar/^{39}Ar$ dates from southeastern Utah, and the stratigraphic relationships do not support the idea that the upper part of the Brushy Basin member is a diachronous unit that becomes markedly older progressing northward toward Dinosaur National Monument (Peterson 1994, p. 252).

By no stretch of the imagination does the $^{40}Ar/^{39}Ar$ method eliminate the problem of discrepant results from tuffs and bentonites! It only makes them easier to rationalize away.

Moreover, owing to the frequent lack of independent evidence for the xenocrystic origin of those individual crystals which happen to yield discrepantly-old $^{40}Ar/^{39}Ar$ dates, this only begs the question about both their xenocrystic origins, and the validity of the $^{40}Ar/^{39}Ar$ method. Ironically, the converse is also true. That is, xenoliths that can be visually identified as such often yield $^{40}Ar/^{39}Ar$ spectra which give little or no evidence of their status as contaminants (Fitch *et al.* 1985, p. 614). When this occurs, it is commonly claimed that the xenoliths had shed their inherited isotopic systematics, and thus had come into isotopic equilibrium with the host magma prior to its crystallization. This, of course, also begs the question about the validity of the dating methods.

Myth: The ^{40}Ar/^{39}Ar method is a virtual panacea for determining which crystals have remained closed systems, and which have been disturbed subsequent to crystallization.

Reality Check: Although this has commonly been claimed in the earlier years of the widespread use of this method, geochronologists have subsequently been forced to retreat from this position in the face of many ^{40}Ar/^{39}Ar flat spectra (or plateaus) that could not possibly be accepted as indicative of the age of the rock. As a result, claims about the scientific value of flat spectra, and their supposedly diagnostic character independent of geologic interpretations, have been relaxed in recent years, as the following examples illustrate:

> The age spectrum will exhibit a plateau if the sample had never been disturbed after formation *or* if the sample had been completely reset by a younger event (Snee *et al.* 1995, p. 367) [emphasis added].

> These cannot be interpreted as magmatic ages, as the field evidence unequivocally requires an early Late Cambrian or older (probably Middle Cambrian) age. . . . It is tempting to hypothesize either a total resetting in Early Ordovician times, or partial resetting at a later time (possibly Permian or later, in the event recorded by phase A) resulting in a geologically meaningless flat plateau (Everard and Villa 1994, p. 270).

> Interpreting the geologic significance of the ^{40}Ar/^{39}Ar results depends upon calibration of the Paleozoic time-scale. . . (Connelly and Dallmeyer 1993, p. 351).

Moreover, at least in some cases, it is questionable if inferred "cooling ages" are meaningful at all:

> It is therefore highly questionable whether *internal* criteria ("good" Arrhenius alignment yielding a closure temperature matching some preconcepted value, e. g., higher than 100°C but lower than 300°C) are able at all to discriminate between usable data and useless ones, in the absence of *external* criteria (petrography, mineralogy, geology . . .) . . . mineral cooling ages may partly be an artifact of the data reduction. . . . Assertions that the apparent precision of the Ar/Ar results corresponds to a self-consistent and *accurate* thermo-chronometrical reconstruction are devoid of foundation (Villa 1996, pp. 260-261) [italics in original].

Other studies (e. g., Coleman and Glazner 1997, Dallmeyer and Villeneuve 1987, Lo and Yui 1996, West *et al.* 1995) have also included discussion of whether or not flat spectra obtained by these authors variously indicate the age of the rock, a later cooling temperature, or a still-later heating event which completely reset the ^{40}Ar/^{39}Ar clock. This, of course, begs the question about the validity of the ^{40}Ar/^{39}Ar method and the significance or otherwise of a flat spectrum, and thus nullifies one of the foundational premises of the ^{40}Ar/^{39}Ar method: that a flat spectrum, or plateau, is diagnostic of the "true" age of the rock:

> One can conclude, therefore, that a plateau spectrum is generally a necessary, but not sufficient, indication that a mineral has not partially lost argon since it last passed through its closure temperature (Hanes 1991, p. 39).

Indeed, excepting metamorphic terranes, where secondary disturbance of igneous minerals is obvious, there is often no way of independently knowing if a mineral has been undisturbed since its crystallization, or if it has been ostensibly completely "reset" by some heating event tens or hundreds of millions of years later. This gives free reign to geologic interpretations. Thus, if a uniformitarian geologist gets a flat plateau that indicates an age that is clearly "too young" to be accepted as the age of a rock, he can always blame it on a "complete resetting" by a later thermal event.

In effect, we are told that the Ar-Ar method can be used to determine whether or not a rock has been disturbed since its emplacement—so long as, ironically, it has not been *too* disturbed since its formation (in which case we would have an Ar-Ar plateau that supposedly dates the secondary effect)! This fact is clear from the following:

> The ^{40}Ar/^{39}Ar method is ideal for resolving the chronological structure of a certain orogen provided that it has not undergone extensive thermal rejuvenation (Al-Saleh *et al.* 1998), p. 173).

Since the presence and presumed magnitude of disturbance often cannot be known from strong, independent geologic evidence, the circular reasoning behind the interpretation of Ar-Ar plateau dates is obvious.

Were the results of Ar-Ar dating actually self-checking and self-informative, they could be interpreted without extraneous information, and the interpretations would be both self-evident and unchangeable. Such is far from the truth. Ar-Ar dates are *not* innately informative as to the ostensible geochronometric significance of the results obtained. For instance, a backpedaling on previous opinions on the geologic significance of Ar-Ar dates took place when new, contradictory U-Pb dates became available (Wang *et al.* 1998b, pp. 332-334). All of a sudden, the Ar-Ar dates were no longer believed to date the time of crustal thickening. Instead, an "excess argon" rationalization was invoked to discount the now-unwelcome Ar-Ar dates.

What if we get "good" Ar-Ar plateau dates—but the dates contradict each other? In such situations, other rationalizations come to the rescue. One of these is the suggestion that the contradictory Ar-Ar plateau dates resulted from regionally-diachronous cooling (Kontak *et al.* 1998, p. 758). In other words, it is conveniently supposed that a strong reheating event had completely "reset" the Ar-Ar "clock" at different times in different locations within the region being subject to geologic investigation.

Moreover, in other instances, flat $^{40}Ar/^{39}Ar$ spectra cannot be straightforwardly fitted-in into any kind of uniformitarian geologic scheme at all:

> However, caution is required, as it is possible to obtain plateau dates that have no meaning (Hanes 1991, p. 38).

> . . . interpretation of release spectra can be ambiguous (Gansecki *et al.* 1996, p. 91).

It should be clear that, on uniformitarians' own terms, a flat spectrum cannot straightforwardly be accepted as a diagnostic indicator of an isotopic system that has been undisturbed since the time of crystallization of the host rock.

Ironically, the converse is also true. The uniformitarian geochronologist can sometimes accept a $^{40}Ar/^{39}Ar$ result as indicative of a valid date even if the spectrum is *not* flat. He thus can disregard, at will, the significance of a staircase-shaped spectrum, which usually he accepts as evidence for a sample having undergone argon loss during its history. As justification for such a conclusion, he can claim that similar-looking minerals (such as phengite and muscovite) have been incorporated in the same mineral separate, and thus have released their argon at different temperatures, creating what they interpret to be a false argon-loss profile (Snee *et al.* 1995, p. 367). The same kind of apparent profile can also be blamed on the different sizes and/or structural types of the same mineral.

Moreover, there are a variety of other technical problems which can at times create a variety of artifacts from the application of the method *itself*. For instance, some $^{40}Ar/^{39}Ar$ results that were "too old" were blamed on recoil effects (Odin *et al.* 1991, p. 217), and such alleged recoil effects on biotite are now believed to be quite common (Obradovich 1993, p. 382). All in all, the elasticity of interpretations available to the uniformitarian geochronologist is positively breathtaking.

Myth: The $^{40}Ar/^{39}Ar$ method can detect the presence of excess argon in a mineral.

Reality Check: On its own terms, it very often cannot. In the $^{40}Ar/^{39}Ar$ method, it is supposed that a sample containing excess argon will produce a spectrum that is shaped like a saddle (or a wide letter "u"), whereas one in which the non-atmosphere-corrected ^{40}Ar all came from *in situ* decay of ^{40}K will yield a flat spectrum. Yet it has now long been recognized that a U-shaped spectrum need not be diagnostic either

of excess argon, ^{39}Ar recoil, or some other effect on terrestrial plagioclases (Albarede 1982, p. 191). Furthermore, there is now a large (and continually growing) body of evidence which indicates that rocks in which excess argon is suspected (because the K-Ar results are "too old" biostratigraphically and/or in comparison with the results of another dating method) need not yield a saddle-shaped spectrum at all:

> The ability of biotite to incorporate large amounts of excess ^{40}Ar has been recognized for many years. It is now equally well documented that biotites containing excess ^{40}Ar can exhibit flat release patterns . . . that are not distinguishable in any obvious way from undisturbed patterns (McDougall and Harrison 1988, p. 110)

Clearly, the presumed diagnostic properties of the $^{40}Ar/^{39}Ar$ dating method *vis-a-vis* excess argon, "work" only on a hit-or-miss basis:

> Excess ^{40}Ar contamination cannot be conclusively proven by conventional K-Ar dating techniques, but *under favourable circumstances*, it is possible to resolve different Ar isotopic components (atmospheric Ar, *in situ* radiogenic Ar, and excess ^{40}Ar) by the $^{40}Ar/^{39}Ar$ step-heating method (Richards and McDougall 1990, p. 1401) [emphasis added].

Some other examples of biotite believed to contain excess argon, despite a flat $^{40}Ar/^{39}Ar$ spectrum and not a saddle-shaped one, are discussed by Maluski (1978), Hanes (1991), Hyodo and York (1993), Renne (1995), and Ruffet *et al.* (1995). This is also the case in igneous K-feldspars (Foster *et al.* 1989; Harrison 1990), igneous plagioclases (Maluski *et al.* 1990, Seidemann *et al.* 1984), igneous hornblendes (Landoll and Foland 1989; Lee 1993), and in metamorphic phengites (Brocker and Franz 1998; Inger *et al.* 1996; Li *et al.* 1994; Lo and Onstott 1995; Ruffet *et al.* 1995, 1997) as well as metamorphic amphiboles (Blanckenburg and Villa 1988; Maboko *et al.* 1991).

Thus, the pointed fact is this: "Excess argon" is invoked for discrepant Ar-Ar dates *in spite of* the existence of a plateau. In such instances, the following convenient line of special pleading is invoked:

> Stepwise heating technique may not have removed all the excess Ar from the hornblende, therefore yielding false plateaus (Cumbest *et al.* 1994; Wang *et al.* 1998b, p. 334).

A variant of this rationalization would have us believe that the excess argon just happened to be sitting in the same sites within the mineral as did the ostensibly radiogenic argon. This, of course, begs the question about the validity of the Ar-Ar method and the identification of excess argon. In addition, minerals are now known to break down during stepwise heating, thus instantly creating a false Ar-Ar plateau (Lee 1993, Lee *et al.* 1991). This too can be invoked whenever an unexpected flat plateau turns up in a suspected "excess argon" situation.

Myth: Whenever the ⁴⁰Ar/³⁹Ar spectrum is not flat, the actual date of the rock can be resolved from one of the steps.

Fact: There is no clear standard by which to decide if a "partially flat" spectrum contains usable geochronometric information. Thus, the subjectivity inherent in the interpretation of a "partially flat" spectrum is obvious from the following statements:

> The disturbed spectrum of sample P35B [figure in cited text] *may* be further evidence of a thermal overprint but because the majority of the steps yield the same age, *we feel confident* in the Late Devonian date (Lamb and Cox 1998, p. 527) [emphasis added].

Moreover, whether or not one or more of the steps of an irregular Ar-Ar spectrum will be recognized as a valid date depends on its "fit" with current geologic ideas:

> The young ages in the low temperature release could be interpreted to represent a recent re-heating event but there is no regional or local evidence for post-crystallization tectonism, thermal overprinting or metamorphism in the area. Consequently, the irregular spectra is believed to be caused by low-K alteration phases in the biotite (Roddick *et al.* 1992, p. 176).

Of course, as the argon-release pattern deviates more and more from a simple, flat spectrum, the subjectivity of interpretation is only increased all the more. Consider the process of interpreting a "staircase"-shaped spectrum:

> If no age plateau exists, the age spectrum is said to be disturbed or discordant and may or may not be interpretable depending on its complexity (Miller *et al.* 1988, p. 658).

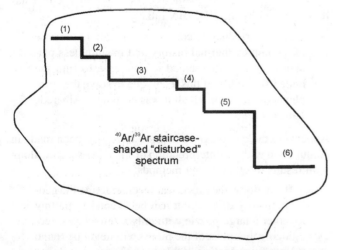

Figure 29. Which of the following fractions gives the correct age of the rock (on uniformitarian terms) (1)? (2)? (3)? (4)? (5)? (6)? (7) None of the above?

In certain rare, favourable circumstances, argon-40/argon-39 age spectrum analysis can be used to help resolve these discrepantly *too high* apparent ages (Fitch and Miller 1983, p. 506) [emphasis in original].

Obviously, then, we have another case of special pleading. Whenever a "disturbed" pattern contains a fraction whose age gives results acceptable to the uniformitarian geochronologist, this is cited as an example of the ⁴⁰Ar/³⁹Ar method having "unraveled" the correct date. But, once again, the absence of "success" is never recognized as evidence against the method. The more-common instances of failure are simply blamed on "unfavorable circumstances." We thus see once again the old **CDMBN** fallacy at work here.

More specifically, whenever it suits conventional geologic interpretations, the oldest/youngest fraction of a "staircase" pattern becomes accepted as the correct age of the rock (or even a minimum/maximum age of the same). Of course, we get a new layer of special pleading whenever such results are unacceptable:

> The spectra that climb to older ages throughout incremental Ar releases are similar to those exhibited by samples that have largely outgassed during a thermal event later than the initial crystallization of the rock [reference cited]. This interpretation would mean that the Peach Springs Tuff is older than 27 Ma, the apparent age of the oldest increment for any of the samples. However . . . these data preclude such an old age for the ash flow unit. . . . We suspect that the discordant age spectra are the result of a two-component K-feldspar mixture: an endogenous K-feldspar and an older disturbed K-feldspar, which were indistinguishable in a hand-picked analytical sample of apparently clear and clean grains. . . (Nielson *et al.* 1990, p. 577).

It should be added that experimental studies also confirm the fact that actual-release patterns are much more complex than previously believed:

> ⁴⁰Ar/³⁹Ar age-spectrum analysis of a hydrothermally treated biotite yields a complex release pattern casting doubt on the general usefulness of such measurements for geochronological purposes (Harrison *et al.* 1985, p. 2461).

In other situations, stepped patterns on age spectra had been subject to different interpretations. Each interpretation calls for the acceptance of a different "real" date for the rock. (Sinton *et al.* 1998, p. 165).

Myth: The ⁴⁰Ar/³⁹Ar method now allows the testing of glauconite dates for reliability.

Reality Check: This situation resembles the one previously discussed regarding the dating of volcanogenic minerals from tuffs and bentonites. In the past, only aggregates of minerals could be dated; now individual grains can. This proliferation of individual dates only produces a string of discordant results, allowing the geochronologist a greater liberty than ever before to pick and choose whichever one he supposes is reliable. This selective manipulation of data is clearly applicable to $^{40}Ar/^{39}Ar$ dating of individual grains of these authigenic minerals:

> Laser-probe argon-argon dating shows that glaucony populations comprise grains with *a wide range of ages*, suggesting a period of genesis several times longer (approximately 5 million years) than previously thought. An estimate of the age of the enclosing sediments (and therefore of time scale boundaries) is given by the *oldest nonrelict grains* in the glaucony populations. . . (Smith *et al.* 1998, p. 1517) [emphasis added].

Of course, as noted earlier, even the oldest K-Ar or $^{40}Ar/^{39}Ar$ result need not be accepted by the uniformitarian as the correct age of the rock, and the "relict" (that is, supposedly reworked) status of grains can always be decided on a posterioritic basis.

Myth: Concordant $^{40}Ar/^{39}Ar$ results, on minerals with different argon-closure temperatures, undoubtedly give the correct age of the rock.

Fact: In actuality, like almost everything else in uniformitarian geochronology, such concordant results are accepted as the age of the rock only if and when such a conclusion fits uniformitarian interpretations:

> Thus, the biotite and hornblende $^{40}Ar/^{39}Ar$ results from eastern border zones of the Burlington Granodiorite suggest either that postmagmatic cooling was delayed relative to more northerly marginal zones (but that once initiated, cooling was relatively rapid) or that the pluton was locally metamorphosed subsequent to its emplacement (with relatively rapid post-metamorphic cooling). The latter interpretation is considered more likely in view of the apparently widespread record of Silurian-Devonian plutonism within the Baie Verte Belt (Dallmeyer and Hibbard 1984, p. 507).

Elsewhere, $^{40}Ar/^{39}Ar$ results on biotite and muscovite were concordant, but much "too young" for the crystallization age of the granite (Lux and Gibson 1998). So it was supposed that the granite was above the argon-retention temperatures for both sets of minerals for tens of millions of years, and then suddenly the granite cooled below the closure temperatures for both sets of minerals!

Myth: $^{40}Ar/^{39}Ar$ plateaus are corroborated by other reliability criteria.

Fact: It is most eye-opening to realize how often an isotopic dating system can pass one "reliability criterion" with flying colors, only to miserably fail one or more other "reliability

criteria." Setterfield *et al.* (1992) subjected a variety of volcanic rocks to the $^{40}Ar/^{39}Ar$ method and then compared plateau criteria itself with other presumed reliability criteria. To be considered fully reliable, a date had to simultaneously pass all of the following tests: (i) at least 50% of ^{39}Ar released over a well-defined plateau consisting of at least 4 steps, (ii) a MSWD of < 2.5 for the isochron for the plateau gas isotope ratios, and (iii) concordant plateau and isochron ages.

A variety of other complications in the interpretation of Ar-Ar spectra (notably for hornblendes) have been discussed by Bingen *et al.* (1998, pp. 165-168). These include various artifacts resulting from thermally-induced changes in the mineral, inhomogeneities in the mineral, secondary mineral contaminates, etc. Such artifacts have caused inconsistencies in the spectra obtained from even the same lithology:

> Although hand-picking was carefully performed, differences in ages and shape of spectra for different aliquots of some samples were observed; they could be related to inhomogeneity at sub-sampling level. . . (Bingen *et al.* 1998, p. 168).

Only a few samples passed all three criteria. Interestingly, however, many samples passed just one or two of the criteria. This indicates that there is a poor correlation between the successful passage of one "reliability criterion" and successful passage of other specific "reliability criteria" (see figure 18). This fact contradicts the premise that these "reliability criteria" are factual and rigorous "self-checking" devices for assessing the geochronometric validity of isotopic dating results.

Myth: All things considered, difficulties with the $^{40}Ar/^{39}Ar$ method amount to just a tiny number of malfunctioning watches.

Reality Check: To begin with, there has been an unmistakable retreat from the bold, earlier claims about the reliability of the $^{40}Ar/^{39}Ar$ method (just as there had been an earlier, definite backing down from the bold, earlier claims of reliability for all the other dating methods). As usual, this retreat has been covered by the **CDMBN** fallacy:

> . . . the irreducible complexity of data in the case of a complex thermal history and meaningless plateau ages . . . all seemed to converge to ruin the hoped-for ability of this technique to solve the complex situations for which it was designed (Albarede 1982).

Appeals to the complexity of nature have also been made in conjunction with the interpretation of $^{40}Ar/^{39}Ar$ spectra, along with results of other dating methods:

> By analogy, the process of reconstructing the geologic history of a region can be likened to putting together a large puzzle with only a few pieces, recognizing that most of the pieces will never be found (Conrad and McKee 1997, p. 1632).

There is no escaping the fact that, not only do problems continue to mount for the $^{40}Ar/^{39}Ar$ method, but these cannot any longer be dismissed as rare or trivial:

> Increasing evidence of the incompatibility between the geologic thermal histories deduced from the $^{40}Ar/^{39}Ar$ incremental-heating technique and those derived from other methods has necessitated a careful evaluation of the assumptions inherent in the former approach . . . independent evidence may be required to establish whether a plateau date from hornblende is truly a geologically significant age (Lee *et al.* 1991, p. 872).

On the other hand, Snee *et al.* (1995, p. 367) assert that many if not most hornblendes do show a "disturbed" spectrum when they had undergone (presumed) partial argon loss in their history. But even this may actually be the result of hidden contamination:

> A large number of published amphibole "diffusive loss" profiles may, in fact, be due to contamination by biotite or other phases which release Ar at low extraction temperatures (Rex *et al.* 1993, p. 271).

A recent study (Slettin and Onstott 1998) on the properties of muscovite has indicated that the diffusion process of Ar is vastly more complex than earlier suspected. And, at least in many applications of the $^{40}Ar/^{39}Ar$ method, it is very questionable if the spectrum obtained has any geologic significance:

> The net effect of this process is to preclude the recovery of any ^{40}Ar concentration gradient which may have formed in the muscovite during geologic processes (Slettin and Onstott 1998, p. 140).

All of these facts have very definitely caused a steady and continuous retreat from the premise that $^{40}Ar/^{39}Ar$ results can be straightforwardly classed into "reliable indicators of age" and "nonreliable dates:"

> For example, an early approach in assessing age spectrum results was to devise rules based on often recognized, but largely unexplained, vagaries (such as, "a hump-shaped spectrum means . . .") or invent what appear to be objective criteria for age assessment (such as, "a plateau contains five consecutive steps consisting of . . . "). Instead, multiple isochronous steps may reflect nothing more than experiment failure. . . . As with all the subjective aspects in $^{40}Ar/^{39}Ar$ dating, common sense remains the most important test. The apparently widespread expectation that a system of rules can uniformly allow all

samples to reveal straightforward age spectra or isochrons is counterproductive (Harrison 1990, p, 219, 227).

All things considered, these uncomfortable facts put the uniformitarian in a vise. On the one hand, he can no longer say that a plateau date is conclusive proof of either closed-system behavior, or of complete resetting of a mineral by some supposed later heating event on the host rock. On the other hand, he cannot wriggle out of the problem by saying that hornblende itself is an unreliable mineral, because (as we have seen) other minerals (such as biotite) have their own tendencies to create $^{40}Ar/^{39}Ar$ plateaus which the uniformitarian cannot accept as the correct age of crystallization or complete rejuvenation. So, for the uniformitarian, the end has come. He has run out of minerals, and has run out of rationalizations.

This, in essence, brings the uniformitarian "back to square one." First he had claimed that conventional K-Ar dates are wonderfully reliable, then he said that they are not always reliable but are at least "self-checking," and finally he said that they must be checked against what he considers to be a reasonable value based on his (uniformitarian) geologic deductions. The same progression in thinking has overcome the $^{40}Ar/^{39}Ar$ spectral method, and the uniformitarian can no longer extol its wonderful diagnostic properties. Instead, he is forced to retreat and admit that even flat spectra of the $^{40}Ar/^{39}Ar$ method must be evaluated as to their ostensible correctness according to what he considers to be the correct age of the rock. This, of course, also means that the $^{40}Ar/^{39}Ar$ method can no longer, by any standard, be reckoned to be inherently self-checking.

In conclusion, it should therefore be obvious that the $^{40}Ar/^{39}Ar$ is not in itself an analytic technique which invariably screens out "disturbed" from "undisturbed" K-Ar results. To the contrary, it has its own assumptions, special pleadings, selective acceptance and disregard of data, etc.

Meanwhile usage of the Ar-Ar method continues to upend earlier long-esteemed "reliable" conventional K-Ar dates, as well as earlier "less strict" Ar-Ar ones. This includes the almost complete demolition of a large part of the database used for oceanic-crust plate-tectonics deductions:

> Of ~35 such ages utilized for deriving plate motion models for the past 130 m.yr., at best, only three [dates given] in the Indian Ocean and one [date] for the Atlantic Ocean may be treated as crystallization ages. . . . This includes two marginal plateau ages, whose utility is debatable (Baksi 1999, p. 13, 23).

Chapter 8

Single-Grain U-Pb Dating of Zircons

Myth: U-Pb dates on zircons will reliably date the plutons even if the results of other dating methods (FT, K-Ar, and Rb-Sr) have all been "rejuvenated."

Reality Check: It has long been known that ore bodies easily become open systems to U and/or Pb (e. g., Snelling 1995), but it has also been supposed that zircons are very resistant to such behavior. (This is yet another appeal to the **ATM** fallacy). Now we have evidence that Pb need not be removed from zircons by heat itself: It can be scavenged by hydrothermal fluids (Bridgwater *et al.* 1989, p. 290, and citations). Thus, the considerable resistance of Pb in zircons to thermally-induced mobility becomes a moot point.

A growing number of researchers (e. g., Black 1986) also rebut the oft-quoted belief that U-Pb in zircons is exempt from open-system behavior, as do the following investigators:

> Our most important finding is that *no* dating technique gives a reliable emplacement age in all cases, but that all methods contribute to determining the intrusive history. Patterns of age concordance or discordance from multiple techniques prove to be much more effective than any single method alone (Fleck *et al.* 1996a, p. 65) [emphasis in original].

In fact zircon, for all its presumed resistance to thermally-induced open-system behavior, is believed to be vulnerable to low-temperature Pb loss. When such loss is superimposed upon xenocrystic zircons, bogus isochrons are formed:

> In such cases, fictitious linear trends can be developed which confuse the issue (Parrish and Roddick 1984, p. III-11).

As always, such interpretations are centered around uniformitarian beliefs about the "true" geologic history of the region, and they beg the question about the validity of the dating methods themselves. Yet they acknowledge, on uniformitarians' own terms, the fallibility of the highly-touted U-Pb method on zircons.

Myth: Explanations involving inheritance, or lead loss, are geologically justified whenever the U-Pb results are in fact found to be discordant.

Reality Check: Geologic interpretations are very plastic. There is no doubt that *some* manner of geologic justification can always be found, as necessary, on *an after-the-fact* basis to explain away a discordant pattern of results. Moreover, discordances occur even in "young" rocks with ostensibly simple geologic histories:

In many cases, the data presented in this chapter are slightly discordant. . . . Assigning precise geologic meaning to slightly discordant U-Pb ages is difficult. For geologically young zircons obtained from magmatic rocks in which there are no textural grounds for a metamorphic or thermal overprint and in which there is little cause to expect inheritance of zircons on the basis of regional geological considerations, it is commonly observed that the ^{207}Pb-^{206}Pb ages are typically slightly older than the Pb-U ages. The cause of this age disparity may stem from one or more of the following: (1) uncertainty in the isotopic composition of common Pb used in the age calculation, (2) Pb-loss, *despite the lack of textural evidence for mechanical or thermal metamorphism of the rock that houses the zircon*, (3) uncertainty in the decay constants of ^{235}U and ^{238}U, and (4) volumetrically small amounts of older, entrained ("inherited") zircon around which magmatic zircon grew. Distinguishing among the possibilities listed above is sometimes possible but was beyond the scope of this study (Walker 1995, p. 251) [emphasis added].

In many instances, there is no independent evidence for a zircon having been contaminated with inherited lead. Instead, such inheritance is *assumed* to be the case as an after-the-fact rationalization when discrepant results arise:

> The U/Pb zircon ages of the bentonite 2 horizon are very discordant, ostensibly resulting from the acquisition of a small amount of an older radiogenic lead during crystallization of the zircon. . . . The minerals from bentonite 1 were similar in every visible respect to those from bentonite 2, yet they yielded coherent results from all of the dating methods (Baadsgaard *et al.* 1993, p. 774).

So-called inherited zircons and their U-Pb dates have taken on a life of their own. For instance, in spite of the fact that, according to conventional plate tectonic theory, the Atlantic Ocean is supposed to be no older than Mesozoic, much older U-Pb dates have been obtained for zircons from gabbroic complexes at the Mid-Atlantic Ridge (Pilot *et al.* 1998). These were explained away as the mineral remnants of old continental crust that had become "chipped" off the drifting continents and "stranded" in the then newly-formed Mesozoic oceanic crust.

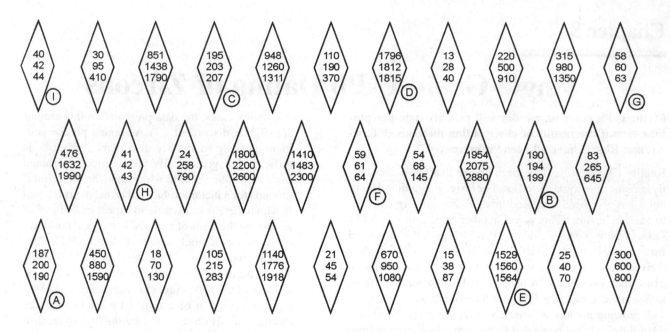

Figure 30. U-Pb SHRIMP dating of individual zircon grains reveals a *colossal* variety of U-Pb ages from the same igneous rock. (The diamond-shaped symbols above denote individual zircons from the same rock. The three numbers indicate dates [in Ma] by the three U-Pb methods.) This wide range of dates allows the geochronologist to "shop around" for a favored date. Results which coincide with the favored date, and are concordant, are assumed to date the rock (zircons A, B, C, above). Those which are concordant but "too old" (D, E) are assumed to be inherited from pre-existing rocks (without having undergone open-system behavior). Those which are concordant but "too young" (F, G, and H, I) are assumed to date later reheating events which resulted in the growth of new zircon crystals. Finally, all the discordant results (the vast majority) are assumed to have resulted from single or repeated episodes of open-system behavior.

Myth: The pristine state of the zircon crystal guarantees closed-system behavior.

Reality Check: Very often, when zircons yield discordant U-Pb dates, this is blamed on such things as crystal defects— all on an after-the-fact basis. However, this cannot be the reason for the discordancy in other cases:

> Nevertheless, some aspects of the data remain puzzling. In particular, the fact that the analyses are discordant in spite of having low U contents, and in spite of the homogeneity and lack of cracks and of alteration of the selected grains (Corfu and Stott 1998, p. 1477).

Myth: Inherited (xenocrystic) zircons can be optically distinguished from ones which crystallized at the same time as the magmatic body did.

Reality Check: To begin with, a uniformitarian geochronologist can always sort and then group zircon crystals according to color, shape, etc. He then can date these, and then interpret these trial balloons in any way he wants to on an after-the-fact basis. For instance, despite yielding a large variety of conflicting ages, zircons need not show any independent evidence of having undergone different histories:

> Zircons from sample La9 (Klein Picho), although morphologically uniform, provided a surprisingly wide array of xenocrystic ages varying between

1112 ± 9 and 1983 ± 10, respectively, and only one grain was found whose age of 584 ± 16 Ma is considered to reflect the time of granodiorite emplacement (Kroner *et al.* 1994, p. 366).

As if to mock the uniformitarian geochronologist, the converse is also true. That is, a population of zircon grains need not be morphologically uniform in order to give fairly consistent U-Pb dates:

> In spite of the heterogeneity of the analyzed zircons, there is no geochronological evidence of inheritance (Paquette and Nedelec 1998, p. 49).

Cox *et al.* (1998, p. 77) also report similar U-Pb ages from zircon grains which were different morphologically from each other, and for which a different history had been suspected.

Let us now consider some efforts to distinguish magmatic from ostensibly-xenocrystic zircon crystals. Roddick and Bevier (1995) discuss a situation where Ordovician granites have yielded U-Pb zircon dates ranging from mildly in excess to the "true" age of the host rock (approximately 450-480 million years) all the way to 1.85 billion years. They also point out that, optically, there is no clear-cut morphological difference between ostensibly-inherited zircons and magmatic ones. Ion-microprobe analysis is supposed to be a better diagnostic tool for screening out supposed xenocrystic zircons, but even the results of such analyses are a matter of diverse interpretations. In fact, it is claimed (Compston and

Williams 1992, p. 61) that ion-probe SHRIMP U-Pb analyses "positively identify any xenocryst or discordant grain that is not otherwise obvious," which, of course, is a tacit admission that supposed xenocrystic zircons can at least sometimes be identified only on an after-the-fact basis:

> . . . grain 13 from the same zircon concentrate, which was chosen for analysis because of its beautifully crystalline shape and with the expectation of the same magmatic age. Instead, it has a reproducible age of 600 Ma, which thereby labels it a xenocryst. [The zircon comes from an Ordovician bentonite, and "should" therefore give an age of about 470 million years.] We failed to identify it *a priori* by any feature of colour or morphology, and cannot distinguish it from the remaining grains in retrospect. (Compston and Williams 1992, p. 61)

Even the most pristine hand-picked zircon grains still contain xenocrysts (Aleinikoff *et al.* 1993, p. 68; Beyth and Reischmann 1996, p. 223; Gaudette *et al.* 1996, p. 189), as do zircon grains which lack any visible inclusions or cores (Lyons *et al.* 1986, p. 493; Nutman *et al.* 1996, p. 158; Williams *et al.* 1997, p. 191). In fact, the term "cryptic cores" has been used by some authors (Buchan *et al.* 1996, p. 1588; Bingen and van Breeman 1998a, p. 146), which, of course, begs the question about their existence in the first place. There is a clear overlap of zircon morphologies regardless of their respective supposed histories:

> Zircon morphology sometimes helps to distinguish between magmatic and xenocrystic zircons, but we also found perfectly euhedral and homogenous varieties which were inherited. Mixture of such grains with magmatic zircons in multigrain analysis tends to produce ages which are invariably too high (Kroner and Jaeckel 1994, p. 181).

> For precise U-Pb dating, it is desirable to separate the genetically distinct zircon components. *Often, however, it is difficult or impossible to identify inherited components* because xenocrysts do not always differ in their physical properties from the bulk population, and cores often show little or no optical contrast to their overgrowth (Hansmann and Oberli 1991, p. 107) [emphasis added].

> *Many studies* of peraluminous granitic rocks have illustrated the difficulty in differentiating between primary igneous zircons and xenocrysts which preserve older systematics. . . (Tomascak *et al.* 1996, p. 188) [emphasis added].

All this, of course, begs the question of the xenocrystic origin of the zircons which are giving U-Pb results that are "too old." It also means that the uniformitarian geochronologist can always rationalize away any discrepantly-old U-Pb result on zircon despite the fact that the zircon grain in question is morphologically identical to the "truly magmatic" zircons:

> Although optically similar to the other zircons, the greater age of these grains identifies them as xenocrysts in the andesite magma, possibly inherited from the source rocks of the magma (Perkins *et al.* 1990, p. 1821).

Whenever a complexly-zoned zircon crystal can clearly be identified optically, and its zones dated separately, the results obtained are subject to their own plastic set of interpretations. If the dating results differ substantially, this is cited as evidence that the zircon crystal acquired its overgrowths at widely different times in geologic history. If, on the other hand, there is little or no difference between the dates of the abraded and unabraded zircon crystals, this is interpreted as evidence that both the central part of the crystal, and the overgrowth, originated at approximately the same time (e. g., Chiarenzelli and McLelland 1991, p. 583). Uniformitarian geochronology is infinitely adaptable to every conceivable possibility! Just indulge in **CDMBN** whenever you want to.

Myth: When there are xenocrystic zircons in a granite, they reliably date the source rocks of the crystals.

Reality Check: If the ages indicated by the real or supposed xenocrystic crystals fit in with the current ideas of what the correct age is for source rock, the dates will probably be accepted as such. However, if they are not, they will be interpreted to have been partly or totally "reset" in the host melt:

> At the same time, the prolonged residence of zircons in melt will undoubtedly cause a disturbance in their U-Pb isotopic system. Thus, the interpretation of ages obtained on zircon-xenocrysts is ambiguous (Bibikova *et al.* 1998, p. 40).

Kroner *et al.* (1998, p. 761) warns that high temperature evaporation techniques may not completely remove metamorphic overgrowths, and thus the U-Pb dates may be geologically meaningless.

Myth: A prognosis of the reliability of a U-Pb zircon date can be made on the basis of its U content.

Fact: While this has long been claimed (Roddick and Bevier 1995, and citations), the actual situation, as usual, is not so simple. High-U zircons need not yield discordant results, and low-U zircons need not be ostensibly reliable. Thus, unexpectedly, highly-discordant results have been obtained from zircons having low U content (Emslie and Hunt 1990, p. 216; Corfu and Stott 1998, p. 1447), and unexpectedly concordant results have resulted from zircons having a high U content (Davis *et al.* 1989, p. 391; Trendall *et al.* 1997, p. 167). In other situations, *no* relationship has been found between degree of discordancy, and U content (Zartman and Leo 1985, p. 277). Similar conflicting opinions, as to U content and reliability, apply to other minerals, such as columbite (Mauthner *et al.* 1995, p. 2096). In conclusion, uniformitarians must once again resort to selective interpretation and special pleading, as they are once again denied a claim of having a reliability criterion for assessing the presumed validity of their dating results. Their **ATM** has failed yet again.

Myth: Discordancy of U-Pb zircons can be predicted on the basis of metamorphic grade.

Reality Check: Even this claim is subject to special pleading, as large geographic areas often show no relationship between metamorphic grade, and degree of discordance between U-Pb zircon results (Zartman and Leo 1985, p. 277).

Myth: Whereas open-system behavior and contamination may be problems for the K-Ar dating of volcanogenic ash, such is not the case for U-Pb dating of zircons from bentonites.

Fact: The following words speak for themselves:

> The surface environment from which the determined zircons occurred due to volcanic emanation, the loose structure of the volcanic ash beds and the very fine grains of zircons all lead to *difficulty in selecting the truly volcanogenic and pure pristine zircon samples as well as obtaining the identical age results for a group of single zircons* (Jie-Dong *et al.* 1996, p. 58) [emphasis added].

Myth: Concordia plots solve the problem of discordant U-Pb results.

Dalrymple (1984, pp. 75-76; 1991, p. 119) would have us believe that the U-Pb concordia-discordia is self-checking.

Fact: To begin with, while the concordia plot does give results which often seem reasonable to the uniformitarian geochronologist, it only begs the question about its own assumptions:

> Ahrens-Wetherill graphs provide information on zircon ages from the analysis of open U-Pb isotope systems only if the perturbations occurred in a single act. If the U-Pb system has been perturbed repeatedly, and if there is considerable discordance in the isotope ratios, linear extrapolation of the discordia to intersection with the concordia may give rise to incorrect dating (Ryvanova *et al.* 1995, p. 49).

An example of such thinking is provided by Paquette *et al.* (1989, p. 280), who report a "geologically meaningless intercept age" that is "an artifact." Comparable rationalizations are invoked by others (Aleinikoff 1985; Aleinikoff *et al.* 1995; Corfu and Easton 1995; Ross and Bowring 1990, Tucker and Gower 1994). In fact, it is now admitted that the concordia method rarely has meaning—on uniformitarians' own terms:

> Lower intercept ages in normally discordant zircons, however, can only rarely be shown to have any geologic significance (Parrish and Roddick 1984, p. III-12).

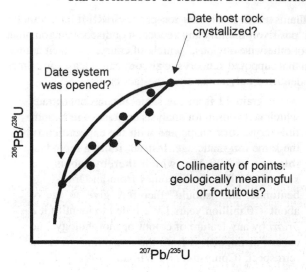

Figure 31. Even if points are collinear on a U-Pb concordia diagram, one or both intercepts can still be rejected as ostensible indicators of correct age and/or disturbance, if they do not fit current ideas.

Failures of the concordia method have been blamed on the rarity of post-crystallization disturbances of U-Pb systems that are in fact limited to one such event per system:

> The real-world problem is that zircon suites with only an age of crystallization and *one* later event are *rare* and that analyses are tedious and expensive so that only a few points of time scale significance have been published (Harland *et al.* 1990, p. 77) [emphasis added].

Of course, the above statement is also a tacit admission that the concordia method rarely "works," and is once again an appeal to the **CDMBN** (**C**redit **D**ating **M**ethods, **B**lame **N**ature) fallacy.

Interestingly, in some situations, intercept ages differing from each other by as much as hundreds of millions of years have been obtained, all depending upon which zircon grains were included in the concordia plot, and which ones were excluded (Aleinikoff *et al.* 1995, Mose *et al.* 1989, Ross and Bowring 1990, Wastenys *et al.* 1996). In several other studies, a "reverse discordancy" has been found. That is, the points actually plot *above* a concordia (Bingen and van Breeman 1998a; Mattinson *et al.* 1996, and citations; Nemchin and Pidgeon 1998; Wang *et al.* 1998a; Williams *et al.* 1984, and citations; Witter 1974).

It is sometimes alleged that a "reliable" concordia will be distinguishable by the excellent statistical collinearity of points on it. But even this claim is an indulgence in special pleading, as such claims had been previously made, only to be retracted when the composite "ages" of bulk-zircon samples became subsequently known. Such cases prompted the following caution:

> Such samples can yield discordia of high statistical quality which nevertheless yield erroneous ages (Dickin 1997, p. 118).

There are also other circumstances under which *both* upper and lower intercepts of concordia diagrams turn out to be of questionable geologic significance:

> Due to the complex nature of the zircons in sample 9015, the linear array of the data points is interpreted to represent a mixing line. . . . This age is, however, obtained from very discordant fractions and both the lower and upper intercept ages must be interpreted with caution (Wang *et al.* 1998b, p. 332).

As is the case with all aspects of conventional geochronology, the concordia is not used in any sort of self-consistent way by uniformitarians. It is always subject to special pleading as to its ostensible geochronometric significance.

In still other situations, and common ones at that, the points scatter considerably, and cannot even be graphed on a concordia plot to begin with (Friedman and Marignole 1995, Mattinson 1990). Of course, whenever the dates on grains of zircon fail to line up on a concordia plot, it can be claimed that a mixed zircon population is still present in the sample—all despite the careful hand-picking of crystals (Gaudette *et al.* 1996, p. 189).

So, in essence, the uniformitarian geochronologist cannot lose, no matter what turns up. If his results are concordant, he says that they had remained closed systems for millions or billions of years. If discordant, but resolvable on a concordia plot, and acceptable to his presuppositions, he claims that they had experienced a simple open-system history. If discordant, and resolvable on a concordia plot, but not acceptable to his presuppositions, he informs us that the linearity of points is fortuitous or otherwise not geologically meaningful. If reversely discordant, he can plead some unusual pattern of isotopic exchange. Finally, if the dates are discordant and do not even form a collinear relationship on a concordia plot to begin with, he rationalizes that the open-system had occurred repeatedly, or had a complex history. As the late creationist scholar Robert Witter (1974) had pointed out, a geochronologist could do as well by throwing darts on a concordia diagram, and then interpreting whatever pattern the darts resulted in on a posterioritic basis [as done comparably in figure 20].

Myth: The abrasion of individual grains of zircon eliminates the problem of discordant U-Pb dates.

Reality Check: With the development of the level of technology that now allows individual zircon grains to be dated, there has also come a tendency to date *components* of individual zircon crystals, and then to check the results for consistency. This methodology, of course, presupposes the validity of what uniformitarians assume to be true, in that zircons have undergone complex histories over vast periods of time, and these complex histories can be unraveled by dating different parts of zircons, such that (if they exist at all), components of individual zircon grains which

exhibit concordant U-Pb dates reliably date the time of crystallization of the host magma.

In particular, there has come the practice of abrading the outer rims of individual zircon grains. This has been based on the assumption that closed-system behavior is more likely to be exhibited by the central parts of the zircon crystal rather than the outer fringes of the same. Indeed, concordant results have often been achieved by following this procedure. However, a series of recent studies involving the use of U-Pb zircon dating for the calibration of the Phanerozoic time scale (Davidek *et al.* 1998; Grotzinger *et al.* 1995; Mundil *et al.* 1996, 1998; Tucker *et al.* 1998) have been unable to escape the reality of variably discordant U-Pb zircon dates despite the use of the air-abrasion technique. In addition, some of the more seriously-discordant results had to be rationalized away by invoking the *ad hoc* existence of invisible inherited components. There are also many examples of where abrasion of zircons, and dating of their centers has, for whatever after-the-fact rationalization, either not decreased the discordance between the results of the U-Pb methods, or sometimes actually *increased* the discordance (Barreiro *et al.* 1998; Childe 1996; Currie 1992; Davis *et al.* 1989; Friedman and Martignole 1995; Paquette and Nedelec 1998; Parrish 1995; Roden *et al.* 1990; Ryvanova *et al.* 1995; Samson and D'Lemos 1999). Elsewhere, abrasion has not been found to be helpful despite much trying:

> For any specimen containing dozens or hundreds of grains and having a total weight of more than 1 mg, abrasive treatment as a rule does not provide concordant values (Ryvanova *et al.* 1995, p. 60).

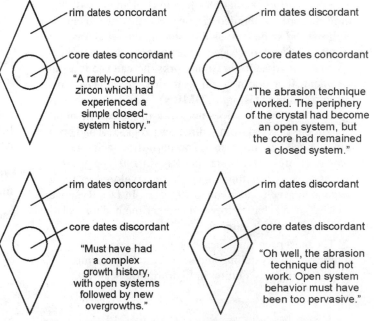

Figure 32. With the dating of individual zircon grains (diamond symbols), a new layer of special pleading has been added to the interpretation of U-Pb dates. A "pick and choose" approach is now done for dates from *parts* of individual grains subjected first to the abrasion technique. Of course, whenever abrasion fails to produce concordant results for the remainder of the grain, this is never counted as evidence against the abrasion technique.

In terms of the degree of discordance, the zircon grains, *in spite of air-abrasion treatment*, can still be more than 50% discordant (Heaman and Tarney 1989, p. 707).

Finally, even when the air abrasion technique does work, there is a fudge factor of sorts in terms of the *amount of zircon grain to be removed*. This has even led to disagreements about how much zircon to abrade away and how to interpret the U-Pb results for the remainder of the grain [compare Mundil *et al.* (1996) and Brack *et al.* (1997) with Hardie and Hinnov (1997)]. Indeed, one only has to examine figure 4 of Mundil *et al.* (1996, p. 145) to see that, despite the decrease in frequency and severity of discordance when 10-20% of the zircon crystals are abraded away, a significant body of discordant dates persist even when about 50% of each crystal is abraded away. Of course, to the extent that different investigators abrade away different amounts of zircon crystal, this allows them to "shop around" for that degree of abrasion that will maximize the degree of concordant results—assuming of course that abrasion works at all in a given instance. Thus, for instance, Samson and D'Lemos (1999) abraded some zircon grains by extensive amounts (and for up to several days) before giving up on getting concordant results from them.

Thanks to the air-abrasion technique, the sampling universe wherein concordant results can be fished out has now suddenly become much larger than before. Since investigators now look for concordance *within* individual crystals, it is hardly surprising that they often find it. After all, the vagaries of migration of isotopes within crystals are bound to increase the degree of concordance within *some* fragment of the crystal solely by chance.

All things considered (figure 32, previous page), we now have a new layer of special pleading to explain away the remaining discordant abraded zircons. So, this new technology follows the same path as did isotopic dating as a whole (see figure 12). And, once again, the uniformitarian geochronologist cannot lose. If abrasion works, he can cite it as an achievement. If it doesn't—oh well, that zircon must have had a more complex history (**CDMBN**). And, even then, it is recognized that abrasion does not work in the case of high-quality zircons derived from sedimentary rocks that had been metamorphosed to uppermost amphibolite-facies metamorphism, or higher (Heaman and Parrish 1991, pp. 92-93).

Of course, other methods have been developed to force the zircons to give concordant U-Pb dates. In fact, Ryanova *et al.* (1995, p. 59) have proposed another method for isolating ostensibly-reliable zircons:

> The most promising means of isolating concordant phases from crystalline and semicrystalline zircons is differential dissolution in hydrofluoric acid.

Mundil *et al.* (1998) also report success with HF acid, having failed to achieve concordance using air abrasion followed by a hot hydrochloric-nitric acid bath!

With the ever-increasing variety of manipulations performed by uniformitarians on isotopic systems, it is becoming more and more easy to shop around for some technique that will give a concordant result. Torture the data long enough, and it will say whatever you want. And if one "torture technique" does not produce the desired result, try another.

Myth: Unlike zircon, the mineral titanite is exempt from inheritance of radiogenic Pb.

Fact: When it is claimed that such-and-such a mineral is exempt from problems in isotopic dating, it is usually just a matter of time before the contrary is demonstrated. After all, attempts to minimize the flaws of isotopic dating commonly use this **ATM** (Appeal To Marginalization) fallacy. Contrary to the earlier beliefs of geochronologists, we now have evidence that, following standard uniformitarian thinking, titanite can also inherit radiogenic lead and thus give results which are "too old" to be accepted (Zhang and Scharer 1996), or even "reversely discordant" (Bingen and van Breeman 1998a).

Myth: The mineral monazite is very reliable for U-Pb dating.

Reality Check:

> Within individual rock samples U-Pb and Pb-Pb ages of single monazite grains vary considerably and range from 40% reversely discordant to 10% normally discordant. . . . The U-Pb ages of essentially concordant grains vary by as much as 20 Ma in a single sample. Backscattered electron imaging reveals no evidence for inheritance (Hawkins and Bowring 1994, p. 131).

We can thus see that monazite, as a mineral for U-Pb dating does not, as claimed by some, overcome the problems of using zircon for dating purposes.

Myth: U-Pb dates conform to conventional geochemical models.

Fact: Some do, some don't:

> Surprisingly, no correlations of major element distributions with U-Pb zircon ages are apparent from the data (Condie *et al.* 1999, p. 106).

Chapter 9

How Often do Dating Methods Agree by Chance? An Exploratory Study

Introduction. As noted earlier in this work, it has never been proved that concordance among dating methods is proof of the accuracy of the dates obtained. It is simply *assumed* to be the case, probably because of a tacit assumption that fortuitous concordances must be very unlikely. Most creationist researchers, notably those involved in the RATE project (Vardiman 1997, 1998), have attempted to solve the apparent riddle of concordant results by investigating the feasibility of multi-magnitude changes in radioactive decay rates. To my knowledge, no one has ever attempted to even estimate the probability of dating methods agreeing by chance, though this had been suggested long ago by creationists Whitcomb and Morris (1961, p. 341). Such an approach is all the more urgent once we realize that both laypersons and scientists are prone to incorrectly ascribe causality to phenomena that are in fact random. Gilovich (1997), Cohen and Stewart (1998), and Martin (1998) provide many examples of this pitfall. Their works make for eye-opening reading.

Geologic Sampling of Dates. When attempting a study of fortuitous concordances, we must also get a handle on the sampling universe we are dealing with. As discussed in the previous work (Woodmorappe 1979, 1993) and current one, isotopic dates from the earth's crust span a considerable range—from negative values to ones in excess of 10 billion years. The vast majority of dates, however, fall within the range of a few million years to about 2.5-3.0 billion years.

In addition to the range of dates, we must also account for their uneven frequency. To approximate this, we need to obtain a plausible distribution of isotopic dates from the earth's crust. This is problematic for several previously-discussed reasons. One is the selective publication of dating results, and the second is the lack of regional standardization of isotopic dates. In addition, with the exception of a few studies (e. g., DePaulo *et al.* 1991, and that primarily for "crust-formation" ages rather than presumed crystallization ages), little if any attempt is made to account for isotopic dates at depth within the crust. In other words, isotopic-dating results are mapped as two-dimensional phenomena whereas the crust is three-dimensional. There do exist some estimates for the volumes of igneous rocks with "age" (e. g., Crisp 1984, Ronov *et al.* 1982), but it is acknowledged (Crisp 1984, p. 187) that these may be off by as much as a factor of ten. This large uncertainty stems from the fact that it is difficult to determine the thicknesses of large plutons (Crisp 1984, p. 179;

Snelling and Woodmorappe 1998), and thus arrive at a reasonably-accurate volume of intrusive rock.

So how is one to account for the uneven frequency of dates from the earth's crust? Indeed, much "old" rock is covered by younger lithologies. It is not surprising, therefore, that dates obtained from the earth's crust are biased towards younger values. Even so, we can still construct our database with this limitation in mind, and thus use the presently-available information for a preliminary study. After all, arguments about the presumed significance of concordant results are, without exception, made within the context of the existing "young rock" bias. Therefore, if for no other reason than methodological consistency, there is no difficulty in working within the constraints of the same bias when challenging the concordance-is-conclusive-proof-of-age argument.

Owing to the preliminary nature of this study, no attempt is made to analyze the data either mathematically or geochemically. Rather, this study attempts to reproduce the *de facto* distribution of earth's radio-isotopic dates, following essentially a "bird's eye" view of the earth's exposed igneous rocks.

Let us therefore first estimate the actual extent of the "young rock" bias. The ratios of global crystalline-rock outcrop areas (Blatt and Jones 1975), expressed in terms of Precambrian:Paleozoic:Mesozoic:Cenozoic, are approximately 6:2:3:4. The median age of earth's igneous rocks, in terms of those outcropping at the surface and therefore accessible for dating, is Mesozoic in age.

Since younger values are much more common than older ones, a linear distribution of numbers will not adequately represent the relative frequencies of the dates. In order to account for the strong bias towards younger ages, two different systems of distribution of dates are examined instead: the log-linear distribution and the log-normal distribution.

Modeling the Global Distribution of Dates. In a log-linear situation, there is an equal probability of "dates" emerging in each of the following bins: 10 million to 100 million years, 100 million years to 1 billion years, and 1 billion to 10 billion years. However, for purpose of this analysis, the range is limited to two spans of relevant dates. The first one (not illustrated), here named "short-running," covers the span of 1 million years to 2.5 Ga. It is intended to mimic the probable global distribution of area-normalized K-Ar dates. The second log-linear distribution, here named "long-running,"

88

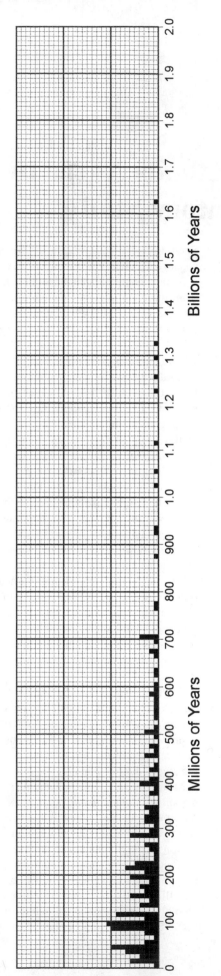

(a) A "long-running" log-normal distribution of global isotopic dates applicable primarily to Rb-Sr, Sm-Nd, and U-Pb dating. 200 random points comprising lists (D) and (H) are all graphed. Median value is 174 million years. 1SD (Standard Deviation) values are 62 million, 490 million years. 2SD values are 22 million, 1.38 billion years. 3SD values are 7.8 million, 3.9 billion years.

Millions of Years

Billions of Years

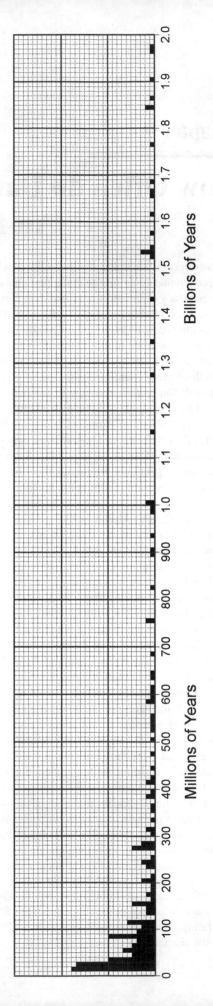

(b) A "long-running" (10 m.y.—3.5 b.y.) log-linear distribution of global isotopic dates, applicable primarily to Rb-Sr, Sm-Nd, and U-Pb dating. 200 random points (of which 23 are greater than 2.0 b.y., and off scale) are graphed, exhausting lists (B) and (C).

Millions of Years

Billions of Years

Figure 33: Graphical depictions showing relative frequencies of dates.

spans the range of 10 million years to 3.5 billion years. It is illustrated in figure 33, (b), and is intended to account for the comparative rarity of Rb-Sr, Sm-Nd, and U-Pb dates younger than 10 million years. The latter distribution also accounts for the fact that Rb-Sr, Sm-Nd, and U-Pb dates appear to become progressively older than simultaneous K-Ar dates as the magnitudes of all the dating results increase. The reason for choosing upper limits of 2.5 Ga and 3.5 Ga for the respective log-linear distributions stems from the relative infrequency of dates, by any method, in excess of these figures.

The log-linear distributions probably create an excessive bias towards very young (i. e., Tertiary) rocks. For this reason, and because of the large numbers of igneous bodies assigned to the Mesozoic (Kauffman 1979), I consider models which allow for the modal date to be Mesozoic in age. In the "short-running" log-normal distribution (figure 34), applicable primarily to K-Ar dates, the median date is 141 million years. One standard deviation spans dates in the range of 52.5 million to 380 million years. The corresponding ranges for two and three standard deviations are, respectively, 19.5 million years to 1.02 billion years and 7.24 million years to 2.75 billion years.

For the "long-running" log-normal distribution [figure 33, (a)], applicable to Rb-Sr, Sm-Nd, and U-Pb dates, the median age is 174 million years. One standard deviation encompasses dates spanning the interval of 63 million years to 490 million years. Ranges for two and three standard deviations are, respectively, 22 million years to 1.38 billion years and 7.8 million years to 3.9 billion years. (A fourth standard deviation spans dates up to 10.9 Ga, accounting for the previously-discussed absurdly-high dates occasionally obtained that are "older than the earth itself.")

The Quasi Monte Carlo Analysis. The modeled distributions of isotopic dates, discussed above, were subject to randomly individual sampling. The well-known program Minitab was used to generate the prescribed random-number distributions and then to choose random-number "dates" from them, 100 "dates" at a time. Minitab is widely used, and has earned a reputation for producing truly random results.

The capital first letters of the alphabet were used to name each list of 100 random "dates." Thus, list (A) consists of the 100 random samples of the "short-running" log-linear distribution. Comparable sampling of the "long-running" log-linear distribution has generated lists (B) and (C). The 100-member number lists (F) and (G) are random samplings of the "short-running" log-normal distribution, while (D), (E), (H), (I), (J), and (K) represent the corresponding samplings of the "long-running" log-normal distribution.

Owing to the limited sample sizes used in this study, the question of representative sampling must be addressed. The statistical robustness of the data points obtained must be accepted with some caution, as this study does not qualify as a true Monte Carlo analysis. The latter typically requires tens of thousands of trials for verification of results. Nevertheless, the data points in this investigation consist of a large sample of the stated numerical distributions. Hence reasonable confidence can be placed in the sampling.

Table 3 illustrates the procedures used in this study. After being listed as described earlier, the random numbers were manually paired from one list to another. Concordance or lack of concordance was then determined by visual inspection. For purposes of this study, results were considered concordant if the 2nd standard-deviation ranges (of analytic uncertainties in a date) overlapped. This was taken to be plus and minus 2.5% of the random date obtained. However, it should be noted that there is no standard "rule" for assessing the maximum divergence of dating results that is compatible with the designation of concordance. Hence, different researchers have used different percentage-differences as cutoff points. For three-way concordances, I allowed for two degrees of strictness in the definition of such a concordance. For what I call a "transitive three-way concordance," the plus and minus 2.5% uncertainty of the first date had to overlap that of the second, and that of the second, in turn, with that of the third. However, the uncertainties of the first date did not have to overlap those of the third. In a "full three-way concordance," however, the plus and minus 2.5% uncertainties

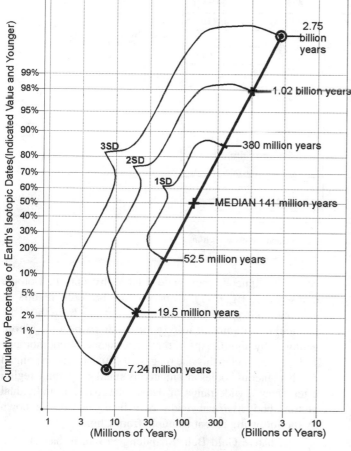

Figure 34: A "short-running" lognormal distribution of global isotopic dates (applicable primarily to K-Ar dating).

	Random Numbers	(range for concordance)		Random Numbers	(range for concordance)	
	List (F)	-2.5%	+2.5%	List (G)	-2.5%	+2.5%
Row	C2	C3	C4	C2	C3	C4
1	66.69	65.02	68.36	469.53	457.79	481.27
2	204.97	199.84	210.09	43.79	42.69	44.88
3	429.35	418.61	440.08	73.90	72.05	75.75
4	55.21	53.83	56.59	269.75	263.00	276.49
5	382.92	373.35	392.49	72.84	71.02	74.66
6	80.07	78.07	82.07	86.52	84.36	88.68
7	118.74	115.77	121.71	30.82	30.05	31.59
8	67.72	66.03	69.41	172.50	168.18	176.81
9	193.32	188.49	198.16	155.33	151.45	159.22
10	906.96	884.29	929.63	147.19	143.51	150.87
11	108.48	105.77	111.19	83.88	81.78	85.97
12	338.48	330.02	346.95	67.62	65.93	69.31
13	237.72	231.77	243.66	1025.88	1000.24	1051.53
14	99.21	96.73	101.69	256.72	250.30	263.13
15	188.37	183.67	193.08	434.13	423.28	444.98
16	213.89	208.54	219.24	1422.46	1386.90	1458.02
17	199.28	194.30	204.26	208.52	203.30	213.73
18	50.40	49.14	51.66	159.65	155.65	163.64
19	296.32	288.91	303.73	52.82	51.50	54.14
20	549.83	536.08	563.57	14.37	14.01	14.73
.	.	.	.	.	.	.
.	.	.	.	.	.	.
.	.	.	.	.	.	.
.	.	.	.	.	.	.
100	——	——	——	——	——	——

} 11 pairs needed for the first-encountered concordant pairing when cumulative trials are considered

← The first-encountered "first try" concordant pair

Table 3. Illustration of concordant pairings involving the actual first 20 (of 100 total) random numbers each in lists (F) vs. (G).

of each member of the triplet of dates had to fully overlap each other.

I began this analysis by testing the frequency of fortuitous "first try" concordances. For this to occur, the Nth number in one list of 100 random dates needed to be concordant with the Nth number in another list of 100 random dates. Assessing the frequency of "first try" concordances corresponded to the dating of one specific igneous lithology by two dating methods, and finding the results in agreement. As illustrated in Table 3, the 17th pair of random numbers of lists (F) and (G) is concordant. Four other concordant pairs exist in the remaining 83 pairings (not shown). All five concordant pairs are enumerated at the intersection of (F) and (G) in Table 4.

A "first try" approach to fortuitous results is overly stringent. This stems from the fact that most regions on earth

containing igneous rock yield a large diversity of isotopic dates (e. g., figure 7). Concordance between results of different dating methods does not have to be from the same particular igneous lithology in order to be considered geologically significant. In the earlier work (Woodmorappe 1979, 1993), and in this one (pages 19-20), it has been pointed out that igneous bodies in a relatively small geographic region often show a wide range of dates. Moreover, an individual plutonic body *itself* can yield widely divergent dates, as shown by the following recent example from China:

Zhaoye Gold Belt, Shandong Province, has extensively been intruded by a range of granitic intrusions. Conventional isotopic dating techniques, such as K-Ar, Rb-Sr, and conventional U-Pb in zircon, have given variable and inconsistent ages which

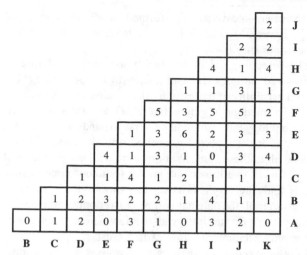

	B	C	D	E	F	G	H	I	J	K	
										2	J
								2	2	I
							4	1	4	H
						1	1	3	1	G
					5	3	5	5	2	F
				1	3	6	2	3	3	E
			4	1	3	1	0	3	4	D
		1	1	4	1	2	1	1	1	C
	1	2	3	2	2	1	4	1	1	B
0	1	2	0	3	1	0	3	2	0	A

Table 4. Number(s) of "first try" concordances with respect to pairings of 100 random numbers (distributions of which are specified in the text). For example, when the 100 numbers in (A) were juxtaposed against the 100 in (F), the 4th 50th and 90th pairs were found concordant. There are thus three concordances for the 100 possible match-ups of (A) vs. (F).

range from Proterozoic to Mesozoic. Therefore, the time of emplacement of these intrusions is controversial. There are three major viewpoints about the timing of these granitoids of the Zhaoye area: (i) they were emplaced during Proterozoic era; (ii) they formed in Mesozoic era; and (iii) the Linglong batholith is a composite batholith consisting of variable plutons whose ages range from early and mid-Proterozoic era, through Hercynian epoch of late Palaeozoic era, to Indo-Chinese and Yanshanian epochs of Mesozoic era (Laicheng *et al.* 1997, p. 361).

The diversity of available dates, of course, greatly increases the likelihood of fortuitous concordances by increasing the number of possible "trials" (pairings) of isotopic dates (figure 35). Furthermore, some dating methods make the involvement of multiple lithologies, over significant geographic areas, virtually inevitable. This is especially true of the isochron-based ones (most commonly Rb-Sr and Sm-Nd) where, as discussed earlier, samples often have to be gathered over large areas of geochemically-differentiated lithologies in order to obtain the requisite spread of data points to construct an isochron. And, to the extent that a variety of contradictory isochrons can be created from much the same suite of lithologies, this procedure itself considerably enhances the multiplicity of "trials." Each of the several isochrons can now be individually compared with the result(s) of other dating method(s), and thus "checked for reliability"—all the while increasing the likelihood of the emergence of at least one fortuitously concordant pair of dates.

Because of the overly-restrictive assumptions inherent in the "first-try" concordances, an additional analysis had been performed in order to account for multiple dates and multiple

chances at fortuitous concordance. Instead of being done one at a time and in isolation towards each other, pairings of random numbers were done on a cumulative basis until the first concordant pairing was encountered. As is illustrated in table 3, this occurred, for list (F) vs. list (G), when the 6th member of the former was found to be concordant with the 11th member of the latter. Since 11 pairs had to be considered before any one member of (F) was found concordant with any one member of (G), this number was entered into the intersection of (F) and (G) in table 5.

Results. Let us first focus on the "first try" concordances. The 5500 individual pairings resulting from the cross-comparison of the fifty-five (table 4) 100-member random-number lists [(A) through (K)] yield 116 fortuitous two-way concordances, amounting to 2.1% of the total. For the evaluation of three-way concordances, 165 non-redundant three-way pairings of the 100-member lists [(A) through (K)] had been performed, generating 16,500 three-member ordered pairs. Of the latter, 4 were "transitively concordant" and 5 were "fully concordant," according to the definitions provided earlier. The "full three-way concordances" amount to 0.03% of the total number of random three-way ordered pairs—a percentage not so small when we take into account the vast magnitude of the sampling universe enjoyed by isotopic dating (more on this shortly).

It is instructive to consider not only the overall frequency of fortuitous "first try" two-way concordances, but also the clusterings of their appearance—which, of course, are also random. Whenever we compare 100 individualized pairings of results of two different dating methods, we almost always obtain at least 1 or 2 fortuitous concordant pairs within those 100 random pairings (table 4). In like manner, albeit subject to the limitations of this analysis, we obtain 3-6 fortuitous

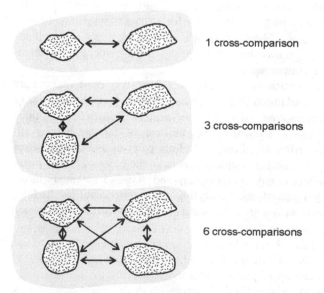

Figure 35: Because orogenic belts typically contain plutons of very divergent "ages," the number of potential cross-comparisons quickly becomes considerable. This alone increases the chances for fortuitous concordances between the results of different dating methods.

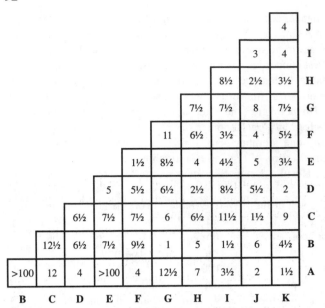

	B	C	D	E	F	G	H	I	J	K
J	4									
I	3	4								
H	8½	2½	3½							
G	7½	7½	8	7½						
F	11	6½	3½	4	5½					
E	1½	8½	4	4½	5	3½				
D	5	5½	6½	2½	8½	5½	2			
C	6½	7½	7½	6	6½	11½	1½	9		
B	12½	6½	7½	9½	1	5	1½	6	4½	
A	>100	12	4	>100	4	12½	7	3½	2	1½

Table 5. Concordance from Assortative Pairings: Number of pairs of random dates which need to be randomly culled from the intersecting lists before a concordant pairing is encountered. This is analogous to the number of random cullings necessary, of men and women at a party, before any one man and any one woman are found to share the same birthday. A "½" denotes that a supernumerary completes a concordant pairing.

concordant pairs nearly one-half of the time (i. e., in 20 of the 55 lists). Furthermore, analysis of the appearance of concordant pairings *within* each set of 100 pairings (not shown) reveals that the concordant pairings often occur in clusters that could easily (but erroneously) be considered geologically meaningful, by uniformitarians, had these random numbers been actual isotopic dates.

When the more geologically-realistic assortative pairings are allowed (table 5), accidental two-way concordances become a common occurrence. Usually only a few to several serial pairings are necessary for a concordant pairing to arise by chance. Furthermore, it is easy to see that the same holds for assortative three-way pairings and the emergence of three-way concordances.

Conclusions. Two and even three-way concordances are not at all unlikely—especially when we keep the vast size of our sampling universe in perspective. Remember that there are many thousands if not millions of dates globally available. After all, if even 1 million pairs of comparative dates are available, we should expect on the order of 21,000 fortuitous two-way concordances and 303-545 fortuitous three-way concordances! And this is for concordant results from the *same* sample. As noted earlier, concordances between

results of assortative dates performed on adjacent lithologies (e. g., figure 35) must be routinely frequent in the world of geochronometry (table 5).

The foregoing discussion tacitly assumes the dating of hand-sized samples. By contrast, with the previously-discussed capability of dating individual grains (e. g., figure 17) and even fractions of grains (figure 32), according to the latest technology, our sampling universe expands manifold. So, of course, do the expected number of fortuitous concordances.

As if all of these considerations were not enough, we must keep in mind that the conditions for fortuitous concordance in this study are very restrictive. This owes to the fact that, in any given trial, the date has complete freedom to take on *any* value (from a few million years to a few billion years) that is commonly encountered from earth's crust.

In other words, this analysis has assumed the serial independence of all the randomly-chosen "dates." That is, no "date" was assumed to have any influence whatsoever on the outcome of any successively-chosen date (whether by the same, or the other, dating method). Had the particular value of a date been allowed to influence the magnitude of a successive date, the number of predicted fortuitous concordances would have increased by a considerable amount.

If the range of dates is more constrained for whatever reason, the number of predicted fortuitous concordances, of course, increases by a large factor. Let us consider one example of mutual constraints on dates. Consider a particular magma chamber where large quantities of argon are being trapped (as shown in (1) of figure 13), thus generating a high K-Ar "date." What if the same processes that had favored the emergence of a high K-Ar "date" also had simultaneously favored the emergence of a high Rb-Sr or U-Pb "date"? The chance of a fortuitous concordance between dating methods would then be considerably higher than in the case of serially-independent isotopic systems.

Now let us consider the possibility of the geochemical species of dating systems *themselves* imposing an additional serial dependence upon the outcome of "dates." As noted earlier, (K) does not behave independently of (Ar). In fact, (K) and (Ar) can replace each other, and can also, in and of themselves, perturb the Rb-Sr system.

We thus can see that the emergence of fortuitous concordances is actually governed by nonrandom processes. It is doubtful that these processes have been examined seriously owing to the ruling uniformitarian paradigm and its preconception about radioactive decay over vast stretches of time being the primary cause of concordant results from different dating methods.

Chapter 10

Future Research

Understanding the Origins of Fission Tracks and "FT Dating"

Up to now, with the notable exception of Bielecki (1998), research on the fission-track phenomenon has been largely limited to the pioneering work of Gentry (1992) on the primordial polonium radiohalos and their evidentiary status for a recently-created Earth. What follows below is entirely different, and is related to fission tracks as a presumed dating method.

Special critical attention needs to be devoted to the assumptions behind fission-track (FT) dating because of its apparent evidence of many millions of years' accumulation of radioactive decays. To begin with, the origin of the tracks should be carefully re-evaluated. The late creationist Rob Witter, who had personal experience with the dating methods, had suggested (personal communication) that various nuclear phenomena can be mistaken for fission tracks. Apropos to this, it is still recognized that alpha-recoil tracks are similar to fission tracks, but are much shorter (Mattinson et al. 1996, p. 367). However, one wonders if the two tracks might not overlap in length once the extent of crystal damage is considered, and all the more so when non-uniformitarian conditions of rock-formation and history are examined and taken into account.

Bielecki (1998) also warned of multiple origins of fission tracks which are tacitly assumed to originate from ^{238}U. These include the spontaneous fission of ^{244}Pu at even low concentrations. Isotopes of some other elements are also potentially relevant in this regard. As for artifactual "tracks," these can result from microlite pits, cracks, fractures, or defects.

We must also keep in mind that, while it seems unlikely that the product (tracks) can be inherited (except, of course, as passengers on xenocrysts), the content of the parent (uranium) can easily be altered in the rock or mineral. Furthermore, the apparent FT "age" is very sensitive to the amount of uranium currently present (see table 6.1 of Herz and Garrison 1998, p. 106; and also figure 2 of Bielecki 1998, p. 84). For instance, with reference to Herz and Garrison's table 6.1, when a rock contains 1/1000 ppm of uranium by weight, the youngest age measured easily is 300 million years, and the same measured with considerable labor is 8 million years. In the case of a uranium concentration of 10 ppm, the respective "age" values become 30,000 years and 800 years, respectively.

Now let us put this information into a creationist-diluvialist context. Consider some rocks and minerals with high U contents starting at Creation. In the 1600 or so years between the Creation and Flood, the host rocks or minerals accumulate considerable numbers of fission tracks. During the Flood, however, all but a trace of the uranium (along with some other elements) is leached away. Consequently, as a result of the rocks or minerals now having a combination of many fission-tracks and small amounts of uranium, they thus pose as having an age of many millions of years. It has long been known that uranium is quite mobile (e. g., Bridgwater et al. 1989, p. 289; Whitcomb and Morris 1961, p. 336) and this fact needs to be examined in more detail.

Although the earth is supposed to be 4.5 Ga old, FT dates from apatite in excess of about 500 Ma seldom occur (Gleadow et al. 1986, p. 411). The usual rationalization for this (that apatite loses tracks from thermal annealing at relatively low temperatures) is not self-consistent. The "500 Ma limit" occurs in regions which are conventionally believed to have been geologically "inert" since much more than 500 Ma ago (Gleadow et al. 1986, p. 411). However, if the earlier-discussed leaching-away of once-high U-content turns out to be the correct explanation for "multimillion-year" FT dates, the "500 Ma limit" is easily explicable in terms of the relative inefficiency of this mechanism for producing "very old" dates. This, of course, contrasts with the isotope-inheritance processes which routinely produce "very old" dates for results of all the other dating methods.

Potential Follow-up Research

Creationist scholars should pay more attention to the significance of fortuitously-occurring isotopic-dating results, and not all assume that multi-magnitude decay-rate changes are the only way of reconciling conventional isotopic dating with a young earth. Obviously, those with a strong background in statistics should delve into this problem.

This exploratory study should, first of all, be followed up by a full-fledged Monte Carlo analysis. It should then include analyses of more complex distributions of "dates" than those attempted here. For instance, a bimodal system of dates could be examined. One mode could be set for middle Mesozoic, and the other mode somewhere in the Precambrian. Such a distribution would take into account the volumes of igneous rocks of different "ages" instead of their relative abundance in terms of areal outcrops (i. e., the "birds-eye" view used in this study). Still more sophisticated statistical experiments could be performed. These should include Markov modeling of particular values of isotope concentrations and their direct effects on the concentration of other isotopes relevant to the presumed dating methods. This should help answer the question whether the isotopes used in isotopic dating interact in such a way that they facilitate concordances between the results of different dating methods, as specified in the ensuing paragraph.

On page 52 of this work, I had already discussed how all of the elements involved in isotopic dating exhibit similar upward-enrichment behavior, and how at least some of them are subject to comparable fractionation processes within the earth. These phenomena must be examined in great detail. In like manner, we must acquire a detailed understanding of how one geochemical species interacts with another. For instance, to what extent are K-Ar and associated Rb-Sr dates modified when K is allowed to replace both Ar and Rb?

Of course, research must also be conducted on gross geochemical patterns of inheritance. For instance, consider the fact that K-Ar dates on biotite are usually younger than those of more mafic minerals such as hornblende. The usual explanation for this is that biotite loses radiogenic argon at lower temperatures than does hornblende. Could the explanation instead have nothing to do with radioactive decay followed and closure temperatures, and instead be a product of geochemical inheritance? That is, minerals with low potassium contents, and inheriting variable amounts of argon, would tend to give higher ages (than high-K minerals such as biotite) by virtue of this fact, and this would be especially true of rocks having very low potassium contents (the ultramafic rocks—which indeed are particularly prone to give absurdly high K-Ar dates: Phillips *et al.* 1998).

In addition to mathematical modeling of the distribution of isotopic dates, studies should be conducted on the distributions of actual dates. To do this, we must acquire access to *all* dates, whether previously published or not. And, as discussed several times in this work, the dates must be normalized according to area of crustal rock (figure 10). Only by normalizing the data can we assign the appropriate weight to particular dating results. This should allow us to answer several questions, such as 1) How common are "good" and "bad" dates; 2) How often are dates from different methods concordant, and how often are they discordant; 3) How often do dating results agree with biostratigraphy and/or magnetostratigraphy; 4) Does a "younging up" trend exist of dates relative to biostratigraphy and 5) If a "younging-up" trend does exist, is it strong enough to warrant a special explanation.

Initially, no dates should be excluded from analysis. Subsequent analyses of the data must treat all information in a self-consistent basis. This is especially true of data which must be excluded from consideration. For instance, consider the fate of altered samples and isotopic dates derived from them. If all "bad" dates on altered samples are to be excluded,

then so also must "good" dates based on samples with a comparable level of alteration. The geologic context of sample selection must also be standardized. For instance, if a date from country rock is suspect because it occurs within a kilometer of a known intrusion, then *all* dates known to occur within a kilometer of an intrusion must also be excluded from analysis. Although such a methodology may seem overly rigid, it at least avoids the special pleading and after-the-fact rejection of dates which is the hallmark of uniformitarian analyses of isotopic dates.

Special consideration must be devoted to isochron-based methods. As we have seen, isochrons are not equal in quality. Any analysis of isochron-based methods must discriminate between isochrons of different quality, and take into the account the relative infrequency of so-called superior isochrons (figure 27). If the isotopic ratios do not show sufficient spread to generate an isochron at all, this should not be treated as a lack of data. To the contrary: Even the inability of an isochron to form at all may be significant in a creationist context—where, according to some models, all isochrons are of inherited origins and none are the products of *in-situ* radioactive decay of parent elements. We must also rigorously evaluate the tendency for multiple isochrons, each defining a different "date," to originate from the same suite of rocks. This is particularly significant when different isochron "dates" result from the selective inclusion and exclusion of samples that are regressed on the isochron diagram. All of the possible isochron "dates" from a region must be included in any comprehensive analysis of dating results.

Detailed geochemical studies should also be undertaken in order to help us better constrain the probable range and probable distribution of fictitious "built-in" dates resulting from inherited isotopes. It can never be stressed often enough that any such study must continually distinguish between empirical analysis and uniformitarian preconceptions.

For instance, we creationist scholars must always treat isotopic dates as geochemical phenomena instead of chronometric ones. Merely eschewing the millions or billions of years is not enough. We must steadfastly resist, for instance, the subtle temptation of believing that a rock yielding a date of 40 million years is necessarily older than one yielding 20 million years. Likewise, the neo-Cuvierist practice of attempting to use either isotopic dates or fossils for *any* type of time horizons must be recognized for the concession to uniformitarianism that it is, and must be rejected once and for all.

As with all areas of the growing creationist-diluvialist paradigm, an overall approach to research which stresses multiple working hypothesis is to be recommended. This allows all riddles of nature to be potentially solved through several different approaches, and prevents the scientific creationist community from becoming prematurely committed to any one approach in preference to another.

Chapter 11

Conclusions

Isotopic dating remains overloaded with numerous layers of assumptions, special pleadings, and selective manipulation of data. Also, contrary to the claims of apologists for isotopic dating, there are no hard and fast reliability criteria for knowing if one has obtained "true" dates for rocks—and that is within uniformitarianism's own terms. Finally, recent advances in analytic methods have not rescued isotopic dating from its fatal flaws. To the contrary: they have forced the invention and proliferation of new layers of rationalizations to account for new sets of unwanted results. Clearly, and by any rational standard, dogmatic claims about the factuality of isotopic dating, and the millions and billions of years obtained, though endlessly repeated by the propaganda organs of the evolutionary-uniformitarian establishment, remain completely unjustified.

The decay constants used in isotopic-dating systems are tainted by past and present practices which raise questions about their objectivity. Nor are measurements on dates themselves necessarily free of compromising biases. And this is the very least that can be said against the validity of isotopic dating.

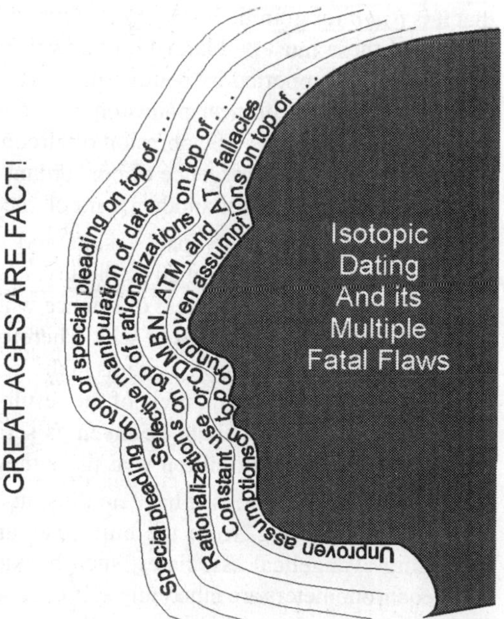

We have seen over and over again that dates are rejected primarily on an after-the-fact basis. They are all essentially trial balloons. And this is not only true of individual dates, but also groups of them. Thus, virtually *any* pattern of dates can be explained *a posteriori* (e. g., figure 4; figure 20). And, contrary to the claims about discrepant dates being rare, they are, in fact, more than common. It has been shown that they are *the rule, not the exception*! If uniformitarians are free to reject dates that don't fit their ideas, then so are creationist scientists. And, if it is correct that only a relatively small number of dates are (supposedly) "highly reliable," this means that creationists end up rejecting only a relatively few more dates than uniformitarians already do. With the aforementioned fact that so-called reliability criteria are themselves subjective, this takes on further significance.

Just because some dates seem "good" or "reasonable" does not in the slightest prove that they are valid. After all, using comparable reasoning, one could argue that dreaming must be valid at least some of the time as a means of predicting the future, because some dreams correspond with events that do in fact take place sometime in the future.

The concordance of dating results is not proof for the validity of the dating methods. Ironically, we now have many instances where *suites* of concordant results have been found from the *same* rock. All of the results can easily be wrong, but they cannot possibly all, concordant or not, correctly give the date of the rock. Furthermore, as shown by a simple statistical analysis, concordant results should occur by chance fairly often.

Some commentators have claimed that the "younging up" of isotopic-dating results relative to biostratigraphy proves the validity of the methods. It does no such thing. First of all, the "younging-up" trend is not proved. The selective publication of dating results guarantees that those very results which would tend to be most effective in randomizing the data set are precisely the ones that are the least likely to be published. Second, even if a "younging up" trend existed, it would not require radioactive decay of parent elements over a long (or, for that matter, short) time to produce it. After all, some clay minerals show a "younging up" in terms of concentration relative to biostratigraphy and no one, of course, suggests for a moment that these clay minerals are dating methods!

Figure 36. Underneath a facade of "absolute factuality" lie the invalid dating methods and all their pretensions. We must never cease from unmasking the dating methods and all the blustery claims made by their apologists.

The claim that dates converge on an age for the earth of 4.5 Ga, though often repeated by apologists for isotopic dating, is not supported by the facts. Instead, we encounter a large range of dates which are *assumed* to date different times of crustal formation, and tectono-magmatic activity, in the earth's past. This, of course, begs the question about the validity of the dating methods and the great age of the earth! Besides this, we also see a steadily-increasing list of dates from different dating methods, all of which are well in excess of 4.5 Ga.

We must also come to grips with the fact that there exists an elaborate Orwellian language surrounding the use of isotopic dates and their selective acceptance. We hear about such entities as delayed-uplift ages, cooling ages, thermochronologic information, rejuvenated dates, inherited isochrons, and many other forms of doublespeak. If we were to take seriously all of this elaborate cover language (as uniformitarians do), we would never know that isotopic dating methods are invalid if in fact they are invalid!

It is laughable to keep hearing that isotopic-dating results are in "tight consensus" with biostratigraphy. The fact is, disagreements with biostratigraphy are routinely used as a presumed reliability criterion in order to reject nonconforming isotopic dates. Much the same can be said about isotopic-dating results relative to magnetostratigraphy. All three systems are subject to manipulation in order to create a contrived agreement between them. And one must grin a little when told that isotopic dates agree with the law of superposition when in fact it is local violations of this law that are used to "ascertain" that the dates are not reliable!

The use of geologic context to excuse unwanted dates is itself an exercise in special pleading because it is used in a self-contradictory manner. Thus, for instance, we may see an unwanted date excused, after-the-fact, because it is too close to a neighboring intrusion. But elsewhere, we see the uniformitarian geologist having no problem accepting a date equally close to a neighboring intrusion as long as the date agrees with his ideas. Much the same can be said about such things as sample alteration, potassium content, identification of xenocrysts, and much more.

So-called testable hypotheses are such only within the narrow confines of uniformitarian thought. And, rather than being predicted in advance, the accumulating flaws in all the dating methods had become evident only *after* each dating method had already enjoyed widespread use in the hands of geologists. The flaws had to be "patched up" after they had become far too common to be wished away as "a few malfunctioning watches" or "a few rotten apples." As a result, it is not at all surprising to learn that geologists have long since scaled back their expectations for all of the dating methods.

One of the advances in isotopic dating over the last few decades has been the ability to date individual mineral grains. However, this has generated suites of mutually-contradictory dates. What had been previously accepted as reliable dates on mineral aggregates has often turned out to be a composite "average" of widely-contradictory dates. Of course, the fact that dates on individual mineral grains are now available only makes it easier for the uniformitarian geochronologist to "shop around" for a favored date.

The closure temperatures inferred for isotopic-dating systems are widely contradictory. Moreover, they are rendered largely irrelevant by the fact that all of the isotopic-dating systems are highly vulnerable to low-temperature fluid-dominated processes.

Isochron-based methods are all severely flawed. Multiple "good" isochrons can form from the same suite of rocks. Uniformitarians have had to retreat from their once-firm conviction that highly-collinear points on an isochron necessarily denote a reliable age. And, arguments to the contrary notwithstanding, there is no objective way of distinguishing an isochron that has resulted from long-term (or, for that matter, short-term) radioactive decay, of parent elements, from an isochron that is solely an artifact of geochemical processes.

The Ar-Ar method has, until recently, been thought of being self-checking as to reliability of the dates obtained. Now, and on uniformitarians' own terms, a flat plateau is recognized as being far from *ipso facto* proof of a "good" date. Special pleading is used to ascertain the presumed meaning of "staircase-shaped" spectra. No longer is it believed that "excess argon" must necessarily produce a "saddle-shaped" spectrum. Geologic information admittedly must be used to evaluate Ar-Ar spectra, and this itself self-refutes the claim that the Ar-Ar method is self-diagnostic.

With advances in U-Pb dating, we now can date parts of individual zircon grains. In doing so, we have also learned that it is *usual* for granitic bodies to contain widely divergent dates, and these must be blamed on xenocrystic contamination—whether supported by petrographic evidence or not. It is now known that collinear points on a concordia plot need not have any meaning. The abrasion of zircon grains sometimes allows for the emergence of concordant dates, but often does not. It is thus yet another form of special pleading.

The conundrum of discrepant results and special pleadings deprive isotopic dating of all credibility. It remains doubtful if there exists any other field of science where data could be so selectively manipulated at will. Therefore, pending a full understanding of isotopic systems in the light of the creationist-diluvialist paradigm, none of the results of these presumed dating systems should be taken as serious proof for the multimillion to multibillion year dates they indicate.

In writing this new book, I have no illusions. No doubt we will continue hearing, from the humanists and their compromising-evangelical associates, such hackneyed mantras as "Geochronometers are inherently self-checking" and "Discrepancies amount to just a few malfunctioning watches." But no matter. Creationist scientists must keep puncturing the self-serving myths of isotopic dating, and shine the light of truth on the fatal flaws of these dating methods even as we continue work to understand isotopic systems in the light of the creationist-diluvialist paradigm (as done, for example, by the RATE Project: Vardiman 1997, 1998).

References

1. Albarede, F. 1982. The $^{40}Ar/^{39}Ar$ technique of dating (pp. 182-197), in Odin, ed., *op. cit.*

2. Albers, J. P., R. W. Kistler, and L. Kwak. 1984. The Mule Mountain Stock, an early Middle Devonian pluton in northern California. *Isochron/West* 41: p. 13.

3. Aleinikoff, J. N. 1985. Isotopic and morphologic evidence for the age of the Fordham Gneiss. *American Journal of Science* 285:459-479.

4. Aleinikoff, J. N., *et al.* 1993. U-Pb ages of zircon, monazite, and sphene from Devonian metagranites and metafelsites, central Brooks Range, Alaska. *U. S. Geological Survey Bulletin* 2068, pp. 59-70.

5. Aleinikoff, J. N., *et al.* 1995. U-Pb ages of metarhyolites of the Catoctin and Mount Rogers Formations, central and southern Appalachians: Evidence for two pulses of Iapetan rifting. *American Journal of Science* 295:428-454.

6. Allegre, C. J., and E. Lewin. 1995. Isotopic systems and stirring times of the earth's mantle. *Earth and Planetary Science Letters* 136:629-646.

7. Al-Saleh, A., A. P., Boyle, and A. E. Mussett. 1998. Metamorphism and $^{40}Ar/^{39}Ar$ dating of the Halaban Ophiolite and associated units. *Journal of the Geological Society of London* 155: 165-175.

8. Alsharhan, A. S., and A. E. M. Nairn. 1997. *Sedimentary Basins and Petroleum Geology of the Middle East.* Amsterdam, New York: Elsevier, 843 p., 99 p. Appendix.

9. Amelin, Y. V. 1998. Geochronology of the Jack Hills detrital zircons by precise U-Pb dilution analysis of crystal fragments. *Chemical Geology* 146:25-38.

10. Amireh, B. S., *et al.* 1998. K-Ar dating, x-ray diffractometry, optical and scanning electron microscopy of glauconites from the early Cretaceous Kurnub Group of Jordan. *Geological Journal* 33:49-65.

11. Anderson, J. L., and R. L. Cullers. 1990. Middle to upper crustal plutonic construction of a magmatic arc (pp. 47-69), in J. L. Anderson, ed., *The Nature and Origin of Cordilleran Magmatism.* Geological Society of America Memoir 174.

12. Anderson, S. L. 1988. Interpretation of K-Ar mineral dates from the Grenville orogenic belt. *American Journal of Science* 288:701-734.

13. Armstrong, R. L. 1981. *Radiogenic isotopes: the case for crustal recycling on a near-steady-state no-continental-growth Earth.* Philosophical Transactions of the Royal Society of London A301:443-472.

14. Armstrong, R. L. 1988. Mesozoic and early Cenozoic magmatic evolution of the Canadian Cordillera (pp. 55-91), in *Processes in Continental Lithospheric Deformation.* Geological Society of America Special Paper 218, 212 p.

15. Armstrong, R. L. 1991a. The persistent myth of crustal growth. *Australian Journal of Earth Sciences* 38:613-630.

16. Armstrong, R. L. 1991b. A brief history of geochronometry and radiogenic isotopic studies (pp. 1-26) in Heaman and Ludden, eds., *op. cit.*

17. Armstrong, R. L., and P. Ward. 1991. Evolving geographic patterns of Cenozoic magmatism in the North American Cordillera. *Journal of Geophysical Research* 96(B8):13201-13224.

18. Arndt, N. T., and S. L. Goldstein. 1987. Use and abuse of crust-formation ages. *Geology* 15: 893-895.

19. Asmerom, Y., *et al.* 1991. Resetting of Rb-Sr ages of volcanic rocks by low-grade burial metamorphism. *Chemical Geology* 87:167-173.

20. Austin, S. A. 1994. *Grand Canyon: Monument to Catastrophe.* El Cajon, CA: Institute for Creation Research, 284 p.

21. Austin, S. A. 1996. Excess argon within mineral concentrates from the new dacite lava dome at Mt. St. Helens Volcano. *Creation Ex Nihilo Technical Journal* 10(3):335-343.

22. Austin, S. A., and A. A. Snelling. 1998. Discordant potassium-argon model and isochron "ages" for Cardenas basalt (middle Proterozoic) and associated diabase of eastern Grand Canyon, Arizona. *Proceedings of the Fourth International Conference on Creationism*, pp. 35-51.

23. Ayuso, R. A., *et al.* 1984. Comparative geochronology in the reversely zoned plutons of the Bottle Lake Complex, Maine: U-Pb on zircons and Rb-Sr on whole rocks. *Contributions to Mineralogy and Petrology* 88:113-125.

24. Baadsgaard, H., *et al.* 1993. Multi-method radiometric age for a bentonite near the top of the *Baculites reesidei* Zone of southwestern Saskatchewan (Campanian—Maastrichtian stage boundary?). *Canadian Journal of Earth Sciences* 30:769-775.

25. Baadsgaard, H., J. F. Lerbekmo, and I. McDougall. 1988. A radiometric age for the Cretaceous-Tertiary boundary based upon K-Ar, Rb-Sr, and U-Pb ages of bentonites from Alberta, Saskatchewan, and Montana. *Canadian Journal of Earth Sciences* 25:1088-1097.

26. Baksi, A. K. 1987. Critical evaluation of the age of the Deccan Traps, India. *Geology* 15:147-150.

27. Baksi, A. K. 1990. Search for periodicity in global events in the geologic record: Quo vadimus? *Geology* 18:983-986.

28. Baksi, A. K. 1999. Reevaluation of plate motion models based on hotspot tracks in the Atlantic and Indian Oceans. *The Journal of Geology* 107:13-26

29. Baksi, A. K., and E. Farrar. 1990. Evidence for errors in the geomagnetic polarity time-scale at 17-15 Ma. *Geophysical Research Letters* 17(8):1117-1120.

30. Baksi, A. K., K. A. Hoffman, and M. McWilliams. 1993. Testing the accuracy of the geomagmatic polarity time-scale (GPTS) at 2-5 Ma, utilizing $^{40}Ar/^{39}Ar$ incremental heating data on whole-rock basalts. *Earth and Planetary Science Letters* 118:135-144.

31. Balakrishnan, S., V. Rajamani, and G. N. Hanson. 1999. U-Pb ages for zircon and titanite from the Ramagiri Area, southern India. *The Journal of Geology* 107:69-86.

32. Balashov, Yu. A., Zh. A. Fedorov, and P. K. Shuf'yin. 1994. Rb-Sr dating of the lower volcanogenic series in the Pechenga Complex, Kola Peninsula. *Geochemistry International* 31(7):85-90.

33. Barovich, K. M., and P. J. Patchett. 1992. Behavior of isotopic systematics during deformation and metamorphism: a Hf, Nd, and Sr isotopic study of mylonitized granite. *Contributions to Mineralogy and Petrology* 109:386-393.

34. Barreiro, B. A., *et al.* 1998. U-Pb systematics and textural studies of monazite and xenotime in semipelites and migmatites of the Grampian Group, Scotland. *Geological Society of America Abstracts with Programs* 30(7):A-240.

35. Bartlett, J. M., et al. 1998. The application of zircon evaporation and model Nd ages to the interpretation of polymetamorphic terranes. Contributions to Mineralogy and Petrology 131: 181-195.

36. Barto-Kyriakidis, A. 1990. Critical Aspects of Plate Tectonics Theory. Athens: Theophrastas Publications, vol. 1, 435 p.

37. Baumann, A., et al. 1991. Isotopic age determinations of crystalline rocks of the Upper Harz Mountains, Germany. Geologische Rundschau 80/3:669-690.

38. Beakhouse, G. P., R. H. McNutt, and T. E. Krogh. 1988. Comparative Rb-Sr and U-Pb zircon geochronology of late- to post-tectonic plutons in the Winnipeg River Belt, northwestern Ontario, Canada. Chemical Geology 72:337-351.

39. Beloussov, V. V. 1990. Certain trends in present-day geosciences (pp. 3-15), in Barto-Kyriakidis, op. cit.

40. Bennett, V. C., and A. P. Nutman. 1998. Discussion: Extreme Nd isotope heterogeneity in the early Archean—fact or fiction? Chemical Geology 148:213-217.

41. Berggren, W. A., et al. 1995. A revised Cenozoic geochronology and chronostratigraphy (pp. 129-212), in Geochronology, Time Scales, and Global Stratigraphic Correlation. SEPM Special Publication No. 54.

42. Beyth, M., and T. Reischmann. 1996. The age of the quartz monzodiorite, the youngest plutonic intrusion in the Timna Igneous Complex. Israel Journal of Earth Sciences 45:223-226.

43. Bibikova, Ye. V., et al. 1994. Belomoride geochronology: Interpretation of a multistage history. Geochemistry International 31(5): 15-34.

44. Bibikova, Ye. V., et al. 1998. Structural transformations of zircons exposed to melt in relation to the disturbance of their U-Pb isotopic system. Geochemistry International 36(1):40-46.

45. Bickford, M. E. 1988. The accretion of Proterozoic crust in Colorado (pp. 411-430), in Ernst, ed., op. cit.

46. Bielecki, J. W. 1998. Search for accelerated nuclear decay with spontaneous fission of [238]U. Proceedings of the Fourth International Conference on Creationism, pp. 79-88.

47. Bingen, B., and O. van Breeman. 1998a. Tectonic regimes and terrane boundaries in the high-grade Sveconorwegian belt of SW Norway, inferred from U-Pb zircon geochronology and geochemical signature of augen gneiss suites. Journal of the Geological Society of London 155: 143-154.

48. Bingen, B., and O. van Breeman. 1998b. U-Pb monazite ages in amphibolite-to-granulite-facies orthogneiss reflect hydrous mineral breakdown reactions. Contributions to Mineralogy and Petrology 132:336-353.

49. Bingen, B., Demaiffe, D., and O. van Breeman. 1998. The 616 Ma old Egersund basaltic dike swarm, SW Norway, and late Neoproterozoic opening of the Iapetus Ocean. The Journal of Geology 106:565-574.

50. Bingen, B., et al. 1998. Hornblende [40]Ar/[39]Ar geochronology across terrane boundaries in the Sveconorwegian Province of S. Norway. Precambrian Research 90: 159-185.

51. Black, L. P. 1986. Isotopic resetting of the systems Rb-Sr and Sm-Nd total rock and U-Pb zircon in Antarctica—the cold facts. Terra Cognita 6(2):155-156.

52. Blackenburg, F. V., and I. M. Villa. 1988. Argon retentivity and argon excess in amphiboles from the garbenschists of the Western Tauern Window, Eastern Alps. Contributions to Mineralogy and Petrology 100:1-11.

53. Blatt, H., and R. L. Jones. 1975. Proportions of exposed igneous, metamorphic, and sedimentary rocks. Geological Society of America Bulletin 86:1085-1088.

54. Bonhomme, M. G. 1982. The use of Rb-Sr and K-Ar dating methods as a stratigraphic tool applied to sedimentary rocks and minerals. Precambrian Research 18:5-25.

55. Bowring, S. A. 1998. Geochronology comes of age. Geotimes 43(11):36-40.

56. Bowring, S. A., and I. S. Williams. 1999. Priscoan (4.00-4.03 Ga) orthogneisses from northwestern Canada. Contributions to Mineralogy and Petrology 134:3-16.

57. Bowring, S. A., and T. Housh. 1996. Response: Sm-Nd isotopic data and Earth's evolution. Science 273:1878-1879.

58. Brack, P., et al. 1997. Biostratigraphic and radiometric age data question the Milankovitch characteristics of the Latemar cycle (Southern Alps, Italy): Reply. Geology 25(5): 471-472.

59. Braddock, W. A., and Z. E. Peterman. 1989. The age of the iron dike—a distinctive Middle Proterozoic intrusion in the northern Front Range of Colorado. The Mountain Geologist 26(4):97-99.

60. Bradley, R. S. 1985. Quaternary Paleoeclimatology. London, Boston: Allen and Unwin, 472 p.

61. Brewer, T. S., and J. F. Menuge. 1998. Metamorphic overprinting of Sm-Nd isotopic systems in volcanic rocks. Chemical Geology 145:1-16.

62. Bridgwater, D., M. Rosing, and L. Schiotte. 1989. The effect of fluid-controlled element mobility during metamorphism on whole rock isotope systems, some theoretical aspects and possible examples (pp. 277-298), in D. Bridgwater, ed., Fluid Movements—Element Transport and the Composition of the Deep Crust. The Netherlands: Kluwer Academic Publishers, 416 p.

63. Briqueu, L., and J. R. Lancelot. 1979. Rb-Sr systematics and crustal contamination models for calc-alkaline igneous rocks. Earth and Planetary Science Letters 43:385-396.

64. Britt, M., et al. 1997. Sm-Nd dating of gabbro- and garnet-bearing contact metamorphic /anatectic rocks from Krutfjellet, Nordland, and some geochemical aspects of the intrusives. Norsk Geologisk Tidsskrift 77:39-50.

65. Brocker, M., and L. Franz. 1998. Rb-Sr isotope studies on Tinos Island (Cyclades, Greece). Geological Magazine 135(3): 369-382.

66. Brookins, D. G. 1983. Geochronologic Studies in Maine—Part III: Geochronologic study of the Ellsworth Schist, Maine, and comparison with the Coldbrook Group, New Brunswick. Isochron/West 38:7-10.

67. Brouwers, E. M., and P. DeDeckker. 1996. Earliest origins of Northern Hemisphere temperate nonmarine ostracode taxa (pp. 205-231), in N. MacLeod and G. Keller, eds., Cretaceous-Tertiary Mass Extinctions. New York, London: W. W. Norton and Co., 575 p.

68. Brush, S. G. 1982. Finding the age of the earth: By physics or by faith? Journal of Geological Education 30(1):48-58.

69. Bryant, B., et al. 1981. Ages of igneous rocks in the South Park—Breckenridge Region, Colorado, and their relation to the tectonic history of the Front Range uplift. U. S. Geological Survey Professional Paper 1199A-E, pp. 15-26.

70. Bubnov, S. N. and Yu. V. Goltsman. 1993. The Rb-Sr systems in intrusive pyroclasts. Geochemistry International 30(10):45-52.

71. Buchan, K. L., H. C. Halls, and J. K. Mortenson. 1996. Paleomagnetism, U-Pb geochronology, and geochemistry of Marathon dykes, Superior Province, and comparison with the Fort Frances swarm. Canadian Journal of Earth Sciences 33:1583-1595.

72. Burchfield, J. D. 1975. Lord Kelvin and the Age of the Earth. New York: Science History Publications, 260 p.

73. Burke, K. 1996. The African Plate. South African Journal of Geology 99(4):341-409.

74. Cattell, A., T. E. Krogh, and N. T. Arndt. 1984. Conflicting Sm-Nd whole rock and U-Pb zircon ages for Archean lavas from Newton Township, Abitibi Belt, Ontario. Earth and Planetary Science Letters 70:280-290.

75. Champion, D. E, M. A. Lanphere, and M. A. Kuntz. 1988. Evidence for new geomagnetic reversal from lava flows in Idaho: discussion of short polarity reversals in the Brunhes and Late Matuyama Polarity chrons. Journal of Geophysical Research 93(B10):11,667-11,680.

76. Chauvel, C., B. Dupre, and G. A. Jenner. 1985. The Sm-Nd age of Kambalda volcanics is 500 Ma too old! *Earth and Planetary Science Letters* 74:315-324.

77. Cherniak, D. J., J. M. Hanchar, and E. B. Watson. 1997. Rare-earth diffusion in zircon. *Chemical Geology* 134:289-301.

78. Chevallier, L., D. C. Rex, and W. J. Verwoerd. 1992. Geology and geochronology of Inaccessible Island, South Atlantic. *Geological Magazine* 129(1):1-16.

79. Chiarenzelli, J. R., and J. M. McLelland. 1991. Age and regional relationships of granitoid rocks of the Adirondack Highlands. *The Journal of Geology* 99:571-590.

80. Childe, F. 1996. U-Pb geochronology and Nd and Pb isotope characteristics of the Au-Ag-Rich Eskay Creek volcanogenic massive sulfide deposit, British Columbia. *Economic Geology* 91:1209-1224.

81. Claoue-Long, J. C., M. F. Thirlwall, and R. W. Nesbitt. 1984. Revised Sm-Nd systematics of Kambalda greenstones, Western Australia. *Nature* 307:697-700.

82. Clark, A. H., D. J. Kontak, and E. Farrar. 1990. The San Judas Tadeo W (-Mo, Au) deposit, Permian lithophile mineralization in southeastern Peru. *Economic Geology* 85:1651-1668.

83. Clauer, N. 1982. The rubidium-strontium method applied to sediments: certitudes and uncertainties (pp. 245-276), in Odin, ed., *op. cit.*

84. Cliff, R. A., and D. Rickard. 1992. Isotope systematics of the Kiruna Magnetic Ores, Sweden. *Economic Geology* 87:1121-1129.

85. Cocherie, A. , C. Guerrot, and Ph. Rossi. 1992. Single-zircon dating by step-wise Pb evaporation. *Chemical Geology* 101:131-141.

86. Cohen, J., and I. Stewart. 1998. That's amazing, isn't it? *New Scientist* 157(2117):24-28.

87. Coleman, D. S., and A. Glazner. 1997. The Sierra Crest magmatic event: Rapid formation of juvenile crust during the Late Cretaceous in California. *International Geology Review* 39:768-787.

88. Coleman, M. E. 1998. U-Pb constraints on Oligocene-Miocene deformation and anatexis within the central Himalaya, Marsyandi Valley, Nepal. *American Journal of Science* 298: 553-571.

89. Coler, D. G., S. D. Samson, and J. A. Speer. 1997. Nd and Sr isotopic constraints on the source of Alleghanian granites in the Raleigh metamorphic belt and Eastern slate belt, southern Appalachians, U.S.A. *Chemical Geology* 134:257-275.

90. Compston, W., and I. S. Williams. 1992. Ion probe ages for the British Ordovician and Silurian stratotypes (pp. 59-67), in B. D. Webby, and J. R. Laurie, eds., *Global Perspectives on Ordovician Geology*, Balkema, Rotterdam, Netherlands, 513 p.

91. Compston, W., *et al.* 1992. Zircon U-Pb ages for the early Cambrian time-scale. *Journal of the Geological Society of London* 149:171-184.

92. Compston, W., I. McDougall, and D. Wyborn. 1982. Possible two-stage ^{87}Sr evolution in the Stockdale Rhyolite. *Earth and Planetary Science Letters* 61:297-302.

93. Condie, K. C., *et al.* 1999. Geochemistry, Nd and Sr isotopes, and U/Pb zircon ages of granitoid and metasedimentary xenoliths from the Navajo Volcanic Field, Four Corners area, southwestern United States. *Chemical Geology* 156:95-133.

94. Connelly, J. B., and R. D. Dallmeyer. 1993. Polymetamorphic evolution of the western Blue Ridge. *American Journal of Science* 293: 322-359.

95. Conrad, J. E., and E. H. McKee. 1997. Reply (to Hanson) on "A tale of 10 plutons." *Geological Society of America Bulletin* 109(12):1631-1632.

96. Conrad, J. E., E. H. McKee, and R. D. Turrin. 1992. Age of tephra beds at the Ocean Point dinosaur locality, north slope, Alaska. *U. S. Geological Survey Bulletin* 1990, 12 p.

97. Copeland, P., *et al.* 1991. An early Pliocene thermal disturbance of the Main Central Thrust, central Nepal. *Journal of Geophysical Research* 96(B5):8475-8500.

98. Corfu, F., and G. M. Stott. 1998. Shebandowan greenstone belt, western Superior Province: U-Pb ages, tectonic implications, and correlations. *Geological Society of America Bulletin* 110(11):1467-1484.

99. Corfu, F., and R. M. Easton. 1995. U-Pb geochronology of the Mazinaw terrane, an imbricate segment of the Central Metasedimentary Belt, Grenville Province, Ontario. *Canadian Journal of Earth Sciences* 32:959-976.

100. Cowie, J. W., and W. B. Harland. 1989. Chronometry (pp. 186-198), in J. W. Cowie, and M. D. Brasier, eds., *The Precambrian-Cambrian Boundary*. Oxford: Clarendon Press, 213 p.

101. Cox, R. A., G. R. Dunning, and A. Indares. 1998. Petrology and U-Pb geochronology of mafic, high-pressure, metamorphic coronites from the Tshenukutish domain, eastern Grenville Province. *Precambrian Research* 90: 59-83.

102. Craig, L. E., A. G. Smith, and R. L. Armstrong. 1989. Calibration of the geologic time scale: Cenozoic and Late Cretaceous glauconite and nonglauconite dates compared. *Geology* 17:830-832.

103. Crisp, J. A. 1984. Rates of magma emplacement and volcanic output. *Journal of Volcanology and Geothermal Research* 20:177-211.

104. Criss, R. E., M. A. Lanphere, and H. P. Taylor. 1982. Effects of regional uplift, deformation, and meteoric-hydrothermal metamorphism on K-Ar ages of biotites in the southern half of the Idaho Batholith. *Journal of Geophysical Research* 87(B8):7029-7046.

105. Cumbest, R. J., E. L. Johnson, and T. C. Onstott. 1994. Argon composition of metamorphic fluids: Implications for ^{40}Ar/^{39}Ar geochronology. *Geological Society of America Bulletin* 106:942-951.

106. Cumming, G. L., and D. Krstic. 1991. Geochronology at the Namew Lake Ni-Cu orebody. *Canadian Journal of Earth Sciences* 28:309-325.

107. Currie, L. 1992. U-Pb geochronology of Cretaceous and Tertiary plutonic rocks of the Tagish Lake area, northeastern Coast Mountains, British Columbia, in Radiogenic Age and Isotopic Studies: Report 6; *Geological Survey of Canada, Paper 92-2*, pp. 163-170.

108. Dallmeyer, R. D., and J. Hibbard. 1984. Geochronology of the Baie Verte Peninsula, Newfoundland. *The Journal of Geology* 92:489-512.

109. Dallmeyer, R. D., and M. Villeneuve. 1987. ^{40}Ar/^{39}Ar mineral age record of polyphase tectonothermal evolution in the southern Mauritanide orogen, southeastern Senegal. *Geological Society of America Bulletin* 98:602-611.

110. Dalrymple, G. B. 1984. How old is the earth? A reply to "scientific" creationism (pp. 66-131) in F. Awbrey, and W. M. Thwaites, eds., *Evolutionists Confront Creationists*. Proceedings of the 63rd Annual Meeting of the Pacific Division, San Francisco, CA: American Association for the Advancement of Science, 213 p.

111. Dalrymple, G. B. 1991. *The Age of the Earth*. California: Stanford University Press, 474 p.

112. Davidek, K., *et al.* 1998. New uppermost Cambrian U-Pb date from Avalonian Wales and age of the Cambrian-Ordovician boundary. *Geological Magazine* 135(3): 305-309.

113. Davis, D. W., K. H. Poulsen, and S. L. Kamo. 1989. New insights into Archean crustal development from geochronology in the Rainy Lake Area, Superior Province, Canada. *The Journal of Geology* 97(4):379-398.

114. Davis, D. W., R. J. Sewell, and D. G. Campbell. 1997. U-Pb dating of Mesozoic igneous rocks from Hong Kong. *Journal of the Geological Society of London* 154:1067-1076.

115. DePaulo, D. J. 1988. *Neodymium Isotope Geochemistry*. Berlin, Heidelberg, New York: Springer Verlag, 187 p.

116. DePaulo, D. J., A. M. Linn, and G. Schubert. 1991. The continental crustal age distribution. *Journal of Geophysical Research* 96(B2):2071-2088.

117. Dhar, S. 1997. Reply to Roy and Sarkar. *Journal of the Geological Society of India* 49:466-469.

118. Di Vincenzo, G., *et al.* 1997. Petrology and geochronology of eclogites from the Lanterman Range, Antarctica. *Journal of Petrology* 38(10):1391-1417.

119. Dickin, A. P. 1988. The North Atlantic Tertiary Province (pp. 111-149), in J. D. MacDougall, ed., *Continental Flood Basalts*, The Netherlands: Kluwer Academic Publishers, 341 p.

120. Dickin, A. P. 1997. *Radiogenic Isotope Geology* (updated paperback edition). U. K., New York: Cambridge University Press.

121. Diehl, J. F., *et al.* 1987. No short reversals of Brunhes Age recorded in the Toba tuffs, north Sumatra, Indonesia. *Geophysical Research Letters* 14(7):753-756.

122. Drake, R. E., *et al.* 1988. New chronology for the Early Miocene mammalian gaunas of Kisingiri, western Kenya. *Journal of the Geological Society of London* 145:479-491.

123. Dunning, G. R., *et al.* 1990. Silurian orogeny in the Newfoundland Appalachians. *The Journal of Geology* 98:895-913.

124. Durrance, E. M. 1986. *Radioactivity in Geology*. Chister, England: Ellis Horwood Ltd., 441 p.

125. Ebihara, M., T. Itaya, and S. Nonura. 1989. Chemical compositions and K-Ar ages of Pliocene volcanic rocks along Aimagawa river, western Gunma, central Japan. *Geochemical Journal (of Japan)* 23:149-160.

126. Emslie, R. F., and P. A. Hunt. 1990. Ages and petrogenetic significance of igneous mangerite-charnockite suites associated with massif anorthosites, Grenville Province. *The Journal of Geology* 98:213-231.

127. Ernst, W. G., ed., 1988. *Metamorphism and Crustal Evolution of the Western United States*. Englewood Cliffs, New Jersey: Prentice Hall, 1153 p.

128. Evans, J. A. 1989. Resetting of the Rb-Sr whole-rock isotope system of an Ordovician microgranite during Devonian low-grade metamorphism. *Geological Magazine* 126(6):675-679.

129. Evans, J. A., I. L. Millar, and S. R. Noble. 1995. Hydration during uplift is recorded by reset Rb-Sr whole-rock ages. *Journal of the Geological Society of London* 152:209-212.

130. Everard, J. L., and I. M. Villa. 1994. Argon geochronology of the Crown Hill Andesite, Mt. Read Volcanics, Tasmania. *Australian Journal of Earth Sciences* 41:265-272.

131. Ferre, E., *et al.* 1996. The Pan-African reactivation of Eburnean and Archaean provinces in Nigeria. *Journal of the Geological Society of London* 153:719-728.

132. Field, D., and A. Råheim. 1979. A geologically meaningless Rb-Sr total rock isochron. *Nature* 282:497-499.

133. Fitch, F. J., and J. A. Miller. 1983. K-Ar age of the East Peripheral kimberlite at De Beers Mine, Kimberley, R. S. A. *Geological Magazine* 120(5):505-512.

134. Fitch, F. J., *et al.* 1985. Reconnaissance potassium-argon geochronology of the Suregei-Asille district, northern Kenya. *Geological Magazine* 122(6):609-622.

135. Fleck, R. J., R. W. Kistler, and J. L. Wooden. 1996a. Geochronological complexities related to multiple emplacement history of the Tuolumne Intrusive Suite, Yosemite National Park, California. *Geological Society of America Abstracts with Programs* 28(5):65-66.

136. Fleck, R. J., *et al.* 1996b. Age and character of basaltic rocks of the Yucca Mountain region, southern Nevada. *Journal of Geophysical Research* 101(B4):8205-8227.

137. Fleming, T. H, *et al.* 1997. ^{40}Ar/^{39}Ar geochronology of Ferrar Dolerite sills from the Transantarctic Mountains, Antarctica: Implications for the age and origin of the Ferrar magmatic province. *Geological Society of America Bulletin* 109(5):533-546.

138. Forsman, N. F. 1983. Volcanic airfall marker bed in the upper Fort Union Formation (Paleocene) of Western North Dakota (pp. 323-325), in J. E. Christopher, and J. Kaldi, eds., *4ᵗʰ International Williston Basin Symposium*. Saskatchewan Geological Society Special Publication No. 6, 325 p.

139. Forster, S. C., and G. Warrington. 1985. Geochronology of the Carboniferous, Permian, and Triassic (pp. 99-113), in Snelling, ed., *op. cit.*

140. Foster, D. A., T. M. Harrison, and C. F. Miller. 1989. Age, inheritance, and uplift history of the Old Woman-Piute Batholith, California, and implications for K-feldspar age spectra. *The Journal of Geology* 97:232-243.

141. Friedman, R. M., and J. Martignole. 1995. Mesoproterozoic sedimentation, magmatism, and metamorphism in the southern part of the Grenville Province (western Quebec): U-Pb geochronological constraints. *Canadian Journal of Earth Sciences* 32:2103-2114.

142. Friedman, R. M., and R. L. Armstrong. 1995. Jurassic and Cretaceous geochronology of the southern Coast Belt, British Columbia, 49 to 51N (pp. 95-139), in *Jurassic Magmatism and Tectonics of the North American Cordillera*. Geological Society of America Special Paper 299, 425 p.

143. Frimmel, H. E., U. S. Klotzli, and P. R. Siegfried. 1996. New Pb-Pb single zircon age constraints on the timing of Neoporoterozoic glaciation and continental break-up in Namibia. *The Journal of Geology* 104: 459-469.

144. Frost, C. D., and B. R. Frost. 1995. Open-system dehydration of amphibolite, Morton Pass, Wyoming: Elemental and Nd and Sr isotopic effects. *The Journal of Geology* 103:269-284.

145. Gale, N. H, R. D. Beckinsale, and A. J. Wadge. 1980. Discussion of a paper by McKerrow, Lambert and Chamberlain on the Ordovician, Silurian, and Devonian time scales. *Earth and Planetary Science Letters* 51:9-17.

146. Gale, N. H. 1982. The physical decay constants (pp. 107-122), in Odin, ed., *op. cit.*

147. Gale, N. H., and R. D. Beckinsale. 1983. Comments on the paper "Fission-track dating of British Ordovician and Silurian stratotypes" by R. J. Ross *et al. Geological Magazine* 120(3):295-302.

148. Gallagher, K., R. Brown, and C. Johnson. 1998. Fission-track analysis and its applications to geological problems. *Annual Review of Earth and Planetary Sciences* 26: 519-572.

149. Gamble, J. A., *et al.* 1999. Constraints on the age of the British Tertiary Volcanic Province. *Journal of the Geological Society of London* 156:291-299.

150. Gansecki, C. A., G. A. Mahood, and M. O. McWilliams. 1996. ^{40}Ar/^{39}Ar geochronology of rhyolites erupted following collapse of the Yellowstone caldera. *Earth and Planetary Science Letters* 142:91-107.

151. Gansecki, C. A., G. A. Mahood, and M. McWilliams. 1998. New ages for the climatic eruptions at Yellowstone: single-crystal ^{40}Ar/^{39}Ar dating identifies contamination. *Geology* 26(4):343-346.

152. Gariepy, C. and B. Dupre. 1991. Pb isotopes and crust-mantle evolution (pp. 191-224), in Heaman and Ludden, eds., *op. cit.*

153. Gaudette, H. E., W. J. Olszewski, and J. O. S. Santos. 1996. Geochronology of Precambrian rocks from the northern part of the Guiana shield, State of Roriama, Brazil. *Journal of the South American Earth Sciences* 9(3/4):183-195.

154. Gazis, C., *et al.* 1998. Isotope systematics of granites and gneisses of the Nanga Parmat Massif, Pakistan Himalaya. *American Journal of Science* 298: 673-698.

155. Gentry, R. V. 1992. *Creation's Tiny Mystery*, 3ʳᵈ ed., Knoxville, Tennessee: Earth Science Associates, 364 p.

156. Gilovich, T. 1997. Some systematic biases of everyday judgment. *Skeptical Inquirer* 21(2):31-35.

157. Gleadow, A. J. W., *et al.* 1986. Confined fission track lengths in apatite: a diagnostic tool for thermal history analysis. *Contributions to Mineralogy and Petrology* 94:405-415.

158. Glen, W. 1982. *The Road to Jaramillo*. California: Stanford University Press, 459 p.

159. Goodwin, M. B., and A. L. Deino. 1989. The first radiometric ages from the Judith River Formation (Upper Cretaceous), Hill County, Montana. *Canadian Journal of Earth Sciences* 26:1384-1391.

160. Gordon, W. R. 1878. *The Science of Revealed Truth Impregnable; as Shown by the Argumentative Failures of Infidelity and Theoretical Geology.* New York: Reformed Church of America, 307 p.

161. Gradstein, F. M. 1985. Stratigraphy and the fossil record (pp. 17-39), in F. M. Gradstein, *et al.*, eds., *Quantitative Stratigraphy.* Dordrecht, Boston: D. Reidel Publishing Co., 598 p.

162. Gradstein, F. M., *et al.* 1994. A Mesozoic time scale. *Journal of Geophysical Research* 99(B12):24,051-24,074.

163. Gradstein, F. M., *et al.* 1995. A Triassic, Jurassic, and Cretaceous time scale (pp. 97-126), in *Geochronology, Time Scales, and Global Stratigraphic Correlation.* SEPM Special Publication No. 54.

164. Graham, I. J. 1985. Rb-Sr geochronology and geochemistry of Torlesse metasediments from the central North Island, New Zealand. *Chemical Geology* 52:317-331.

165. Graham, I. J., and G. Mortimer. 1992. Terrane characterization and timing of metamorphism in the Otago Schist, New Zealand, using Rb-Sr and K-Ar geochronology. *New Zealand Journal of Geology and Geophysics* 35:391-401.

166. Grau, G., C. Chauvel, and B. M. Jahn. 1990. Anomalous Sm-Nd ages for the early Archean Onverwacht Group volcanics. *Contributions to Mineralogy and Petrology* 104:27-34.

167. Green, P. F. 1986. On the thermo-tectonic evolution of Northern England: evidence from fission track analysis. *Geological Magazine* 123(5):493-506.

168. Grimes, J., *et al.* 1997. Tectonic implications of Ordovician U-Pb zircon dates from the Farmsville Metagranite, Alabama Piedmont. *Geological Society of America Abstracts with Programs* 29(3):20.

169. Gritsch, E. W. 1993. The unrefined reformer. *Christian History* 39(12):35-37.

170. Grotzinger, J. P., *et al.* 1995. Biostratigraphic and geochronologic constraints on early animal evolution. *Science* 270: 598-604.

171. Hacker, R. B., *et al.* 1998. U/Pb zircon ages constrain the architecture of the ultrahigh-pressure Qinling-Dabie Orogen, China. *Earth and Planetary Science Letters* 161:215-230.

172. Hallam, A., *et al.* 1985. Jurassic to Paleocene: Part I. (pp. 118-140), in Snelling, ed., *op. cit.*

173. Ham, K. 1998. *Creation Evangelism for the New Millennium.* Arkansas: Master Books, 176 p.

174. Hamilton, W. B. 1998. Archean tectonics and magmatism. *International Geology Review* 40:1-39.

175. Hanes, J. A. 1991. K-Ar and ^{40}Ar/^{39}Ar geochronology: methods and applications (pp. 27-57), in Heaman and Ludden, *op. cit.*

176. Hansmann, V., and F. Oberli. 1991. Zircon inheritance in an igneous rock suite from the southern Adamello batholith (Italian Alps). *Contributions to Mineralogy and Petrology* 107:501-518.

177. Haq, B. U., J. Hardenbol, and P. R. Vail. 1988. Response to Gradstein *et al. Science* 241:601-602.

178. Hardie, L. A., and L. A. Hinnov. 1997. Biostratigraphic and radiometric age data question the Milankovitch characteristics of the Latemar cycle (Southern Alps, Italy): comment. *Geology* 25(5): 470-471.

179. Harlan, S. S., L. W. Snee, and J. W. Geissman. 1996. ^{40}Ar/^{39}Ar geochronology and paleomagnetism of Independence volcano, Absaroka Volcanic Supergroup, Beartooth Mountains, Montana. *Canadian Journal of Earth Sciences* 33:1648-1654.

180. Harland, W. B. 1983. More time scales. *Geological Magazine* 120(4): 393-400.

181. Harland, W. B., *et al.* 1990. *A geologic time scale 1989.* Cambridge, New York: Cambridge University Press, 263 p.

182. Harmer, R. E., and B. M. Eglington. 1990. A review of the statistical principles of geochronometry: towards a more consistent approach for reporting geochronological data. *South African Journal of Geology* 93(5/6):845-856.

183. Harper, C. L., and S. B. Jacobsen. 1996. Evidence for ^{182}Hf in the early Solar system and constraints on the timescale of terrestrial accretion and core formation. *Geochimica et Cosmochimica Acta* 60(7):1131-1153.

184. Harper, C. T., ed. 1973. *Geochronology.* Benchmark Papers in Geology. Stroudsburg, Pennsylvania: Dowden, Hutchinson, and Ross, Inc., 469 p.

185. Harrison, T. M. 1990. Some observations on the interpretation of feldspar ^{40}Ar/^{39}Ar results. *Chemical Geology* 80:219-229.

186. Harrison, T. M., I. Duncan, and I. McDougall. 1985. Diffusion of ^{40}Ar in biotite. *Geochimica et Cosmochimica Acta* 49:2461-2468.

187. Hartz, E. H., T. H. Torsvik, and A. Andresen. 1998. Reply. *Geology* 26(3):285-286.

188. Haute, P. Van den *et al.* 1998. The parameters that govern the accuracy of fission-track age determinations: A reappraisal (pp. 33-46), in Van den Haute and De Corte, *op. cit.*

189. Haute, P. Van den, and F. De Corte. 1998. *Advances in Fission-Track Geochronology.* Boston, London: Kluwer Academic Publishers, Dordrecht.

190. Hawkins, D. P., and S. A. Bowring. 1994. Complex U-Pb systematics of Paleoproterozoic monazite from the Grand Canyon, Arizona, USA (p. 131), in Lanphere *et al.*, *op. cit.*

191. Hayatsu, A., and C. E. Waboso. 1985. The solubility of rare gases in silicate melts and implications for K-Ar dating. *Chemical Geology* 52:97-102.

192. Hayward, A. 1985. *Creation and Evolution: The Facts and the Fallacies.* London: Triangle Books, 232 p.

193. Heaman, L. M., and J. Tarney. 1989. U-Pb baddeleyite ages for the Scourie dyke swarm, Scotland. *Nature* 340:705-708.

194. Heaman, L., and J. N. Ludden. 1991. *Applications of Radiogenic Isotope Systems to Problems in Geology.* Short Course Handbook, vol. 19, 498 p.

195. Heaman, L., and R. Parrish. 1991. U-Pb geochronology of accessory minerals (pp. 59-102), in Heaman and Ludden, *op. cit.*

196. Heidlauf, D. T., A. T. Hsiu, and G. D. Klein. 1986. Tectonic subsidence analysis of the Illinois Basin. *The Journal of Geology* 94:779-794.

197. Heimann, A., *et al.* 1994. A short interval of Jurassic continental flood basalt volcanism in Antarctica as demonstrated by ^{40}Ar/^{39}Ar geochronology. *Earth and Planetary Science Letters* 121:19-41.

198. Helmick, L. S., and D. P. Baumann. 1986. A demonstration of the mixing model to account for Rb-Sr isochrons. *Creation Research Society Quarterly* 26(1):20-23.

199. Herz, N, and E. G. Garrison. 1998. *Geological Methods for Archaeology.* New York: Oxford University Press.

200. Hess, J. C., and H. J. Lippolt. 1986. Kinetics of Ar isotopes during neutron irradiation. *Chemical Geology* 59:223-236.

201. Hess, J. C. *et al.* 1999. High-precision ^{40}Ar/^{39}Ar spectrum dating on sanidine from the Donets Basin, Ukraine. *Journal of the Geological Society of London* 156:527-533.

202. Hess, J. C., H. J. Lippolt, and R. Wirth. 1987. Interpretation of ^{40}Ar/^{39}Ar spectra of biotites. *Chemical Geology* 66:137-149.

203. Hetherington, N. S. 1983. Just how objective is science? *Nature* 306:727-730.

204. Hickman, M. H. and W. E. Glassley. 1984. The role of metamorphic fluid transport in the Rb-Sr isotopic resetting of shear zones. *Contributions to Mineralogy and Petrology* 87:265-281.

205. Higgins, M. D. 1984. A test of two alteration indices as predictors of argon loss in basic rocks. *Isotope Geoscience* 2: 175-180.

206. Hilgren, F. J., W. Krijgsman, and J. R. Wijbrans. 1997. Direct comparison of astronomical and $^{40}Ar/^{39}Ar$ ages of ash beds. *Geophysical Research Letters* 24(16):2043-2046.

207. Holdsworth, R. E., and R. A. Strachan. 1988. The structural age and possible origin of the Vagastie Bridge Granite and associated intrusions, central Sutherland. *Geological Magazine* 125(6):613-620.

208. Holland, J. G., and R. St. J. Lambert. 1995. The geochemistry and geochronology of the gneisses and pegmatites of the Tollie antiform in the Lewisian complex of northwestern Scotland. *Canadian Journal of Earth Sciences* 32:496-507.

209. Hong, Z., *et al.* 1990. Early Archean inheritance in zircon from Mesozoic Dalngshan granitoids in the Yangtze Foldbelt of southeast China. *Geochemical Journal (of Japan)* 24:133-141.

210. Hunt, P. A., and J. C. Roddick. 1991. A compilation of K-Ar ages, Report 20, in Radiogenic Age and Isotopic Studies: Report 4; *Geological Survey of Canada*, Paper 90-2, p. 113-143.

211. Hunt, P. A., and J. C. Roddick. 1992. A compilation of K-Ar ages, Report 21, in Radiogenic Age and Isotopic Studies: Report 5; *Geological Survey of Canada*, Paper 91-2, p. 207-261.

212. Hunt, P. A., and J. C. Roddick. 1993. A compilation of K-Ar and $^{40}Ar-^{39}Ar$ ages, Report 23, in Radiogenic Age and Isotopic Studies: Report 7; *Geological Survey of Canada*, Paper 93-2, p. 127-154.

213. Hurford, A. J. 1998. Zeta: The ultimate solution to fission track analysis calibration, or just an interim measure (pp. 19-32), in Van den Haute and De Corte, *op. cit.*

214. Hurford, A. J., and P. F. Green. 1982. A users' guide to fission-track calibration. *Earth and Planetary Science Letters* 59:343-354.

215. Hyodo, H., and D. York. 1993. The discovery and significance of a fossilized radiogenic argon wave (argonami) in the earth's crust. *Geophysical Research Letters* 20(1):61-64.

216. Inger, S., *et al.* 1996. Metamorphic evolution of the Sesia-Lanzo Zone, western Alps. *Contributions to Mineralogy and Petrology* 126:152-168.

217. Intasopa, S., T. Dunn, and R. St. J. Lambert. 1995. Geochemistry of Cenozoic basaltic and silicic magmas in the central portion of the Loei-Phetchabun volcanic belt, Lop Buri, Thailand. *Canadian Journal of Earth Sciences* 32:393-409.

218. Itaya, T., and H. Takasugi. 1988. Muscovite K-Ar ages of the Sanbagawa schists, Japan, and argon depletion during cooling and deformation. *Contributions to Mineralogy and Petrology* 100:281-290.

219. Ivanenko, V. V., and M. I. Karpenko. 1988. $^{40}Ar-^{39}Ar$ data on excess argon-40 in nepheline from the Kovdor Massif, Kola Peninsula. *Geochemistry International* 25(1):77-82.

220. Jacobs, J., and R. J. Thomas. 1996. Pan-African rejuvenation of the c. 1.1 Ga Natal Metamorphic Province (South Africa): K-Ar muscovite and titanite fission track evidence. *Journal of the Geological Society of London* 153:971-978.

221. Jagoutz, E. 1994. Isotopic systematics of metamorphic rocks (p. 156), in Lanphere *et al., op. cit.*

222. Jahn, B., and H. Cuvellier. 1994. Pb-Pb and U-Pb geochronology of carbonate rocks: an assessment. *Chemical Geology* 115:125-151.

223. Jambon, A. 1994. Earth degassing and large-scale geochemical cycling of volatile elements (pp. 479-517), in M. R. Carroll, and J. R. Holloway, eds., Volatiles in Magmas. *Reviews in Mineralogy* 30, 517 p.

224. Jenkin, G. R. T. 1997. Do cooling paths derived from mica Rb-Sr data reflect true cooling paths? *Geology* 25(10):907-910.

225. Jie-Dong, Y., *et al.* 1996. Sm-Nd isotopic age of Precambrian-Cambrian boundary in China. *Geological Magazine* 133(1):53-61.

226. Jones, B. G., P. F. Carr, and A. J. Wright. 1981. Silurian and Early Devonian geochronology—a reappraisal, with new evidence from the Bungonia Limestone. *Alcheringa* 5:197-207.

227. Juteau, M., V. 1984. Isotopic heterogeneities in the granitic intrusion of Monte Capanne (Elba Island, Italy) and dating concepts. *Journal of Petrology* 25(2):532-545.

228. Kalsbeek, F., and M. Hansen. 1989. Statistical analysis of Rb-Sr isotope data by the "bootstrap" method. *Chemical Geology* 73:289-297.

229. Kamber, B. S., Moorbath, S., and M. J. Whitehouse. 1998. Reply to Bennett and Nutman. *Chemical Geology* 148:219-224.

230. Kamo, S. L., G. K. Czamanske, and T. E. Krogh. 1996. A minimum U-Pb age for Siberian flood-basalt volcanism. *Geochimica et Cosmochimica Acta* 60(18):3505-3511.

231. Kappelman, J., E. L. Simons, and C. C. Swisher III. 1992. New age determinations for the Eocene-Oligocene boundary sediments in the Fayum Depression, northern Egypt. *The Journal of Geology* 100:647-668.

232. Karner, E. B., and P. R. Renne. 1998. $^{40}Ar/^{39}Ar$ geochronology of Roman volcanic province tephra in the Tiber River valley. *Geological Society of America Bulletin* 110(6): 740-747.

233. Kauffman, E. G. 1979. Cretaceous (p. A445), in Robison, R. A., and C. Teichert, eds, *Treatise on Invertebrate Paleontology, Part A.* University of Kansas Press.

234. Kawano, Y., and H. Kagami. 1993. Rb-Sr whole rock and mineral isochron ages of granitic rocks of the Ryukyu Arc, Japan. *Geochemical Journal (of Japan)* 27:171-178.

235. Kennan, L, S. Lamb, and C. Rundle. 1995. K-Ar dates from the Altiplano and Cordillera Oriental of Bolivia. *Journal of South American Earth Sciences* 8(2):163-186.

236. Kerr, A., G. R. Dunning, and R. D. Tucker. 1993. The youngest Paleozoic plutonism of the Newfoundland Appalachians: U-Pb ages from the St. Lawrence and Francois granites. *Canadian Journal of Earth Sciences* 30:2328-2333.

237. Kerr, R. A. 1995. A volcanic crisis for ancient life? *Science* 270:27-28.

238. Ketchum, J. W. F., *et al.* 1998. Timing and thermal influence of late orogenic extension in the lower crust. *Precambrian Research* 89:25-45.

239. Kohn, B. P., B. Lang, and G. Steinitz. 1993. $^{40}Ar/^{39}Ar$ dating of the Atlit-1 volcanic sequence, northern Israel. *Israel Journal of Earth Sciences* 42:17-28.

240. Kontak, D. J. *et al.* 1998. $^{40}Ar/^{39}Ar$ dating of ribbon-textured veins and wall-rock material from Meguma lode gold deposits, Nova Scotia. *Canadian Journal of Earth Sciences* 35:746-761.

241. Kostitsyn, Yu. A. 1992. The Rb-Sr isotope system in Altytau (Central Kysylkum) granites: Open in rocks and closed in feldspars. *Geochemistry International* 29(5):76-42.

242. Kroner, A. 1982. Rb-Sr geochronology and tectonic evolution of the Pan-African Damara Belt of Namibia, southwestern Africa. *American Journal of Science* 282:1471-1507.

243. Kroner, A., and A. P. Willner. 1998. Time of formation and peak of Variscan HP-HT metamorphism of quartz-feldspar rocks in the central Erzgebirge, Saxony, Germany. *Contributions to Mineralogy and Petrology* 132:1-20.

244. Kroner, A., and P. Jaeckel. 1994. Precise dating of granitoids by single zircon geochronology: a nightmare! (p. 181), in Lanphere *et al., op. cit.*

245. Kroner, A., *et al.* 1994. Geochronology and Nd-Sr systematics of Lusatian granitoids. *Geologische Rundschau* 83:357-376.

246. Kroner, A., *et al.* 1998. Further evidence for an early Carboniferous (~340 Ma) age of high-grade metamorphism in the Saxonian granulite complex. *Geologische Rundschau* 86: 751-766.

247. Kumar, A., *et al.* 1996. Sm-Nd ages of Archaean metavolcanics of the Dharwar craton, South India. *Precambrian Research* 80:205-216.

248. Kunk, M. J., and J. F. Sutter. 1984. $^{40}Ar/^{39}Ar$ age spectrum dating of biotite from Middle Ordovician bentonites—eastern North America (pp. 11-22), in D. L. Bruton, ed., *Aspects of the Ordovician System.* University of Oslo Press, 228 p.

249. Kwan, T. S., R. Krahenbuhl, and E. Jager. 1992. Rb-Sr, K-Ar and fission track ages for granites from Penang Island, West Malaysia. *Contributions to Mineralogy and Petrology* 111:527-542.

250. Laeter, de. J. R., W. G. Libby, and A. F. Trendall. 1981. The older Precambrian geochronology of western Australia. *Special Publication of the Geological Society of Australia* 7:145-157.

251. Laicheng, M., *et al.* 1997. Zircon sensitive high resolution ion microprobe (SHRIMP) study of granitoid intrusions in Zhaoye Gold Belt of Shandong Province and its implication. *Science in China* D40(4):361-369.

252. Lamb, M. A., and D. Cox. 1998. New ^{40}Ar/^{39}Ar age data and implications for porphyry copper desposits of Mongolia. *Economic Geology* 93: 524-529.

253. Landing, E., *et al.* 1998. Duration of Early Cambrian: U-Pb ages of volcanic ashes from Avalon and Gondwana. *Canadian Journal of Earth Sciences* 35:329-338.

254. Landoll, J. D., and K. A. Foland. 1989. Excess argon in amphiboles from fluid interaction and short intrusion interval at the epizonal Marangudzi Complex, Zimbabwe. *Journal of Geophysical Research* 94(B4):4053-4069.

255. Lanphere, M. A., G. B. Dalrymple, and B. D. Turrin. 1994. Abstracts of the Eight International Conference on Geochronology, Cosmochronology, and Isotope Geology. *U. S. Geologic Survey Circular* 1107, 384 p.

256. Lawlor, P. J. *et al.* 1999. U-Pb geochronology, geochemistry, and provenance of the Grenvillian, Huiznopalal Gneiss of eastern Mexico. *Precambrian Research* 94:73-99.

257. Lee, J. K. W. 1993. The argon release mechanisms of hornblende *in vacuo*. *Chemical Geology* 106:133-170.

258. Lee, J. K. W., *et al.* 1991. Incremental heating of hornblende *in vacuo*: Implications for ^{39}Ar/^{40}Ar geochronology and the interpretation of thermal histories. *Geology* 19:872-876.

259. Leitch, C. H. B., *et al.* 1991. Geochronometry of the Bridge River Camp, southwestern British Columbia. *Canadian Journal of Earth Sciences* 28:195-208.

260. Levchenkov, O. A., *et al.* 1998. Kinetics of Pb and U loss from metamict zircon under different P-T-X conditions. *Geochemistry International* 36(11):1006-1013.

261. Leveson, D. J., and D. E. Seidemann. 1996. Richard Milton—a non-religious creationist ally. *Journal of Geoscience Education* 44: 428-438.

262. Li, S., *et al.* 1994. Excess argon in phengite from eclogite. *Chemical Geology* 112:343-350.

263. Lippolt, H. J., *et al.* 1994. (Uranium + thorium)/helium dating of apatite. *Chemical Geology* 112:179-191.

264. Lippolt, H. J., H. Schleicher, and I. Raczek. 1983. Rb-Sr systematics of Permian volcanites in the Schwarzwald (SW-Germany), Part I. *Contributions to Mineralogy and Petrology* 84:272-280.

265. Lo, C.-H., and T. C. Onstott. 1995. Rejuvenation of K-Ar systems for minerals in the Taiwan Mountain Belt. *Earth and Planetary Science Letters* 131: 71-98.

266. Lo, C.-H., and T.-F. Yui. 1996. ^{40}Ar/^{39}Ar dating of high-pressure rocks in the Tananao Basement Complex, Taiwan. *Journal of the Geological Society of China* 39(1):13-30.

267. LoBello, Ph. , *et al.* 1987. ^{40}Ar/^{39}Ar step-heating and laser fusion dating of a Quaternary pumice from Neschers, Massif Central, France. *Chemical Geology* 66:67-71.

268. Lubenow, M. L. 1992. *Bones of Contention*. Grand Rapids, Michigan: Baker Book House, 295 p.

269. Ludwig, K. R., and J. A. Cooper. 1984. Geochronology of Precambrian granites and associated U-Ti-Th mineralization, northern Olary province, South Australia. *Contributions to Mineralogy and Petrology* 86:298-308.

270. Lutz, T. M., and L. Srogi. 1986. Biased isochron ages resulting from subsolidus isotope exchange: A theoretical model and results. *Chemical Geology* 56:63-71.

271. Lux, D. R., and D. Gibson. 1998. Post-crystallization cooling history of the Sebago Granite. *Geological Society of America Abstracts with Programs* 30(1):59.

272. Lyons, J. B., J. N. Aleinikoff, and R. E. Zartman. 1986. Uranium-thorium-lead ages of the Highlandcroft Plutonic Suite, northern New England. *American Journal of Science* 286:489-509.

273. Maboko, M. A. H., *et al.* 1991. Discordant ^{40}Ar-^{39}Ar ages from the Musgrave Ranges, central Australia: implications for the significance of hornblende ^{40}Ar-^{39}Ar spectra. *Chemical Geology* 86:139-160.

274. Maboko, M. A. H., I. S. Williams, and W. Compston. 1991. Zircon U-Pb chronometry of the pressure and temperature history of granulites in the Musgrave Ranges, central Australia. *The Journal of Geology* 99:675-697.

275. MacIntyre, R. M., and G. W. Berger. 1982. A note on the geochronology of the Iberian Alkaline Province. *Lithos* 15:133-136.

276. Magaritz, M., and H. P. Taylor. 1986. Oxygen 18/Oxygen 16 and D/H studies of plutonic granitic and metamorphic rocks across the Cordilleran batholiths of southern British Columbia. *Journal of Geophysical Research* 91(B2): 2193-2217.

277. Maluski, H. 1978. Behavior of biotites, amphiboles, plagioclases, and K-feldspars in response to tectonic events with the ^{40}Ar-^{39}Ar method. *Geochimica et Cosmochimica Acta* 42:1619-1633.

278. Maluski, H., *et al.* 1990. Location of extraneous argon in granulitic-facies minerals: A paired microprobe-laster probe ^{40}Ar/^{39}Ar analysis. *Chemical Geology* 80:193-217.

279. Mankinen, E. A., and G. B. Dalrymple. 1979. Revised geomagnetic polarity time-scale for the interval 0-5 m. y. B. P. *Journal of Geophysical Research* 84(B2):615-627.

280. Marsh, T. M., M. T. Einaudi, and M. McWilliams. 1997. ^{40}Ar/^{39}Ar geochronology of Cu-Au and Au-Ag mineralization in the Potrerillos District, Chile. *Economic Geology* 92:784-806.

281. Marshall, L. G. *et al.* 1986. Geochronology of Type Santacrucian (middle Tertiary) land mammal age, Patagonia, Argentina. *The Journal of Geology* 94:449-457.

282. Martin, B. 1998. Coincidences: Remarkable or random? *Skeptical Inquirer* 22(5):23-28.

283. Mattinson, J. M. 1990. Petrogenesis and evolution of the Salinian magmatic arc (pp. 237-250), in J. L. Anderson, ed., *The Nature and Origin of Cordilleran Magmatism*. Geological Society of America Memoir 174.

284. Mattinson, J. M., *et al.* 1996. U-Pb reverse discordance in zircons: The role of fine-scale oscillatory zoning and sub-micron transport of Pb (pp. 355-370), in A. Basu and S. Hart, eds., *Earth Processes: Reading the Isotopic Code*. Geophysical Monograph 95, American Geophysical Union, 437 p.

285. Mauthner, M. H. F., *et al.* 1995. Geochronology of the Little Nahanni pegmatite group, Selwyn Mountains, southwestern Northwest Territories. *Canadian Journal of Earth Sciences* 32:2090-2097.

286. McConnell, J. V. 1986. Science and pseudoscience. *Skeptical Inquirer* 11(1):104-105.

287. McCulloch, M. T., and V. C. Bennett. 1994. Progressive growth of the earth's continental crust and depleted mantle: geochemical constraints. *Geochimica et Cosmochimica Acta* 58(21):4717-4738.

288. McDougall, I., and T. M. Harrison. 1988. *Geochronology and Thermochronology by the ^{40}Ar/^{39}Ar Method*. New York: Oxford University Press, 212 p.

289. McDowell, F. W. 1983. K-Ar dating: Incomplete extraction of radiogenic argon from alkali feldspar. *Chemical Geology* 1:119-126.

290. McLelland, J., F. Wasteneys, and C. M. Fanning. 1997. Single grain zircon dating in the Adirondack Lowlands, New York: Revised ages and plate tectonic implications for the Adirondack-Prontenac region. *Geological Society of America Abstracts with Programs* 29(6):A-466.

291. McWilliams, M. 1994. Relative chronology of events at and near the Cretaceous-Tertiary boundary (p. 214), in Lanphere *et al.*, *op. cit.*

292. Meijer, A., T-T. Kwon, and G. R. Tilton. 1990. U-Th-Pb partitioning behavior during partial melting in the upper mantle. *Journal of Geophysical Research* 95(B1):433-448.

293. Miller, E. L., *et al.* 1988. Metamorphic history of the east-central Basin and Range Province (pp. 649-682), in Ernst, ed., *op. cit.*

294. Miller, F. K., and D. M. Morton. 1980. Potassium-argon geochronology of the eastern Transverse Ranges and southern Mojave Desert, southern California. *U. S. Geological Survey Professional Paper* 1152, 30 p.

295. Miller, W. M., *et al.* 1991. Fluid disturbed hornblende K-Ar ages from the Dalradian rocks of Connemara, western Ireland. *Journal of the Geological Society of London* 148:985-992.

296. Milton, R. 1997. *Shattering the Myths of Darwinism.* Vermont: Park Street Press, 308 p.

297. Mitchell, J. G, P. N. Rands, and P. R. Ineson. 1989. Perturbation of the K-Ar age system in the Cleveland dyke, U. K. *Chemical Geology* 79:49-64.

298. Mitchell, J. G., and M. G. Euwe. 1988. A model of single-stage concomitant potassium-argon exchange in acidic lavas from the Erlend Volcanic Complex, north of Shetland Islands. *Chemical Geology* 72:95-109.

299. Moller, A., K. Mezger, and V. Schenk. 1998. Crustal age domains and the evolution of the continental crust in the Mozambique Belt of Tanzania. *Journal of Petrology* 39(4):749-783.

300. Mondal, M. E. A., *et al.* 1998. Ion microprobe ^{207}Pb/^{206}Pb zircon for gneiss-granitoid rocks from Bundelkhand massif. *Current Science* 74(1):70-75.

301. Montanari, A., *et al.* 1985. Radiometric time scale for the upper Eocene and Oligocene based on K/Ar and Rb/Sr dating of volcanic biotites from the pelagic sequence of Gubbio, Italy. *Geology* 13:596-599.

302. Moorbath, S., and M. J. Whitehouse. 1996. Sm-Nd isotopic data and Earth's evolution. *Science* 273:1878.

303. Moorbath, S., P. N. Taylor, and N. W. Jones. 1986. Dating the oldest terrestrial rocks—fact and fiction. *Chemical Geology* 57:63-86.

304. Moran, J. E. 1996. Origin of iodine in the Anadarko Basin, Oklahoma: An ^{129}I study. *American Association of Petroleum Geologists Bulletin* 80(5):685-694.

305. Morozova, I. M., *et al.* 1996. Inheritance of radiogenic argon by newly formed minerals during glauconite transformation. *Transactions (Doklady) of the Russian Academy of Sciences: Earth Science Sections* 344(7):52-57.

306. Morozova, I. M., *et al.* 1997. Radiogenic argon as an indicator of the inheritance of material during glauconite hydrothermal transformations. *Geochemistry International* 35(8):716-723.

307. Morton, J. P., and L. E. Long. 1984. Rb-Sr ages of glauconite recrystallization: Dating times of regional emergence above sea level. *Journal of Sedimentary Petrology* 54(2):495-506.

308. Mose, E. G., *et al.* 1989. Radiometric ages of rift-associated latest Precambrian alkalic granites in the Grenville terrane of the Appalachians. *Northeast Geology* 11(1):1-21.

309. Muecke, G. K., *et al.* 1994. ^{40}Ar/^{39}Ar geochronology of Late Cretaceous volcanic events in the Canadian Arctic Islands: Arctic biotic heterochroneity (p. 229), in Lanphere *et al.*, *op. cit.*

310. Muller-Sohnius, D., and P. Horn. 1994. K-Ar dating of ring complexes and fault systems in Northern Kordofan, Sudan. *Geologische Rundschau* 83:604-613.

311. Mundil, R., and K. R. Ludwig. 1998. Improving the accuracy of high resolution single zircon U/Pb data. *Geological Society of America Abstracts with Programs* 30(7):A-312.

312. Mundil, R., *et al.* 1996. High resolution U-Pb dating of Middle Triassic volcaniclastics. *Earth and Planetary Science Letters* 141: 137-151.

313. Munsksgaard, N. C. 1984. High δ^{18}O and possible pre-eruptional Rb-Sr isochrons in cordierite-bearing Neogene volcanics from SE Spain. *Contributions to Mineralogy and Petrology* 87:351-358.

314. Nagler, Th. F., and J. D. Kramers. 1998. Nd isotopic evolution of the upper mantle during the Precambrian. *Precambrian Research* 91:233-252.

315. Nakata, J. K. 1991. K-Ar and fission-track ages (dates) of volcanic, intrusive, altered, and metamorphic rocks in the Mohave Mountains area, west-central Arizona. *Isochron/West* 57:21-27.

316. Negrey, Ye. V., *et al.* 1996. Rb-Sr and δ^{18}O isotope studies on a tantaliferous lithium-flourine granite dome. *Transactions (Doklady) of the Russian Academy of Sciences: Earth Science Sections* 344(7):236-241.

317. Nelson, S. T., J. P. Davidson, and K. R. Sullivan. 1992. New age determinations of central Colorado Plateau laccoliths, Utah. *Geological Society of America Bulletin* 104:1547-1560.

318. Nemchin, A. A., and R. T. Pidgeon. 1998. Precise conventional and SHRIMP baddeleyite U-Pb age for the Binneringle Dyke, near Narrogin, Western Australia. *Australian Journal of Earth Sciences* 45:673-675.

319. Nielson, J. E., *et al.* 1990. Age of the Peach Springs Tuff, southeastern California and western Arizona. *Journal of Geophysical Research* 95(B1):571-579.

320. Nutman, A. P., *et al.* 1996. SHRIMP U/Pb zircon ages of acid volcanic rocks in the Chitradurga and Sandur Groups, and granites adjacent to the Sandur Schist Belt, Karnataka. *Journal of the Geological Society of India* 47:153-164.

321. Oard, M. 1998. How reliable are Quaternary methods? *Creation Ex Nihilo Technical Journal* 12(3):258-259.

322. Obradovich, J. D. 1984. An overview of the measurement of geologic time and the paradox of geologic time scales (pp. 11-30), in *Proceedings of the 27th International Geological Congress*, vol. 1.

323. Obradovich, J. D. 1988. A different perspective on glauconite as a chronometer for geologic time scale. *Paleoceanography* 3(6):757-770.

324. Obradovich, J. D. 1993. A Cretaceous time scale (pp. 379-396), in W. G. E. Caldwell, and E. G. Kauffman, eds., *Evolution of the Western Interior Basin*. Geological Association of Canada Special Paper 39, 680 p.

325. Obradovich, J. D., and W. A. Cobban. 1975. A time-scale for the Late Cretaceous of the western interior of North America (pp. 31-54), in W. G. E. Caldwell, ed., *The Cretaceous System in the Western Interior of North America*. Geological Association of Canada Special Paper 13.

326. Odin, G. S. 1982. Effects of pressure and temperature on clay-mineral potassium-argon ages (pp. 307-319), in Odin, ed., *op. cit.*

327. Odin, G. S. 1985. Key rules for numerical time-scale calibration (pp. 41-46), in Snelling, N. J., ed., *op. cit.*

328. Odin, G. S., ed. 1982. *Numerical Dating in Stratigraphy*, 2 vols., New York: John Wiley and Sons, 1040 p.

329. Odin, G. S., *et al.* 1986. K-Ar biotite data for Ludlovian bentonites from Great Britain. *Chemical Geology* 59:127-131.

330. Odin, G. S., *et al.* 1991. Reliability of volcano-sedimentary biotite ages across the Eocene-Oligocene boundary (Appenines, Italy). *Chemical Geology* 86:203-224.

331. Olsen, P. E., A. R. McCune, and K. S. Thomson. 1982. Correlation of the early Mesozoic Newark Supergroup by vertebrates, principally fishes. *American Journal of Science* 282:1-44.

332. Paces J. B., and J. D. Miller. 1993. Precise U-Pb ages of Duluth Complex and related mafic intrusions, northeastern Minnesota. *Journal of Geophysical Research* 98(B8):13,997-14,013.

333. Pankhurst, R. J., *et al.* 1973. Mineral age patterns in ca. 3700 my old rocks from West Greenland. *Earth and Planetary Science Letters* 20:157-170.

334. Pankhurst, R. J., *et al.* 1998. Geochronology and geochemistry of pre-Jurassic superterranes in Marie Byrd Land, Antarctica. *Journal of Geophysical Research* 103(B2):2529-2547.

335. Paquette, J. -L., and A. Nedelec. 1998. A new insight into Pan-African tectonics in the east-west Gondwana collision zone by U-Pb dating of granites from central Madagascar. *Earth and Planetary Science Letters* 155:45-56.

336. Paquette, J. -L., C. Chopin, and J.-J. Peucat. 1989. U-Pb, Rb-Sr, and Sm-Nd geochronology of high- to very-high-pressure meta-acidic rocks from the western Alps. *Contributions to Mineralogy and Petrology* 101:280-289.

337. Parrish, R. R. 1995. Thermal evolution of the southeastern Canadian Cordillera. *Canadian Journal of the Earth Sciences* 32:1618-1642.

338. Parrish, R. R., and J. C. Roddick. 1984. *Geochronology and Isotope Geology for the Geologist and Explorationist.* Geological Association of Canada Cordilleran Section, Short Course No. 4, 71p.

339. Patchett, P. J. 1992. Isotopic studies of Proterozoic crustal growth and evolution (pp. 481-508), in K. C. Condie, ed., *Proterozoic Crustal Evolution.* Amsterdam, New York: Elsevier Publishing Co., 537 p.

340. Patton, W. W., *et al.* 1987. New U/Pb ages from granite and granite gneiss in the Ruby Geanticline and southern Brooks Range, Alaska. *The Journal of Geology* 95:118-126.

341. Paul, C. 1980. *The Natural History of Fossils.* New York: Holmes and Meier Pub. Co.

342. Pearson, D. G., *et al.* 1995. Re-Os, Sm-Nd, and Rb-Sr isotope evidence for thick Archaean lithospheric mantle beneath the Siberian craton modified by multistage metasomatism. *Geochimica et Cosmochimica Acta* 59(5):959-977.

343. Perkins, C., *et al.* 1990. $^{40}Ar/^{39}Ar$ and U-Pb geochronology of the Goonumbla porphyry Cu-Au deposits, New South Wales, Australia. *Economic Geology* 85:1808-1824.

344. Peterson, F. 1994. Sand dunes, sabkhas, streams, and shallow seas: Jurassic paleogeography in the southern part of the Western Interior basin (pp. 233-272), in M. V. Caputo, J. A. Peterson, and K. J. Franczyk, eds., *Mesozoic Systems of the Rocky Mountain Region, USA.* SEPM (Society of Economic Paleontologists and Mineralogists), 536 p.

345. Phillips, D. *et al.* 1998. A petrographic and $^{40}Ar/^{39}Ar$ geochronological study of the Voorspoed kimberlite, South Africa. *South African Journal of Geology* 101(4): 299-306.

346. Pigage, L. C., and R. G. Anderson. 1985. The Anvil plutonic suite, Faro, Yukon Territory. *Canadian Journal of Earth Sciences* 22:1204-1216.

347. Pilkey, O. H. 1996. Mathematical modeling of beach behavior. *GSA Today* (May):11-12.

348. Pilot, J., *et al.* 1998. Palaeozoic and Proterozoic zircons from the Mid-Atlantic Ridge. *Nature* 393: 676-679.

349. Poths, J., H. Healey, and A. W. Laughlin. 1993. Ubiquitous excess argon in very young basalts. *Geological Society of America Abstracts with Programs* 25(6):462.

350. Poty, B. 1989. Geological conditions governing the use of dating methods (pp. 35-44), in E. Roth and B. Poty, eds., *Nuclear Methods of Dating.* Dordrecht, Boston, London: Kluwer Academic Publishers, 600 p.

351. Premo, W. R., *et al.* 1998. Isotopic ages, cooling histories, and magmatic origins for Mesozoic tonalitic plutons from the Northern Peninsular Ranges Batholith, southern California. *Geological Society of America Abstracts with Programs* 30(5):59-60.

352. Prothero, D. R. 1994. *The Eocene-Oligocene Transition.* New York: Columbia University Press, 291 p.

353. Prothero, D. R., and F. Schwab. 1996. *Sedimentary Geology.* New York: W. H. Freeman and Co., 575 p.

354. Pukhtel, I. S., *et al.* 1991. Petrography and Sm-Nd age of a differentiated sheet of komatiitic basalt in the Vetra Belt, Baltic shield. *Geochemistry International* 28(12):14-23.

355. Queen, M., *et al.* 1996. $^{40}Ar/^{39}Ar$ phlogopite and U-Pb perovskite dating of lamprophyre dykes from the eastern Lake Superior region. *Canadian Journal of Earth Sciences* 33:958-965.

356. Reid, D. L., A. J. Erlank, and D. C. Rex. 1991. Age and correlation of the False Bay dolerite dyke swarm, south-western Cape, Cape Province. *South African Journal of Geology* 94(2/3):155-158.

357. Renne, P. R. 1995. Excess ^{40}Ar in biotite and hornblende from the Noril'sk 1 intrusion, Siberia: implications for the age of the Siberian Traps. *Earth and Planetary Science Letters* 131: 165-176.

358. Renne, P. R., *et al.* 1998. Intercalibration of standards, absolute ages and uncertainties in $^{40}Ar/^{39}Ar$ dating. *Chemical Geology* 145:117-152.

359. Rex, D. C., P. G. Guise, and J.-A. Wartho. 1993. Disturbed $^{40}Ar-^{39}Ar$ spectra from hornblendes: Thermal loss or contamination? *Chemical Geology* 103:271-281.

360. Reynolds, S. J., *et al.* 1988. Geologic setting of Mesozoic and Cenozoic metamorphism in Arizona (pp. 466-501), in Ernst, ed., *op. cit.*

361. Reznitskiy, L. Z., *et al.* 1994. First U-Pb isotope dates for accessory zircons from the granulites of the Slyudanka complex (south Baikal region). *Transactions (Doklady) of the Russian Academy of Sciences: Earth Science Sections* 321A(9):38-43.

362. Richards, J. P., and I. McDougall. 1990. Geochronology of the Porgera gold deposit, Papua New Guinea: Resolving the effects of excess argon on K-Ar and $^{40}Ar/^{39}Ar$ age estimates for magmatism and mineralization. *Geochimica et Cosmochimica Acta* 54:1397-1415.

363. Roberts, D., J. G. Mitchell, and T. B. Andersen. 1991. A post-Caledonian dolerite dyke from Mageroy, North Norway: age and geochemistry. *Norsk Geologisk Tidsskrift* 71:289-294.

364. Roddick, H. C., F. B. Quigg, and P. A. Hunt. 1992. Miscellaneous $^{40}Ar-^{39}Ar$ ages and analytical procedures, in Radiogenic Age and Isotopic Studies: Report 6; *Geological Survey of Canada,* Paper 92-2, p. 171-177.

365. Roddick, J. C., and M. L. Bevier. 1995. U-Pb dating of granites with inherited zircon. *Chemical Geology* 119:307-329.

366. Roden, M. K. 1991. Apatite fission-track thermochronology of the southern Appalachian basin: Maryland, West Virginia, and Virginia. *The Journal of Geology* 99:41-53.

367. Roden, M. K., R. R. Parrish, and D. S. Miller. 1990. The absolute age of the Eifelian Tioga Ash Bed, Pennsylvania. *The Journal of Geology* 98:282-285.

368. Ronov, A. B. 1982. The Earth's sedimentary shell, Part 1. *International Geology Review* 24(11):1313-1363.

369. Ross, G. M., and S. A. Bowring. 1990. Detrital zircon geochronology of the Windermere Supergroup and the tectonic assembly of the southern Canadian Cordillera. *The Journal of Geology* 98:879-893.

370. Rowley, P. D., *et al.* 1994. Isotopic ages and stratigraphy of Cenozoic rocks of the Marysvale volcanic field and adjacent areas, west-central Utah. *U. S. Geological Survey Bulletin* 2071, 35 p.

371. Roy, A., and A. Sarkar. 1997. Comment on the paper "Sr, Pb, and Nd isotope studies and their bearing on the petrogenesis of the Jalor and Siwana complexes, Rajasthan, India." *Journal of the Geological Society of India* 49:464-466.

372. Rublev, A. G. 1985. The possibility of correcting for excess argon in K-Ar dating. *Geochemistry International* 22(4):73-79.

373. Ruffet, G., *et al.* 1995. Plateau ages and excess argon in phengites. *Chemical Geology* 121:327-343.

374. Ruffet, G., *et al.* 1997. Rb-Sr and $^{40}Ar-^{39}Ar$ laser probe dating of high-pressure phengites from the Sesia zone (western Alps). *Chemical Geology* 141:1-18.

375. Russell, J. 1995. Direct Pb/Pb dating of Silurian macrofossils from Gotland, Sweden. (pp. 175-200), in R. E. Dunay and E. A. Hailwood, eds., *Non-Biostratigraphical Methods of Dating and Correlation.* Geological Society of London Special Publication No. 89.

376. Ryan, P. D., and J. F. Dewey. 1997. Continental eclogites and the Wilson cycle. *Journal of the Geological Society of London* 154:437-442.

377. Ryvanova, N. G., *et al.* 1995. Comparison of zircon phase separation methods for geochronological purposes. *Geochemistry International* 32(3):49-60.

378. Saal, A. E., *et al.* 1998. Re-Os isotope evidence for the composition, formation and age of the lower continental crust. *Nature* 393: 58-61.

379. Sadler, P. M., and D. J. Strauss. 1990. Estimation of completeness of stratigraphical sections using empirical data and theoretical models. *Journal of the Geological Society of London* 147:471-485.

380. Samson, S. D. 1997. Good dates, bad dates, hot dates, and blind dates: examples from the Appalachian Orogen. *Geological Society of America Abstracts and Programs* 29(3):66.

381. Samson, S. D., and R. S. D'Lemos. 1998. U-Pb geochronology and Sm-Nd isotopic composition of Proterozoic gneisses, Channel Islands, UK. *Journal of the Geological Society of London* 155:609-618.

382. Samson, S. D., and R. S. D'Lemos. 1999. A precise late Neoproterozoic U-Pb zircon age for the syntectonic Perelle quartz diorite. *Journal of the Geological Society of London* 156:47-54.

383. Saull, V. A. 1986. Wanted: Alternatives to plate tectonics. *Geology* 14(6):536.

384. Schaaf, P., W. Heinrich, and T. Besch. 1994. Composition and Sm-Nd isotopic data of the lower crust beneath San Luis Potosi, central Mexico. *Chemical Geology* 118:63-84.

385. Schaltegger, U. 1990. Post-magmatic resetting of Rb-Sr whole rock ages—a study in the Central Aar Granite (Central Alps, Switzerland). *Geologische Rundschau* 79(3):709-724.

386. Scherer, E. E., *et al.* 1997. Lu-Hf geochronology applied to dating Cenozoic events affecting lower crustal xenoliths from Kilbourne Hole, New Mexico. *Chemical Geology* 142:63-78.

387. Schleicher, H., *et al.* 1998. Enriched subcontinental upper mantle beneath southern India. *Journal of Petrology* 39(10):1765-1785.

388. Schleicher, H., H. J. Lippolt, and I. Raczek. 1983. Rb-Sr systematics of Permian volcanites in the Schwarzwald (SW-Germany), Part II. *Contributions to Mineralogy and Petrology* 84:281-290.

389. Schuchert, C. 1931. Geochronology. *Bulletin of the National Research Council* 80:10-64.

390. Scott, D. J. 1998. An overview of the U-Pb geochronology of the Paleoproterozoic Torngat Orogen, northeastern Canada. *Precambrian Research* 91:91-107.

391. Seidemann, D. E. 1988. The hydrothermal addition of excess ^{40}Ar to the lava flows from the early Jurassic in the Hatford Basin (northeastern U. S. A.): implications for the time scale. *Chemical Geology* 72:37-45.

392. Seidemann, D. E. 1989. Age of the Triassic/Jurassic boundary: A view from the Hartford Basin. *American Journal of Science* 289:553-562.

393. Seidemann, D. E. 1992. The significance of Rb-Sr glauconite ages, Bonneterre Formation, Missouri: Late Devonian-Early Mississipian brine migration in the mid-continent: a discussion. *The Journal of Geology* 100: 639-641.

394. Seidemann, D. E., *et al.* 1984. K-Ar dates and ^{40}Ar/^{39}Ar age spectra for Mesozoic basalt flows of the Hartford Basin, Connecticut, and the Newark Basin, New Jersey. *Geological Society of America Bulletin* 95:594-598.

395. Setterfield, T. N, A. E. Mussett, and R. D. J. Oglethorpe. 1992. Magmatism and associated hydrothermal activity during the evolution of the Tavua Caldera. *Economic Geology* 87:1130-1140.

396. Shane, P. 1998. A radiometric age constraint from a tephra bed at the Miocene-Pliocene boundary in New Zealand. *New Zealand Journal of Geology and Geophysics* 41:111-114.

397. Shatagin, K. N., and V. N. Volkov. 1998. Rb-Sr system in hydrothermally altered acid volcanics: a case study. *Geochemistry International* 36(2):128-133.

398. Sheth, H. C., *et al.* 1997. Deccan Trap dioritic-gabbros from the western Satpura-Tapi region. *Current Science* 72(10):755-757.

399. Shimizu, H., *et al.* 1986. ^{138}La-^{138}Ce geochronology of an Amitsoq gneiss, Greenland, and a Mustikkamaki pegmatite, Finland. *Terra Cognita* 6(2):145.

400. Shirey, S. B. 1991. The Rb-Sr, Sm-Nd, and Re-Os isotopic systems (pp. 103-166), in Heaman and Ludden, eds., *op. cit.*

401. Shirey, S. B., and R. J. Walker. 1998. The Re-Os isotope system in cosmochemistry and high-temperature geochemistry. *Annual Review of Earth and Planetary Sciences* 26: 423-500.

402. Siebel, W. 1995. Anticorrelated Rb-Sr and K-Ar age discordances, Leuchtenberg granite, NE Bavaria, Germany. *Contributions to Mineralogy and Petrology* 120:197-211.

403. Singer, B. S., and M. S. Pringle. 1996. Age and duration of the Matuyama-Brunhes geomagnetic polarity reversal from ^{40}Ar/^{39}Ar incremental heating analysis of lavas. *Earth and Planetary Science Letters* 139:47-61.

404. Singer, B. S., *et al.* 1998. Inherited argon in a Pleistocene andesite lava: ^{40}Ar/^{39}Ar incremental-heating and laser-fusion analysis of plagioclase. *Geology* 26(5):427-430.

405. Singer, B. S., *et al.* 1999. Dating transitionally magnetized lavas of the late Matuyama Chron: Toward a new ^{40}Ar/^{39}Ar timescale of reversals and events. *Journal of Geophysical Research* 104(B1):679-693.

406. Sinton, C. W., K. Hitchen, and P. A. Duncan. 1998. ^{40}Ar-^{39}Ar geochronology of silicic and basic volcanic rocks on the margins of the North Atlantic. *Geological Magazine* 135(2):161-170.

407. Skobelin, E. A., I. P. Sharapov, and A. F. Bugayov. 1990. Deliberations of state and ways of Perestroika in geology (pp. 17-37), in Barto-Kyriakidis, A., *op. cit.*

408. Slettin, V. W., and T. C. Onstott. 1998. The effect of instability of muscovite during *in vacuo* heating on ^{40}Ar/^{39}Ar step-heating spectra. *Geochimica et Cosmochimica Acta* 62(1):123-141.

409. Smalley, P. C., D. Field, and A. Råheim. 1983. Resetting of Rb-Sr whole-rock isochrons during Sveconorwegian low-grade events in the Gjerstad Augen Gneiss, Telemark, southern Norway. *Isotope Geoscience* 1:269-282.

410. Smith, P. E., *et al.* 1994a. Cretaceous Park: ^{40}Ar/^{39}Ar ages from Mesozoic lacustrine basins, northeast China (p. 297), in Lanphere *et al.*, *op. cit.*

411. Smith, P. E., *et al.* 1994b. A laser ^{40}Ar-^{39}Ar study of minerals across the Grenville Front: investigation of reproducible excess Ar patterns. *Canadian Journal of Earth Sciences* 31:808-817.

412. Smith, P. E., *et al.* 1998. Single-grain ^{40}Ar-^{39}Ar ages of glauconites: implications for the geologic time scale and global sea level variations. *Science* 279:1517-1519.

413. Snee, L. W., *et al.* 1995. An ^{40}Ar/^{39}Ar chronicle of the tectonic development of the Salmon River suture zone, western Idaho. *U. S. Geological Survey Professional Paper* 1428:359-414.

414. Snelling, A. A. 1995. The failure of U-Th-Pb "dating" at Koongarra, Australia. *Creation Ex Nihilo Technical Journal* 9(1):71-92.

415. Snelling, A. A. 1998. The cause of anomalous potassium-argon "ages" for recent andesite flows at Mt. Ngauruhoe, New Zealand, and the implications for potassium-argon "dating." *Proceedings of the Fourth International Conference on Creationism*, pp. 503-525

416. Snelling, A. A., and J. Woodmorappe. 1998. The cooling of thick igneous bodies on a young earth. *Proceedings of the Fourth International Conference on Creationism*, pp. 527-545.

417. Snelling, N. J. 1985. *The Chronology of the Geological Record*. Geological Society of London Memoir 10.

418. Sole, J., M. Delaloye, and P. Enrique. 1998. K-Ar ages in biotites and K-feldspars from the Catalan Coastal Batholith. *Eclogae geologicae Helvetae* 91: 139-148.

419. Spell, T. L., and I. McDougall. 1992. Revisions to the age of the Brunhes-Matuyama boundary and the Pleistocene Geomagnetic Polarity Timescale. *Geophysical Research Letters* 19(12):1181-1184.

420. Stein, H. J., and S. A. Kish. 1992. The significance of Rb-Sr glauconite ages, Bonneterre Formation, Missouri: Late Devonian-Early Missisippian brine migration in the mid-continent *The Journal of Geology* 100: 641-645.

421. Steiner, M. B., and J. D. Walker. 1996. Late Silurian plutons in Yucatan. *Journal of Geophysical Research* 101(B8):17,727-17,735.

422. Stemmerik, L., and S. E. Bendix-Almgreen. 1998. Carboniferous age for the East Greenland "Devonian" basin. *Geology* 26(3):284-285.

423. Stern, R. A., and W. Bleeker. 1998. Age of the world's oldest rocks refined using Canada's SHRIMP. *Geoscience Canada* 25(1):27-31.

424. Stern, R. J., and C. E. Hedge. 1985. Geochronologic and isotopic constraints on late Precambrian crustal evolution in the Eastern Desert of Egypt. *American Journal of Science* 285:97-127.

425. Stern, R. J., et al. 1981. Isotopic U-Pb ages of zircon from the granitoids of the central Sierra Nevada, California. *U. S. Geological Survey Professional Paper* 1185, 17 p.

426. Strahler, A. N. 1987. *Science and Earth History: The Evolution/ Creation Controversy*. Buffalo, New York: Prometheus Books, 552 p.

427. Suarez, M., A. Puig, and M. Herve. 1986. K-Ar dates on granitoids from Archipelago Cabo de Hornos, southernmost Chile. *Geological Magazine* 123(5):581-584.

428. Sundeen, D. A. 1989. Note concerning the petrography and K-Ar age of Cr-spinel-bearing olivine tholeiite in the subsurface of Choctaw County, north-central Mississippi. *Southeastern Geology* 30(2):137-146.

429. Suzuki, K., H. Shimizu, and A. Masuda. 1996. Re-Os dating of molybdenites from ore deposits in Japan. *Geochimica et Cosmochimica Acta* 60(16):3151-3159.

430. Swisher, C. C., L. Dingus, and R. F. Butler. 1993. $^{40}Ar/^{39}Ar$ dating and magnetostratigraphic correlation of the terrestrial Cretaceous-Paleocene boundary and Puercan Mammal Age, Hell Creek—Tullock formations, eastern Montana. *Canadian Journal of Earth Sciences* 30:1981-1996.

431. Sykes, L. R. 1978. Intraplate seismicity, reactivation of preexisting zones of weakness, alkaline magmatism, and other tectonism postdating continental fragmentation. *Reviews of Geophysics and Space Physics* 16(4):621-688.

432. Tabor, R. W., R. K. Mark, and R. H. Wilson. 1985. Reproducibility of the K-Ar ages of rocks and minerals: An empirical approach. *U.S. Geological Survey Bulletin* 1654, 5 p.

433. Tanner, G., and T. Dempster. 1988. Comment and Reply on "Tectonically reset Rb-Sr system during Late Ordovician terrane assembly in Iapetus, western Ireland. *Geology* 16(8):762-763.

434. Tanner, G., T. Dempster, and F. Rogers. 1997. New constraints upon the structural and isotopic age of the Oughterard Granite, and on the timing of events in the Dalradian rocks of Connemara, western Ireland. *Geological Journal* 32:247-263.

435. Tauxe, L., et al. 1992. Pinning down the Brunhes/Matuyama and upper Jaramillo boundaries. *Earth and Planetary Science Letters* 109:561-572.

436. Tegner, C., et al. 1998. $^{40}Ar-^{39}Ar$ geochronology of Tertiary mafic intrusions along the East Greenland rifted margin. *Earth and Planetary Science Letters* 156:75-88.

437. Teich, A. H., and M. S. Frankel. 1992. *Good Science and Responsible Scientists*. American Association for the Advancement of Science., 35 p.

438. Terekado, Y., and S. Nohda. 1993. Rb-Sr dating of acidic rocks from the middle part of the Inner Zone of southwestern Japan. *Chemical Geology* 109:69-87.

439. Thompson, T. A., G. S. Fraser, and G. Olyphant. 1988. Establishing the altitude and age of past lake levels in the Great Lakes. *Geological Society of America Abstracts with Programs* 20(5):392.

440. Thoni, M., and E. Jagoutz. 1992. Some new aspects of dating eclogites in orogenic belts: Sm-Nd, Rb-Sr, and Pb-Pb isotopic results from the Australoalpine Saualpe and Koralpe type-locality (Carinthia/ Styria, southeastern Austria). *Geochimica et Cosmochimica Acta* 56:347-368.

441. Togashi, S., et al. 1992. Trace elements and Nd-Sr isotopes of island arc tholeiites from frontal arc of northeast Japan. *Geochemical Journal (of Japan)* 26:261-277.

442. Tomacsak, P. B., E. J. Krogstad, and R. J. Walker. 1996. U-Pb monazite geochronology of granitic rocks from Maine: Implications for late Paleozoic Tectonics in the northern Appalachians. *The Journal of Geology* 104:185-195.

443. Toulkeridis, T., et al. 1998. Sm-Nd, Rb-Sr, and Pb-Pb dating of silicic carbonates from the early Archaean Barberton Greenstone Belt, South Africa. *Precambrian Research* 92: 129-144.

444. Tregenza, T., and N. Wedell. 1997. Natural selection bias? *Nature* 386:234.

445. Trendall, A. F., et al. 1997. A precise zircon U-Pb age for the base of the BIF of the Mulaingiri Foramtion, (Bababudan Group, Dharwar Supergroup) of the Karnataka craton. *Journal of the Geological Society of India* 50:161-170.

446. Tucker, R. D., and C. F. Gower. 1994. A U-Pb geochronological framework for the Pinware Terrace, Grenville Province, southeast Labrador. *The Journal of Geology* 102:67-78.

447. Tucker, R. D., et al. 1998. New U-Pb zircon ages and the duration and division of Devonian time. *Earth and Planetary Science Letters* 158: 175-186.

448. Tucker, R. D., and W. S. McKerrow. 1995. Early Paleozoic chronology: a review in light of new U-Pb zircon ages from Newfoundland and Britain. *Canadian Journal of Earth Sciences* 32:368-379.

449. Tucker, R. D., L. D. Ashwal, and Zinner, E. K. 1998. Slow cooling of deep crustal granulites and Pb-diffusion in zircon. *Geological Society of America Abstracts with Programs* 30(7):A-213.

450. Vandamme, D., et al. 1991. Paleomagnetism and age determinations of the Deccan Traps (India). *Reviews of Geophysics* 29(2):159-190.

451. Vardiman, L. 1997. The first young-earth conference on radioisotopes. *ICR Impact* #290, 4 p.

452. Vardiman, L. 1998. Radioisotopes and the age of the earth. *ICR Impact* #301, 4 p.

453. Venkatesan, T. R., K. Pande, and Z. G. Ghevariya. 1996. $^{40}Ar-^{39}Ar$ ages of Anjar Traps, western Deccan province (India) and its relation to the Cretaceous-Tertiary boundary events. *Current Science* 70(11):990-996.

454. Vervoort, J. D., and P. Patchett. 1998. Early Earth Nd isotopes: An unreliable record of crust-mantle evolution? *Geological Society of America Abstracts with Programs* 30(7):A-207.

455. Villa, I. M. 1996. Comment on "Age and cooling history of the Manaslu granite: implications for Himalayan tectonics" by Copeland et al. *Journal of Volcanology and Geothermal Research* 70:255-261.

456. Villa, I. M., and M. Puxeddu. 1994. Geochronology of the Larderello geothermal field: new data and the "closure temperature" issue. *Contributions to Mineralogy and Petrology* 115: 415-426.

457. Wagner, G. A. 1988. Apatite fission-track geochrono-thermometer to 60C: projected length studies. *Chemical Geology* 72:145-153.

458. Walker, N. W. 1995. Tectonic implications of U-Pb zircon ages of the Canyon Mountain Complex, Sparta Complex, and related multiplutonic rocks of the Baker terrace, northeastern Oregon. *U. S. Geological Survey Professional Paper* 1428:247-269.

459. Wallace, A. R. 1995. Isotopic geochronology of the Leadville 1 x 2 quadrangle, west-central Colorado—Summary and Discussion. *U. S. Geological Survey Bulletin* 2104, 51 p.

460. Walter, R. C., et al. 1996. New radiometric ages for the Hadar Formation above the disconformity. *Geological Society of America Abstracts with Programs* 28(6):69.

461. Wang, Q. *et al.* 1998a. Geochronology of supracrustal rocks from the Golden Grove area, Murchison Province, Yilgarn Craton, Western Australia. *Australian Journal of Earth Sciences* 45: 571-577.

462. Wang, X.-D. *et al.* 1998b. U-Pb and Sm-Nd dating of high-pressure granulite-and upper amphibolite facies rocks from SW Sweden. *Precambrian Research* 92:319-339.

463. Wastenys, H. A., *et al.* 1996. Wellesley Island leucogranite dated at 1172 ± 5 Ma by single zircon U-Pb method and implications for the geologic history of the Adirondack lowlands. *Geological Society of America Abstracts with Programs* 28(3):108-109.

464. Wastenys, H. A., R. J. Wardle, and R. E. Krogh. 1996. Extrapolation of tectonic boundaries across the Labrador shelf: U-Pb geochronology of well samples. *Canadian Journal of Earth Sciences* 33:1308-1324.

465. Waterhouse, J. B. 1979. Chronologic, ecologic, and evolutionary significance of the Phylum Brachiopoda (pp. 497-518), in E. G. Kauffman, and J. E. Hazel, eds., *Concepts and Methods of Biostratigraphy*. Pennsylvania: Dowden, Hutchinson, and Ross, 658 p.

466. Weaver, C. E. 1967. Potassium, illite, and the ocean. *Geochimica et Cosmochimica Acta* 31:2181-2196.

467. Wel, van de L., J. M. Barton, and P. D. Kinny. 1998. 1.02 Ga granite magmatism in the Tati Granite-Greenstone Terrane of Botswana. *South African Journal of Geology* 101(1): 67-72.

468. Wendt, I. 1993. Isochron or mixing line? *Chemical Geology* 104:301-305.

469. West, D. P., C. V. Guidotti, and D. R. Lux. 1995. Silurian orogenesis in the western Penobscot Bay region, Maine. *Canadian Journal of Earth Sciences* 32:1845-1858.

470. Wetherill, G. W. 1998. Contemplation of things past. *Annual Review of Earth and Planetary Sciences* 26: 1-21.

471. Whitcomb, J., and H. M. Morris. 1961. *The Genesis Flood*. Pennsylvania: Presbyterian and Reformed, 518 p.

472. Whitehouse, M. J. 1989. Pb-isotopic evidence for U-Th-Pb behaviour in a prograde amphibolite to granulite facies transition from the Lewisian complex of north-west Scotland. Implications for Pb-Pb dating. *Geochemical et Cosmochimica Acta* 53:717-724.

473. Whitehouse, M. J. 1990. Isotopic evolution of the southern Outer Hebridean Lewisian gneiss complex. *Chemical Geology* 86:1-20.

474. Whitehouse, M. J., M. B. Fowler, and C. R. L. Friend. 1996. Conflicting mineral and whole-rock isochron ages from the Late-Archaean Lewisian Complex of northwestern Scotland. *Geochimica et Cosmochimica Acta* 60(16):3085-3102.

475. Willett, S. D. 1997. Inverse modeling of annealing of fission tracks in apatite 1: A controlled random search method. *American Journal of Science* 297:939-969.

476. Willett, S. D., *et al.* 1997. Inverse modeling of annealing of fission tracks in apatite 2: Application to the thermal history of the Peace River Arch region, western Canada sedimentary basin. *American Journal of Science* 297:970-1011.

477. Williams, A. R. 1992. Long-age isotope dating short on credibility. *Creation Ex Nihilo Technical Journal* 6(1):2-5.

478. Williams, E. A., *et al.* 1997. An Eifelian U-Pb zircon date for the Enagh Tuff Bed from the Old Red Sandstone of the Munster Basin in NW Iveragh, SW Ireland. *Journal of the Geological Society of London* 154:189-193.

479. Williams, I. S., *et al.* 1984. Unsupported radiogenic Pb in zircon: a cause of anomalously high Pb-Pb, U-Pb, and Th-Pb ages. *Contributions to Mineralogy and Petrology* 88: 322-327.

480. Wise, D. U. 1998. Creationism's geologic time scale. *American Scientist* 86:140-173.

481. Witter, R. 1974 (since promoted to Glory). Radioactive dating. . . *Bible-Science Newsletter* (June issue), pp. 1, 3, 6.

482. Woodburne, M. O. 1987. Introduction (pp. 1-8), in M. O. Woodburne, ed., *Cenozoic Mammals of North America*. Berkeley, London: University of California Press, 336 p.

483. Wooden, J. L., P. A. Mueller, and D. W. Mogk. 1988. A review of the geochemistry and geochronology of the Archean rocks of the northern part of the Wyoming Province (pp. 383-410), in Ernst, ed., *op. cit.*

484. Wooden, J. L., R. W. Kistler, and R. J. Fleck. 1996. Problems using the U-Pb zircon technique to determine the time of crystallization— Lessons from the western U. S. Cordillera. *Geological Society of America Abstracts with Programs* 28(5):126.

485. Woodmorappe, J. 1979. Radiometric Geochronology Reappraised. *Creation Research Society Quarterly*, reprinted in Woodmorappe, J. 1993, 1999. Studies *in Flood Geology*. El Cajon, California: Institute for Creation Research.

486. Woodmorappe, J. 1985. A reply to G. Brent Dalrymple. *Creation Research Society Quarterly* 21(4):84-86.

487. Yang, T. F., *et al.* 1995. Fission-track dating of volcanics in the northern part of the Taiwan Luzon Arc. *Journal of Southeast Asian Earth Sciences* 11(2):81-93.

488. Zartman, R. E., and G. W. Leo. 1985. New radiometric ages on gneisses of the Oliverian domes in New Hampshire and Massachusetts. *American Journal of Science* 285:267-280.

489. Zartman, R. E., and R. S. Naylor. 1984. Structural implications of some radiometric ages of igneous rocks in southeastern New England. *Geological Society of America Bulletin* 95:522-539.

490. Zeitler, P. K., *et al.* 1987. U-Th-He dating of apatite: A potential thermochronometer. *Geochimica et Cosmochimica Acta* 51:2865-2868.

491. Zeuner, F. E. 1950. *Dating the Past*. London: Methuen and Co., 474 p., plates.

492. Zhang, L.-S., and U. Scharer. 1996. Inherited Pb components in magmatic titanite and their consequences for the interpretation of U-Pb ages. *Earth and Planetary Science Letters* 138:57-65.

493. Zheng, Y.-F. 1989. Influences of the nature of the initial Rb-Sr system on isochron validity. *Chemical Geology* 80:1-16.

494. Ziegler, U. R. F., and G. F. U. Stoessel. 1993. *Age Determinations in the Rehoboth Basement Inlier, Namibia*. Geological Survey of Namibia Memoir 14, 106 p.

Study Questions

Questions are listed along with the page number on which the answer may be found. FAQs (frequently asked questions) are listed first.

1. Is there any basis to the assertion of compromising evangelicals that questioning of such things as isotopic dating and the old earth brings discredit to the Christian faith, and hinders others from accepting the Gospel? (p. 5)

2. Can it be shown that the above-mentioned compromise, far from winning unbelievers over, actually does nothing more than encourage unbelievers to continue their rejection of Biblical truth, and to use the compromise itself as a weapon against true Bible believers? (p. 5)

3. When apologists for isotopic dating assert that discrepant isotopic dating results are very rare overall (comparable perhaps to a few malfunctioning watches, or a few rotten apples), are they speaking the truth? (pp. 27-30, 32-33, 71, 78-79, etc.)

4. Even if most dates are bad, some (or many) are "eminently reasonable." Is one therefore obligated to believe them? (p. 3, 95)

5. Is it fact, or uniformitarian wishful thinking, that there exists a tight consensus of dating results for the Phanerozoic geologic column? (p. 13, 42-43, 50)

6. Apropos to the previous question, would we *actually* need some sort of massive conspiracy in place in order to force agreement on "correct" dates? (pp. 13-15)

7. True or False: All of the dating methods converge on a 4.5 Ga (billion-year) age for our planet? (p. 2, 24-26)

8. Historically speaking, has the overall validity of the isotopic dating methods been established prior to their widespread usage, or have dating methods been accepted with little criticism as long as they produced results congenial to uniformitarian thought? (p. 34, 36)

9. Reality or Rhetoric: Isotopic-dating results are usually internally consistent. (p. 29, etc.)

10. Scientific Fact or Anti-Creationist Propaganda: Isotopic dates are unambiguously divisible into "credible" and "non-credible" categories. (p. 37, 41-45)

11. Assuming for the sake of argument the validity of the "self-checking" methodologies, do we find that geochronologists at least agree among themselves on the reliability or unreliability of particular dating results? (p. 37, 39-42)

12. Leaving aside the question of the validity or otherwise of the methodologies for a moment, do presumed reliability criteria *even agree with each other* in predicting which dating results will be reliable and which ones will not? (pp. 45-47)

13. Results of dating methods typically fall in the multimillion-year to multibillion-year range. Does this prove that the correct ages of rocks are at least approximately in the millions to billions of years? (pp. 18-20).

14. As a corollary to the previous question, would we not expect the results of the dating methods to consistently indicate essentially zero ages if the earth was only a few thousand years old? (p. 18)

15. Has it been proven that there exists a "younging-up" trend in isotopic dates (that is, an overall older-to-younger progression of isotopic dates relative to biostratigraphy)? (pp. 21-23, 94-95; see also question #18)

16. Even if the "younging-up" trend in isotopic dates does in fact exist, does this constitute *ipso facto* proof for the validity of the dating methods? (p. 18, 23, 95)

17. True or False: If isotopic dating methods were invalid, we would necessarily expect to find as many "zero" dates, and "future" dates, as those that seem to indicate million-to-billion year values. (p. 24)

18. Do isotopic dates confirm the relative age of fossil-bearing sedimentary rock, or are they actually *dependent* upon faunal ages to check their presumed accuracy? (pp. 7-8, 42-43, 50, 57)

19. Are dating results confirmed by the Geomagnetic Polarity Time-Scale (GPTS), or does each of the two systems tacitly assume that the other one is valid? (pp. 54-56, see also p. 9)

20. Can it be truthfully said that isotopic, biostratigraphic, and geomagnetic results independently corroborate each other? Or is each one of the systems force-fitted in order to compel its agreement with the other two systems? (pp. 54-57)

21. What about the claim that assessing the reliability of isotopic dates is a rigorous, scientific procedure? (p. 8, 37-46, etc.)

22. Fact or Fable: The presumed reliability of isotopic dates can be assessed objectively from analytic data, and independent of any uniformitarian geologic interpretations. (pp. 43-44)

23. What of the claim that dating results are usually concordant when a rock is dated by more than one dating method? (pp. 29-30)

24. Is it fair to say that geochronologists disregard particular dating results as unreliable only after rigorous analysis? (pp. 37-39)

25. True or False: An overwhelming preponderance of "good" over "bad" dates is necessary for the acceptance of the reliability of a dating method on a given material. (p. 36)

26. When apologists of isotopic-dating methods assert that all discrepant isotopic results have a rational geologic explanation that corresponds closely with the known geology of the region, are they speaking a partial truth, a trivial truth, or both? (pp. 8-10, 75, 77, 81, etc.)

27. Does the geologic complexity of Precambrian terrains excuse the discordance of isotopic dates obtained from them? (p. 12)

28. When uniformitarians tell us that isotopic geochronology leads to testable hypotheses, what are they actually saying? (p. 8, 35)

29. Begging the Question: Where can we see the Law of Superposition employed to reject non-conforming dates, and then hear that isotopic-dating methods must be valid because they conform to their stratigraphic context? (pp. 20-21, 43, 46, 50, 54)

30. Even if all isotopic dates did show a local progression in conformity with the Law of Superposition, would one be therefore justified to leap to the conclusion that isotopic-dating methods are therefore validated? (pp. 20-21, 31)

31. If conventional geochronometric dating methods are invalid, why are they still being used? (p. 16)

32. What of the claim that, as analytical tools improve, the validity of isotopic dating is strengthened? (pp. 7-8, 73-74)

33. If we point out that uniformitarian geochronologists often don't publish discrepant dates, are we thereby accusing them of being dishonest? (pp. 15-16)

34. Don't lead-isochron dates from the earth, and from meteorites, themselves establish the earth's age at 4.5 billion years? (p. 24)

35. Fact or Wishful Thinking: Excess argon is a trivial phenomenon. (p. 3, 30-32, 41)

36. Is it true that the assumed equilibration of magmatic and atmospheric argon gas is a well-founded assumption? (pp. 30-31)

37. Most recent volcanics give essentially zero K-Ar ages. When uniformitarians claim that this proves that excess argon is infrequent and unimportant, what biased assumption are they tacitly making? (p. 31)

38. Reality or Rhetoric: On uniformitarians' own terms, do Rb-Sr isochrons that fail to indicate the correct age of the rock occur infrequently? (pp. 32-33)

39. True or False: Inherited (xenocrystic) zircons, a source of U-Pb results which are "too old," seldom occur. (p. 29, 33, 82-83)

40. Are tuffs and bentonites largely exempt from the xenocrystic-zircon problem for U-Pb dating? (p. 33, 84)

41. When some anti-creationists assert that glauconite dating has been abandoned, and insinuate that I am being dishonest in bringing up the dating of glauconite, what does this tell us about how informed and/or honest *they* are? (p. 2, 9, 39, 78)

42. Can it be said with a straight face that conventional K-Ar dates are self-checked for validity and accuracy? (pp. 37-57)

43. Is it correct to say that reliable results can be predicted for unaltered samples of rock? (pp. 46-47)

44. On uniformitarians' own terms, is potassium content a good reliability criterion to screen out unreliable K-Ar dates? Conversely, is high potassium content a near-guarantee for the accuracy of K-Ar dating results? (p. 8, 45, 47)

45. On theoretical grounds alone, are unrecognized xenocrysts likely to have little influence on the magnitude of K-Ar dates? (p. 49)

46. Is it true that xenocrystic crystals (in lavas, tuffs, and bentonites) can invariably be identified and removed before the host rock is dated? Or is a xenocryst labeled as such on an after-the-fact basis because the date from that mineral grain had turned out unacceptably old? (p. 48, 82-84)

47. True or False: Interpretation of discordantly-young K-Ar results, from plutons, as "cooling ages," is corroborated by independent geologic evidence. (pp. 10-11)

48. Are fission-track (FT) dates, most of which are "too young," unambiguously interpreted in terms of annealing caused by geologic heating events, or are such presumed events invented as an *ad hoc* basis precisely because the dates are "too young?" (p. 10, 12, etc.)

49. Are uniformitarians at least following a self-consistent methodology when they tell us that "excess argon" can independently be ruled out if the K-Ar results are homogenous over a wide geographic area? (p. 49)

50. On uniformitarians' own terms, is reproducibility and consistency of isotopic dates proof for their presumed chronometric validity? (pp. 43-44)

51. Can we believe the claim that mineral-pair concordances, by minerals with different isotope-retentive closure temperatures, reliably indicate the correct age of the dated rock? (p. 50, 57-58)

52. True or False: If a U-Pb dating result on a zircon grain is reproducible, it is thereby self-checked, and must necessarily give a reliable crystallization age for the host rock. (p. 44, 50)

53. When uniformitarians argue that concordant results by different dating methods are virtually conclusive proof for the accuracy of the dates, are they at least using their own argument in a self-consistent manner? (pp. 50-54, 95)

54. As a matter of fact, how likely is it for results of different methods to agree (i. e., be concordant) by chance? (pp. 87-92)

55. All things considered, is the closed-system behavior of K-Ar and Rb-Sr systems, over the assumed millions or billions of years, a robust scientific assumption, or is it closer to wishful thinking? (pp. 57-60)

56. When it comes to closure temperatures, are the tested high temperatures necessary to cause open-system behavior in rocks and minerals *ipso facto* evidence for the uniformitarian belief that isotopic dating systems must have remained closed systems for millions and billions of years? (pp. 57-59, 96)

57. As a corollary to the previous question, is a significant thermal event the *only* way in which a rock or mineral can become an open system to the isotopes used in presumed age determination? Conversely, what is the Achilles' heel of all the dating methods? (pp. 58-59, 81)

58. Studies have been conducted on patterns of "rejuvenation" at contact-metamorphic aureoles. Do these patterns accredit the premise about isotopic dating systems likely remaining closed systems over millions to billions of years? (p. 59-60)

59. Even if we were to grant the uniformitarian belief of an old earth, could we nevertheless discount the validity of isochron-based dating systems by empirically questioning the central assumption of the initial isotopic homogeneity of consanguineous magmas? (pp. 61-62)

60. Fact or Myth: The onetime consanguinity of magmas, a foundational assumption behind all of the isochron-based dating methods, is readily determined? (pp. 62-63)

61. Regardless of dating assumptions, does the choice of points which will be placed on the isochron diagrams themselves at least follow from a rigorous and objective methodology? (p. 63)

62. True or False: The fact that points are collinear on the isochron diagram validates both the method and the individual dating result obtained. (p. 59, 63-64)

63. "Superior Isochrons:" Failing the previous argument, are uniformitarians correct when they say that the existence of strongly-collinear points on an isochron diagram prove the age-indicative validity of that particular isochron? (pp. 64-65)

64. What is the significance, if any, of situations where the MSWD value for points on an isochron is very low? (p. 64)

65. Does the value for initial $^{87}Sr/^{86}Sr$ ratio in a Rb-Sr isochron determine its chronometric validity? (p. 65)

66. Are apologists for isotopic dating speaking the truth, or are they just "blowing smoke," when they want us to believe that true Rb-Sr isochrons can easily be distinguished from those resulting as an artifact of mixing effects? (pp. 39, 44, 70-71)

67. Are uniformitarians correct in asserting that inverse plots of isotopic ratios objectively distinguish age-indicative isochrons from mixing lines? (pp. 69-71)

68. Fact or Myth: On uniformitarians' own terms, even if K-Ar dates are conceded to be easily "rejuvenated," Rb-Sr isochron dates remain very reliable owing to their resistance to open-system behavior. (p. 30, 32-33, 65-66)

69. Considering their overall rarity, how can "superior isochrons" be explained by complex mixing processes? (p. 71)

70. True or False: The pitfalls of Rb-Sr mineral-isochrons dating is circumvented by the usage of Rb-Sr whole-rock isochrons. (p. 66)

71. Is to correct to say that, just because REE's (rare earth elements) are presumably immobile, Sm-Nd isochrons dates are therefore a highly reliable indicator of a rock's age? (p. 59, 66-67)

72. In like manner to Rb-Sr isochrons, can geochronologists objectively determine, on their own terms, which Sm-Nd isochrons are fortuitous, which are mixing lines, and which are supposedly indicative of the correct age of the rock? (pp. 70-72)

73. What assumptions are there behind the uniformitarian claim that Sm-Nd model ages date the time since the formation of earth's crust in different geographic areas of our planet? (p. 67)

74. What are some of the flaws of the new lutetium-hafnium (Lu-Hf) dating method? (p. 58, 68)

75. Reality or Rhetoric: On theoretical grounds alone, it is fair to suppose that Pb/Pb isochrons likely have remained undisturbed for millions of years. (p. 68)

76. Even if it is conceded that assumptions about atmospheric argon contents are questionable when it comes to conventional K-Ar dating, is the K-Ar isochron technique exempt from such doubts? (pp. 68-69)

77. Even granting its assumptions, what is the Achilles' heel of the Ar-Ar method and its reputed ability to date rocks and minerals with pinpoint accuracy? (p. 50, 57, 73-74)

78. Can we fairly say that the Ar-Ar method is a panacea for virtually eliminating the interpretative guesswork of K-Ar dating? (pp. 74-75)

79. Has uniformitarian confidence in the presumed diagnostic capabilities of the Ar-Ar method increased with time, or have uniformitarians actually been forced to backpedal away from the early rosy beliefs about the presumed capabilities of this method? (pp. 75-76, 78-79)

80. Is it true that, given the validity of uniformitarian assumptions, the shape of an Ar-Ar spectrum is diagnostic of closed-system behavior over long periods of geologic time? (pp. 74-77, 96)

81. Can apologists for isotopic dating legitimately wish away the difficulties of the Ar-Ar method as "just a tiny number of malfunctioning watches in a sea of properly-functioning ones?" (pp. 78-79)

82. Regardless of whether or not we accept uniformitarian presuppositions, are we forced by the empirical evidence to agree with the claim that the Ar-Ar method at least follows a rigorous and self-consistent methodology for the analysis and interpretation of spectra (or plateaus)? (p. 74, 78-79)

83. What is the obvious special pleading behind the claim that the isochrons used in conjunction with the Ar-Ar method independently detect the presence of excess argon? (pp. 69-70)

84. In what self-serving sense does the Ar-Ar method solve the problem of xenocrystic contamination in lavas, tuffs, and bentonites? (p. 44, 48, 74-75)

85. What role does selective manipulation of data play in the "resolution" of the ostensibly-correct age of a rock from one of the steps of a "staircase-shaped" $^{40}Ar/^{39}Ar$ spectrum? (p. 77)

86. Can we say that the $^{40}Ar/^{39}Ar$ method now allows the testing of glauconite dates for reliability? (p. 78)

87. True or false: If minerals have different argon-closure temperatures, then concordant Ar-Ar results undoubtedly give the correct age of the rock. (p. 78)

88. If adhering to uniformitarian preconceptions, must we conclude that $^{40}Ar/^{39}Ar$ plateau dates are correct if found to be corroborated by other reliability criteria? (p. 78)

89. Fact or Myth: U-Pb dates on zircons are almost certain to be reliable because such dates cannot be "rejuvenated." (p. 81)

90. Should we legitimately let the uniformitarian off the hook when he tells us that explanations involving inheritance, or lead loss, are geologically justified whenever the U-Pb results are in fact found to be discordant? (p. 81)

91. Is it true that inherited (xenocrystic) zircons can be optically distinguished from ones which crystallized at the same time as did the host rock? (pp. 82-83)

92. Are uniformitarians at least following a self-consistent chain of reasoning when they tell us that xenocrystic zircons in a granite reliably date the source lithologies responsible for the origin of the crystals? (p. 83)

93. Can a prognosis of the (presumed) reliability of a U-Pb zircon date be made on the basis of its uranium content? (pp. 83-84)

94. Is it an empirically-verifiable fact that the discordance of U-Pb zircon dates can be predicted on the basis of the metamorphic grade of the host rock? (p. 84)

95. Reality or Rhetoric: Discordance of U-Pb dates can be independently predicted on the basis of the degree of alteration of the zircon crystal being dated. (p. 82)

96. Why is the use of concordia plots a transparent exercise in special pleading? (p. 53, 84, 96)

97. If one grants uniformitarian presuppositions for the sake of argument, can one then truthfully say that the use of concordia plots to interpret discordant U-Pb dates is at least a self-consistent procedure? (pp. 84-85)

98. True or False: The abrasion of individual grains of zircon eliminates the problem of discordant U-Pb dates. (p. 51, 85-86)

99. In what way does the use of the air-abrasion technique on zircons open up a Pandora's box of uncertainties and assumptions, thus providing a new set of special pleadings for the uniformitarian geochronologist to use at will? (p. 85)

100. What has happened to the claims about titanite and monazite being particularly reliable minerals for U-Pb dating? (p. 53, 86)

Index

Note: Entries in this index include concepts as well as terms. For this reason, the exact wording in the index and that of the cited page do not always coincide.

abraded zircons; *most* igneous bodies *nevertheless* yield contradictory U-Pb dates, 33

abrasion technique, U-Pb zircons, 44-45, 51, 83, 85-86, 96

absurdly old dates, 2, 19-20, 22, 25, 32, 67, 87, 89, etc.

accepted dates, skewed by rejection of even slightly-deviant dates, 38

accreted terranes, see collage...

Achilles' heel of all isotopic-dating methods, 58-60; see also 63-68, 72

acid (sialic) volcanics, Rb-Sr isochrons *usually* "too young," 36; see also 29

acidic solutions, readily open K-Ar systems, 58-59

after-the-fact rationalizations, see posterioritic reasoning

after-the-fact xenocrystic contamination invoked, see xenocrystic contamination...

age, earth, 4.5 Ga, myth of consensus for, 2, 24-25, 32; see also 89, 96

age, minimum, arbitrarily assumed true of K-Ar dating, 38

agreement, dates by same method, see reproducibility
    remarkable, with geology, for since-discredited dates, 13-14
    different dating methods, see concordance

alpha-recoil tracks and fission tracks, potential confusion of, 93

alteration indices, dating, predictive failure of, 46

alteration, sample, as trial balloon for date, 3, 8, 54; see also K-content, low...
    samples, lacking, dates nevertheless discrepant, 46-47, 66, 81-82

American Biology Teacher, professional periodical, anti-religious bigotry in, 6

amphiboles, excess argon common in, 32

analytic-method improvements, no credit to dating methods, 7, 28, 40, 43-44, 95

annealing rationalizations, "too young" FT dates, not self-consistent, 93; see also 10, 12

anomalous dates, see bad dates, discrepant dates

anomalously-high ages, can be very reproducible, 43

anti-creationists, duplicitous remarks by, 1, 16, 63-64

Ar-Ar biotite/hornblende concordances, non-evidence of date validity, 78

Ar-Ar dates, "good plateaus," ambiguities in interpretation of, 75
    absurdly old, 25
    geologically meaningless, 54, 69, 76
    precision of, greatly overstated, 73-74
    use of, 10, 25, 28, 35, 45-46, 48, 49, 54-56, 73-79

Ar-Ar flat release pattern, non-evidence for date validity, 76

Ar-Ar method, fails to diagnose excess argon, 76-77; see also 45, 69
    monitor minerals and, 50, 57, 73-74
    not ignored in my 1979 paper, 2
    retreat from once-held high expectations, 35, 79, 96
    so-called false argon-loss profile, 76
    staircase-shaped spectrum, special pleading and, 76-77
    upends K-Ar dates previously accepted as reliable, 47, 50, 79; see also 41
    xenocrystic-contamination "diagnosis," 74-75, 77; see also 44, 48

Ar-Ar plateau dates, "highly reliable," subsequently rejected, 75-76
    conflict with other "good" dates, 39-40, 57
    contradict each other, 76

Ar-Ar saddle-shaped spectrum, not exhibited by suspected excess argon, 77-78

Ar-Ar xenocrystic contamination rationalizations, see xenocrystic...

Archean Rb-Sr isochron dates, largely invalid, 32

argon 40/36 ratio, contra-indicated, see excess argon..., nonradiogenic...

argon 36 content, as reliability check, contradicts other "reliability checks," 45

argon correction, see non-radiogenic argon correction

argon, excess, as rationalization for "too old" dates, see excess argon

arsonist, taking credit for reporting fire, metaphor for dating apologists, 35

ash, volcanogenic, dating of, see bentonites, tuffs

astrology, compared with validity of dating methods, 3

astronomical cycles, agreement with Ar-Ar dates, fudged, 74

ATM (Appeal-to-Marginalization) Fallacy, 2-3, 24, 27, 32, 38, 40, 49, 81, 84, 86, 95

atmospheric initial argon-isotope ratio, see non-radiogenic argon correction

ATT (Appeal-to-Technicalities) Fallacy, 3, 9, 37, 95

aureoles, contact-metamorphic, isotopic-date patterns and, 59-60

Austin, Steven A., 6, 18, 23, 31-33, 64, 97

Australopithecus hominid fossils, see Hadar, KBS tuff

authigenic minerals, see glauconite, clay minerals

backpedaling, on dates once believed to be reliable, 37, 39-40, 43-46, 66, 79, 84-85

bad C-14 dates, arbitrarily rejected, 41

bad dates, "just a list of," fallacious stereotype of my 1979 paper, 1
    can be very reproducible, 43
    need *not* be outnumbered by (supposed) good dates, 36
    Orwellian cover words for, see euphemisms...
    rule, not the exception, 27-28, 33
    see also discrepant...
    usually not published, 1, 16, 22

balloons, trial, dating methods as, 3, 37, 41, 54, 62-63, 95, etc.

basalts, flood, see flood basalts
    Hawaiian, bogus anti-creationist arguments about, 2

basic solutions, readily open K-Ar systems, 46, 52, 58-59

bentonites, dating of, 22, 29, 33-34, 46-48, 52, 56, 59, 65, 74, 84

Berkeley team, highly-regarded "reliable" dates proved false, 40-41

best data, isotopic dates, tainted with doubts, 37

bias, experimenter, dating, not accounted for, 15-16
    experimenter, effect on dating results, 17-18, 49, 94
    laboratory and/or interlaboratory, isotopic-dating results, 7-8, 52, 56-57, 74

biased data sampling, need to overcome, 22-23, 30, 87-89

biostratigraphic dating, assumed "check" on dates, see faunal dating

biostratigraphic progression, dates, alleged, see younging up

biotic heterochroneity, euphemism for fossil/date conflict, 52

biotite, Ar-Ar method fails to diagnose excess argon in, 76-77
    excess argon common in, 32, 76
    superior argon retention, fallacious argument about, 28; see also 94

biotite-hornblende concordances, see concordant mineral-pair...

Brunhes Polarity Chron, 55

burden of proof, on dating methods, not on creationists, 5-6

C-14 dates, discrepant, arbitrarily rejected, 41

Cambrian-Precambrian boundary, dating of, 13-14, 22

Canadian Cordillera, date compendium from, 30, 42

Canadian Shield, dates from, 18

capabilities, once believed and now rejected, for all dating methods, 34-35

CDMBN (Credit-Dating-Methods, Blame-Nature) Fallacy, 2-3, 10, 16, 27, 42, 49, 67, 77-78, 83-86, 95

censorship of dissenting views in science, dating and, 14-15

chance concordances, see fortuitous concordances

CHUR (chondritic uniform reservoir), uniformitarian beliefs about, 25, 67

clay minerals, spoof of "younging-up" argument for isotopic dates, 18, 23

clay-mineral dates vs. igneous dates, double standard on credibility, 22-23

closure temperatures, isotopes, dating, see temperatures...

closure-temperature ages, euphemism for "too young" K-Ar dates, see cooling...

collage, euphemism for regionally-contradictory dates, 19

collinearity, excellent, isochron points, non-evidence for validity, 59, 62, 64, 69, 70

collinearity, points on concordia diagram, non-evidence for validity, 84-85

comagmatic samples, isochron-construction, see consanguineous...

complexity, geologic, no necessary relationship to dates, 12

composite batholith, euphemism for contradictory dates obtained, 90-91; see also 10

compromising evangelicals, curry favor with humanists, 5, 95
    steeped in rationalism, 2

concordance, dates from different methods, inconsistent argument, 51-54, 82, 95

concordance, fortuitous, see fortuitous concordance

concordant dates, sets of, in mutual contradiction, 52-53

concordant mineral-pair dates, Ar-Ar, non-evidence for validity, 78
    K-Ar, non-evidence for validity, 50

concordant pattern, dates, fortuitous, 22, 38, 44, 55, 74

concordia, U-Pb dating, excellent collinearity of points, eventually rejected, 84-85
    U-Pb dating, special pleading in usage, 53, 84-85

consanguineous magmas, central assumption behind isochron dating, violated, 61-63

consensus mentality, dating methods and, 14-15

consensus, 4.5 Ga of earth, myth of, 24-25
    Phanerozoic time scale, canard about, 13, 37-38, 42-44, 50, 52, 56-57, 60

consistency, dates by same method, see reproducibility
    dates, obvious circular reasoning about, 29

conspiracy, imagined, to force agreement on "good" dates, 13, 16
    to suppress doubts about dates, 14-16

contact-metamorphic aureoles, meaning of dates near, 59-60

contact-metamorphic zones, *ad hoc* reinterpretations for dates, 9; see also 59-60

contamination, C-14 dating and, impossibility of ruling out, 41
    xenocrystic, alleged, see xenocrystic...

continental crust, alleged growth of, 15

continental drift, see plate tectonics

contours, using dates as "cooling ages," artificiality of, 10; see also 57-58, 91

contradictions between concordant sets of dates, 52-53

contradictory dates, same igneous body, illustrated, 11
    U-Pb zircons, from same igneous body, the *rule*, not exception, 33

cooling ages, admission that *most* K-Ar dates are "too young," 28
    euphemism for discrepantly-young dates, 10, 16, 28, 34, 49, 57
    fundamentally speculative, 58

Cordillera, Canadian, widely contradictory dates from, 30

cosmogenic origin, isotopes, assumed, 26

cover words for discrepant dates, see euphemisms

cratonic nuclei, isotopic dates and, 20

creation evangelism, significance of, 5

Creation, reason for high apparent ages after, 24, 31, 70, 93

creationist significance of K, Ar exchange, 68

credible/non-credible dates, a contrived and false dichotomy, 42-49; see also 79

Cretaceous-Tertiary boundary, dating of, 52

CRS algorithm, for FT dating, 10-12

crustal-enrichment trends, chemical elements used in dating systems, 52

cryptic cores, euphemism for *ad hoc* U-Pb zircon xenocrysts, 83

crystals, mineral, individual, dating of, see mineral grains...

Dalrymple, G. Brent, 1-2, 5, 24, 27-28, 31, 42, 49, 51, 54, 64, 69, 84, 99, 103

data skewing, dating methods and, 15-16, 95, etc.

data, isotopic dating, torture of, 86

dates, global distribution, "birds-eye" view, 87-89, 93
    isotopic, admitted subjectivity of interpreting, 8, 37-38, 42
    isotopic, clash with geologic field relationships, 8-9, 25, 60, 93, etc.
    magnitude of, *reductio ad absurdum* of argument about, 18
    multimillion to multibillion, geochemical alternatives to, 18

dating methods, admittedly non-experimental and nonstatistical, 1
    retreat from once-held high expectations, 34-36

dating results, overall, log-linear distribution of, 87-88
    overall, log-normal distribution of, 88-89

decay rates indeed calibrated by other dating methods, 16-17, 95

decay-rate increases, alternatives to, 6, 18, 21-23, 31-32, 70, 87-94

deductions, dating methods, see predictive failures...

delayed-uplift ages, euphemism for "too young" K-Ar dates, see cooling...

dinosaur-bearing strata, dating of, 57

discordance, a *rule* for both K-Ar and Rb-Sr mineral dates, 29
    a *rule* for dates from different dating methods, 29-31
    reverse, see reverse discordance

discordances, multi-magnitude, from same lithological associations, 18-19

discrepant results, "rational" geologic explanations for, 8
    majority unpublished, 1, 16
    not rare (and probably the rule), 1, 24, 27-34, 71
    still arbitrarily rejected, 13, 39, 52, etc.

dishonesty, scientific, infrequency of, 15-16

distribution, dates, global, see global...

diverse values, dates, small geographic areas, 18-20, 29, 90-91; see also 25

DM (depleted mantle), 25

doublespeak, routinely used in dating, see euphemisms

dreams, compared with validity of dating methods, 3, 95

dyke (also spelled dike) orientations, clash with dating results, 9; see also 8

earth, some dates say "older than 4.5 Ga," 2, 25, 32, 87, 96

earth's age, see age, earth

elements, chemical, major, unpredictable relation to isotopic dates, 9, 71, 86
    in dating systems, crustal-enrichment trends, 52, 94

empirical analyses, dating results, subordinate to uniformitarian preconceptions, 35

errorchrons, see scatterchrons

euphemisms for bad dates, as types of Orwellian "isotopic" language, 16, 96
    see biotic..., closure..., collage..., composite..., cooling..., cryptic..., delayed..., excess..., hybrid..., rejuvenation..., reverse..., stratigraphic..., thermochronological..., xenocrystic...

evangelicals, compromising, see compromising evangelicals

evaporation technique, U-Pb zircon treatment, dates inconclusive, 83

events, improbable (dating coincidences), see improbable events

Evernden glauconite study, bogus anti-creationist arguments about, 2

Evernden K-Ar dates, "very reliable," later proved false, 40-41

excess argon, admitted impossibility of proving, 41
    Ar-Ar "diagnostic capabilities" regarding, 76
    definition of, 30
    euphemism for "too old" K-Ar dates, 19, 32, 39, 42, 46-47, 49-50
    fallacy of limited occurrence, 3, 30-33, 38
    special pleading on Ar-Ar isochron "diagnosis" of, 47, 96
    special pleading on K-Ar isochron "diagnosis" of, 68

exclusion, arbitrary, of deviant dates, 43, etc.

excursions, geomagnetic, contrived, 55

experimenter bias, see bias, experimenter

extinct radioactivity, old earth *assumed*, 26

extraneous argon, definition of, 30; see also argon

faunal dating, altered to conform with isotopic dates, 52
    disregard of dates which conflict with, 43-44, 50, 57, 60, etc.

few malfunctioning watches, myth of, 1, 24, 27-33, 71, 78-79
few-malfunctioning-watch argument turned around, 36
field geology, contradicted by isotopic dates, see geologic context...
fissiogenic origin, isotopes, assumed, 26
fission track dating, see FT
fission tracks, why so many produced between Creation and Flood, 93
flood basalts, dates from, usually highly inconsistent, 28-29
Flood, reason for high apparent ages, 18, 24, 31, 70, 93
fluid movement, Achilles' Heel of all dating methods, 58-60, 63-68, 72, 96
fortuitous concordances, high probability of, demonstrated, 87-92
    invoked by uniformitarians whenever needed, 50-54
    rates increased, by dating of single mineral grains, 44, 74, 85, 92
    rates increased, by stringent reliability criteria, 38
fortuitous isochrons, see isochrons, meaningless
fossil succession, forced agreement of dates with, 43-44
    see also younging up, faunal dating...
four-and-half billion years, earth's presumed age, exceeded by isotopic
    dates, 2, 25, 32, 89, 96
fraud, intentional, rarity in scientific research, 15-16
Free Inquiry magazine, anti-religious bigotry in, 6
fresh samples, see alteration
Freudian slip, 6
FT (fission track) apatite dates, almost all "too young," 25, 34, 93
FT dates, "too young," contrived thermotectonic events, 10, 57, 59, 93
    "too young," despite fresh minerals, 46
    incorrect, "corroborate" magnetic polarity scales, 55
    rarely date the rock, 27
    sphenes and zircons, "too young," 46
    widely contradictory, 19, 29
FT dating, uranium leaching increases dates, 93
    zeta and, 14
FT method, retreat from once-held high expectations, 35
FT tracks, biased counting of, 18
FT, spontaneous fission decay constant unknown, 17
    xenocrystic contamination rationalizations, see xenocrystic...
fudged isochrons, see isochrons, fudging of
fudging, trimming, massaging, torture, of data, dating methods and, 15-
    16, 56, 74, 86
funding, scientific studies, dating and, 15
future ages, bogus anti-creationist argument about, 24
futurechrons, 24

garnet and clinopyroxene, bad Sm-Nd dates not published from, 16; see
    also 24
Gauss Polarity Chron, 55
Gentry, Robert V., 93, 100
geochemical trends, isotopes, conducive to fortuitous concordances, 51-
    52, 94
geochemistry, see elements
geochron, fallacy about, 24-25
geographic proximity of very contradictory dates, 19-20, 90-91; see also 25
geologic complexity, dating and, 12
geologic context, special pleading, isotopic dating, 8-9, 25, 35, 59, 60, 66,
    79, 93, 96, etc.
geologic time scale, see Phanerozoic time scale
geologists, usually uncritically accept dating methods if they "fit," 35, 67,
    etc.
geomagnetic polarity time scale, data-manipulation and, 54-56
geothermal fluids, see fluid movement
glauconite dates, arbitrary rejection of, admitted, 39; see also 77-78
    fail to show expected geologic event, 9
glauconite dates/igneous dates, double standard, 28
glauconite dating, bogus anti-creationist argument about, 2
    depth of samples, effect on results, 2
glauconite Rb-Sr dates, reason for acceptance, 34; see also 40
global distribution of dates, approximated for analysis, 87-89
global tectonics, see plate tectonics
good dates, despite proximity to intrusions, 59, 60
    so-called, doubtful significance of, 42
    so-called, preponderance *not* necessary, 36

Gordon, William Robert, 5
Gospel, discredited by questioning old earth, canard about, 5
GPTS, see geomagnetic polarity time scale
grains, individual mineral, dating of, see mineral grains...
Grand Canyon, absurd Pb-Pb isochron date from, 33
greenstone belts, *ad hoc* diverse dates from, 25

Hadar Formation, Ethiopia, hominid fossils and dating, 21
Ham, Ken, 5, 101
Hawaiian basalts, bogus arguments about, 2
helium method, advocated revival of, 16
hornblende, excess argon common in, 32
    K-Ar dating, easily opened by fluids, 59
    K-content, special pleading and, 47; see also 94
hotspots, oceanic, dates from, 79
Hualalai volcano, xenoliths, inconsistent argument about, 49
humanists, love believers' concessions to old earth, 5
hybrid dates, euphemism for unusable isotopic dates, 11
hydrofluoric-acid treatment, zircons, for U-Pb dating, 86
hydrothermal fluids, see fluid movement
hypotheses, testable, dating, see predictive failures

Idaho Batholith, artificial dating interpretations about, 10
illite, non-dating stratigraphic trend, 18
improbable events, likelihood increased by numerous trials, 71, 92
incomplete record, perennial uniformitarian excuse for nonconforming
    data, 79
individual grains, see mineral grains
inherited argon, definition of, 30; see also excess argon
inherited isochrons, see isochrons, inherited
inherited mineral grains, see xenocrystic contamination
intercept ages, U-Pb method, see concordia
intrusions, contemporaneity of, contradicted by dates, 9, 44
    K-Ar dates *usually* "too young," 28
    loose biostratigraphic brackets, dates and, 22; see also 10, 57
    unpredictable effects on country-rock isotopic dates, 60
inverse discordance, see reverse discordance
inverse plots, see mixing lines...
Iodine 129, secondary origin assumed, 26
isochron dates, confessedly no way of determining their validity, 71
    reasonable intercepts, non-evidence for validity, 65
isochron validity, disagreements about, 63
isochrons, absurdly high ages from, 19-20, 25
    Ar-Ar, see Ar-Ar isochrons
    conventional K-Ar, meaningless, 68; see also 30
    dates, *majority* are of mediocre quality, 65, 70-71
    fudging of, by selective inclusion of points, 61-62, 94
    inherited, 44, 61-62, 65, etc.
    initial-isotope homogeneity assumption, violated, 61-62
    intercepts, absurd values of, 65, 69
    meaningless, 39, 59, 61-63, 65-68, 71-72, 81, etc.
    mineral, ambiguous meaning of, 66
    multiple, contradictory, from same rock, 62-63, 91
    once accepted as reliable age-indicators, now rejected, 64, 66, 69
    reference, see scatterchrons
    rejuvenated, secondary, see isochrons, rotated
    rotated, and "too young" isochron dates, 30, 32-33, 36, 47, 54, 64-
        66, 68-69
    see also mixing lines
    see also scatterchrons
    tightly collinear, non-evidence for validity, 59, 62, 64, 69-70, 96
    whole-rock vs. mineral, reversed expectations of reliability, 66
    whole-rock, essentially only two-point isochrons, 39-40, 70

Journal of Geoscience Education, anti-religious bigotry in, 6

K, Ar exchange, significance for creation studies, 68, 92
K-Ar dates, "older than earth," 25, 32
    global distribution, "birds-eye" view, 87, 89
    usually "too young," from extrusives, 28-29

usually "too young," from intrusives, 34
very consistent, later rejected, 45-46
vintage of, non-problem, 1
K-Ar dating, overall retreat from once-high expectations, 34
xenocrystic contamination rationalizations, see xenocrystic...
K-Ar isochrons, see isochrons, conventional K-Ar
K-Ar method, dates previously accepted as reliable, overthrown by Ar-Ar
dating, 47, 50, 79; see also 41
now disparaged in general by some geochronologists, 45
K-Ar systems, easily opened by fluid transport, 58-59
K-Ar, minimum age, arbitrarily assumed, 38
KBS Tuff controversy, 18, 21, 54-55
K-Ca ratios, fail to independently identify xenocrysts, 48
K-content, low, yet K-Ar dates nevertheless accepted because they "fit,"
8, 47; see also 3
presumed reliability criterion, contradicted, 45
presumed reliability criterion, detailed description of, 47
kimberlites, see ultramafic rocks...
Kirkpatrick Basalt (Antarctica), dating of, 28-29
Krogh technique, see abrasion technique, U-Pb zircons
K-T boundary, dating of, 52

La-Ce dating, uncertain decay constant, fixed by Sm-Nd, 17
lanthanum-cerium dating method, see La-Ce
lava flows, inverted dates from, 21
lavas, dates from, usually highly inconsistent, 28-29
law of superposition, dating results violate, 20-21, 46, 54
lead-lead dates, see Pb-Pb
Leadville quadrangle, Colorado, USA, 19
light, velocity of, old measurements, 17
Lu-Hf method, flaws in, 68
Lu-Hf, uncertain closure temperature of, 58
lutetium-hafnium dating method, see Lu-Hf
Luther, Martin, 6

magma generation rate, entrapment of argon, 31
magnetically-separated mineral fractions, K-Ar dating and, 45; see also 29
magnetochrons, dates, *ad hoc* revisions of, 55-56
magnetostratigraphy, see geomagnetic...
malfunctioning watches, see few malfunctioning watches, myth of
manipulation of isotopic, biostratigraphic, and magnetochronologic data,
37, 56-57
mantle-extraction ages, not obtained by Sm-Nd or Re-Os, 67-68; see also
72
Matuyama Polarity Chron, 55
meaningless concordia diagrams, 84-85, 96
meaningless isochrons, see isochrons, meaningless
Mesozoic bias, isotopic dates, contra "younging up" of dates, 22; see also
89
metamorphic grade, does not predict degree of U-Pb date discordance, 84;
see also 8
metamorphism, invented, as date rationalization, see rejuvenation; also FT
metasomatic processes, see fluid movement...
meteorites, dating of, 24-25
microcontinents, *ad hoc* inventions from dating results, 19
Mid-Atlantic Ridge, dates from, 81
Milankovitch cycles, agreement with Ar-Ar dates, fudged, 74
mineral grains, singly dated, proliferate dates to choose from, 7, 33, 44,
74, 78, 82, 85-86, 92
mineral-pair concordances, see concordances, mineral-pair...
mineral-pair trends in dates, inversions of, 58
minimum age, arbitrarily assumed true of K-Ar dating, 38
mixing lines instead of isochrons, 18, 39, 61, 64, 69-72, 96
mixing lines not disproved by collinear inverse plots, 69-71
mixing lines on concordia diagrams, U-Pb dating, 85
model ages, Sm-Nd, in the future, 24
Sm-Nd, "too young," 67
modernists, tools of humanists, 5
monitor minerals, Ar-Ar dating and, 50, 57, 73-74

Monte Carlo analysis, quasi, to estimate frequency of fortuitous
concordances, 52, 89-92
Morris, Henry M., *iv, vi,* 13, 35-36, 87, 93, 108
Moses, cosmogony of, 5
Mount St. Helens, dates from 1980 lavas, 32
MSWD, low, non-evidence for isochron validity, 44, 47, 63, 65

negative ages, from various dating methods, 24
negativity, allegations about criticisms of dating methods, science and, 3
neodymium-isotope evolution, self-fulfilling conclusions, 67
Newspeak, an essential part of isotopic-dating vocabulary, 16
non-radiogenic argon correction, 7, 30-31, 37, 47
non-temporal younging up, geologic column, dates, 18, 23, 95

Oard, Michael, 55, 104
occluded argon, see excess argon
oceanic-rock dating, fallacies of, 79; see also 8
ophiolites, dates usually of doubtful validity, 29
opinions, not facts, govern "date's reliability," 37-41
ores, U-Pb dates from, myth of 4.5 Ga consensus, 24
orogens, overlapping in "age," 19-20
Orwell, George, 16
Orwellian constructs, common in isotopic dating, 16, 96
Orwellian doublethink, dating, see euphemisms
out-of-step dates, arbitrary disregard of, 29, 37, 39
over-interpretation of isotopic dates, 10-11

Pahrump diabase, red herring about, 2
palaeoisochrons, transposed, see isochrons, rotation of
paleomagnetism, see geomagnetic...
paleomagnetically-based correlations, contradicted by dates, 9
paleontologic dating, "isotopic-date progression," see younging up
assumed "check" on dates, see faunal dating
Paleozoic rocks, almost all were open systems, 27
Pb-Pb dates, carbonate rocks, 36
consistent, yet invalid, 45
Pb-Pb isochron dates, often spurious, 68
Pb-Pb isochron, absurd, from Grand Canyon, 33
peer pressure, dating-method conformity and, 14-15
Permian Period, boundaries of, 13
Phanerozoic time scale, consensus-of-dates-myth, see consensus,
Phanerozoic
even "good" dates contradict, 7, 37-38, 42-43
phenocrysts, see xenocrystic contamination...
plate tectonics, 8, 15, 19, 79, 81
plateaus, Ar-Ar, see Ar-Ar, plateaus
Pleistocene Magnetic Polarity Scale, see geomagnetic...
plutons, dating results, artificial cooling histories from, 10; see also
intrusions
posterioritic reasoning, endemic to isotopic dating, 3, 16, 37-38, 42, 48,
51, 62-63, 66, 72, 78, 81-82, 85, 95
potassium content, see K-content
potassium-argon dating, see K-Ar, Ar-Ar, indirect references to
Precambrian lithologies, artificially divided by isotopic dates, 25
simple histories of some, 12
predictions, dates, vitiated by posterioritic reasoning (which see)
successful, non-evidence for dating methods, 3
predictive failures, Ar-Ar spectrum, diagnostic capabilities of, 76-77
capabilities of methods themselves, 34-35, 96, etc.
dating methods, alteration indices of samples, 46
biostratigraphy and, 43-44, 60, etc.
chemical element concentration, 71, 86, etc.
comagmatic suites of samples, 62
distance and extent of contact metamorphism, 60
greenstone belts, 25; see also 46
in absence of "confirmatory" geologic data, 27, 39-40
isochron-based, generally, 71, etc.
isotope-closure temperatures and, 57-59
Law of Superposition, 20-21, etc.

metaphoric textures and, 12, 66, 84
   mineralogy and geochemistry, 9, 62
   structural geology and, 9, 44
   suitable geologic materials for Sm-Nd dating, 16
   xenocrysts and, 48-49, etc.
progression, dates, alleged, see younging up
pseudo-isochrons, see isochrons, meaningless
publishing, dates, selective, proof of, 1, 16; see also 22, 46

radioactive decay, see decay rates...
radioactive isotopes, short-lived, assumed secondary origins of, 26
radioactivity, extinct, see extinct radioactivity
radiogenic content, K-Ar dating, see non-radiogenic argon correction
radiometric dating, usage of term, 5
rarity, discrepant dates, not, 1, 24, 27-34, 71, etc.
ratchet wheel, dating usage resembles, 3
RATE Project, 6, 18, 87, 96
rationalism, dating methods, a sacred cow of, 6
Rb-Sr dates, global distribution of, "birds-eye" view, 88-89
Rb-Sr dating, doubted in many geologic studies, 12, 32-33
   said to be discredited for age determination, 27
Rb-Sr isochron dates, once accepted as reliable, subsequently rejected, 66
Rb-Sr isochron method, retreat from once-held high expectations, 35
Rb-Sr isochrons as unacceptable dates, very common, 29-30, 32-33, 36
Rb-Sr isochrons, inherited, see isochrons, inherited
   initial-isotope homogeneity assumption violated, 61-62
   meaningless, see isochrons, meaningless
Rb-Sr isotopic systems, easily opened by fluid transport, 58-59, 63
Rb-Sr method, once believed virtually foolproof, 34-35; see also
   isochrons...
Rb-Sr whole-rock dating, reckoned as unreliable, 33
recoil effect, Ar-Ar dating and, 76
REE (rare-earth elements), see Sm-Nd...
reference isochrons, see scatterchrons, errorchrons
   use of, 2
regional geology, geographic scale of discrepant dates, 18-20, 29, 90-91
reheating, rationalizations, see rejuvenation
reinforcement syndrome, "correct" decay constants and, 17
   "correct" isotopic dates and, 14, 46, 56, 62, 67
rejuvenated isochrons, see isochrons, rotated
rejuvenation, euphemism for "too young" dates, 10-11,19, 21, 29, 39, 46-
   47, 49, 51, 57-58, 75
   mutual, rationalization for "too young" concordant dates, 53
reliability criteria, alleged, contradict each other, 8, 45, 78
reliability, dates, lack of agreement of which ones are, 39-40, 41-49; see
   also 83-84
   dates, successive dogmatic claims about, 36
   samples for dating, see alteration
reliable dates, once believed, subsequently rejected, 39-40, 43-46, 66, 79,
   84-85
reliable/non-reliable dates, an artificial dichotomy, 42-49, 78
Re-Os dates, discrepant, 49, 68
Re-Os isochron dates, often older than those of other methods, 67-68
Re-Os isochrons, meaningless, 68
Re-Os model ages, absurdly old, 25
repression of scientific dissent, implications for dating, 14-15
reproducibility dates, special pleading and, 43, 45-46, 49-54
reproducibility, dates, non-evidence for validity, 43, 50, etc.
resetting, rationalization for "too young" dates, see rejuvenation
reverse discordance, blamed on excess argon, 58
   euphemism for older dates from less-retentive minerals
   U-Pb dates, common, 24, 84-85
review, scientific peer, dating results and, 15
rhenium-osmium dating method, see Re-Os
rhetorical terms for discrepant dates, see euphemisms
rifting, tectonic, presumed dating of, 8
rotated isochrons, "too young" isochron rationalization, see isochrons,
   rotated
rubidium-strontium dating method, see Rb-Sr, individual references to

samarium-neodymium dating method, see Sm-Nd, individual references to
samples, suitable for dating, see alteration
sampling of earth, uneven, isotopic dates, 22
sampling universe, considerably enlarged by single-grain dating, 44, 74,
   78, 86, 92
   fortuitous concordances in perspective, 91
scatterchrons, 2, 71
scientific peer pressure, dating method conformity and, 14-15
secondary status, ephemeral radioactive isotopes, assumed origins of, 26
sedimentation rates, calibrated early isotopic dates, 13-14
   highly variable, 13
self-checking, dates, wishful thinking about, 10, 37-60, 62, 95, etc.
   dating systems, see also reliable..., reliability...
SHRIMP, U-Pb dating, described, 44; see also 63, 66, 82-83, etc.
Siberian traps, dating controversy, 42
smectite, apparent younging up of, 18, 23
Sm-Nd dates, global distribution of, "birds-eye" view, 88-89
Sm-Nd dating, source-area effects, presumed, special pleading, 25, 71-72
Sm-Nd isochron method, once believed virtually foolproof, 34-35, 66-67
Sm-Nd isochrons, contradict earlier ostensibly-reliable Sm-Nd isochrons,
   46
   initial-isotope homogeneity assumption violated, 61-62
   meaningless, see isochrons, meaningless
   spurious, not rare, 71
Sm-Nd isotopic systems, readily opened by fluid transport, 58-59, 66-67, 72
Sm-Nd method, see also isochrons...
Sm-Nd mixing line, 64, 71
Sm-Nd model ages, meaningless, 24-25, 67
Sm-Nd, dating of garnet, clinopyroxene, etc., , 16, 24, 58
   uncertain closure temperature of, 58
smokescreens for discrepant dates, see euphemisms
Snelling, Andrew A., iv, 2, 5, 16, 18, 23-25, 31-32, 106-107
solutions, open systems, see fluid movement
source-area effects, see Sm-Nd dating...; U-Pb dating...
spectrum, Ar-Ar, arbitrary rules for interpreting, 75, 79; see also Ar-Ar
   plateau
statistically-excellent isochrons, non-evidence for validity, 44, 59, 62, 64,
   69, 70, 96
statistics, not usually used for collections of dates, 1
   simple, suggest frequent fortuitous concordances, 87-92
Strahler, Arthur N., irresponsible arguments of, 2, 107
stratigraphic control, euphemism for discarded dates, 43-44, 46
stratigraphic trends, dates, see trends, stratigraphic, non-evidence
stratigraphic-consistency tests, see superposition, faunal dating
strontium, initial ratios inferred from Rb-Sr isochrons, absurd values, 65
superior isochrons, non-evidence for chronometric validity, 70
superposition, law of, circular "check" of dates, 20-21, 43, 46, 50, 54
systematic errors, see bias, experimenter...

tectonically-disturbed environments, "good" dates from, 8
tectonics, plate, see plate tectonics
temperatures, closure, inconsistent estimates of, 57-59
   closure, vitiated by low-temperature fluid transport, 58-60, 96
tendentious publication, dates, trends are artifacts of, 21-22
tephrochronology, see tuffs, bentonites
Tertiary K-Ar dates, long highly-regarded, later proved false, 40-41
testable hypotheses, see predictive failures...
Th-Pb bad dates the rule, not the exception, 33; see also 29
thermochronological information, euphemism for failed methods, 34, 96;
   see also cooling...
thermotectonic events, ad hoc, see rejuvenation...
transposed palaeoisochrons, see isochrons, rotation of
trends, stratigraphic, non-evidence for dating methods, 18, 20-22, 95
trial balloons, dating methods as, 3, 8, 37, 41, 54, 62-63, 95
tuffs, ad hoc xenocrystic contamination invoked, 40-41, 48
   dating of, 21, 33, 40-41, 48, 54-56
   inverted dates from, 21

ultramafic rocks, possible key to understanding "excess argon," 94 unaltered samples, see alteration

unsupported isotopes, non-evidence old earth, 26

U-Pb bad dates, zircon (abrasion notwithstanding), the *rule*, not the
    exception, 33, 96

U-Pb crystals, xenocrystic, see xenocrystic contamination, U-Pb....

U-Pb dates, carbonate rocks, 36
    global distribution of, "birds-eye" view, 88-89
    ores, non-evidence for 4.5 Ga earth age, 24
    reverse discordance, monazites, common, 24, 53
    usually discordant, 29-30
    whole rocks, rarely acceptable, 33

U-Pb dating, bulk zircons, once accepted as reliable, 40, 45
    columbite, 49
    concordia, see concordia...
    monazites, 24, 33, 53, 86
    source-area effects, special pleading and, 83
    titanite, unpredictable behavior of, 60, 86
    zircons, 21, 25, 33, 37, 44, 57

U-Pb isotopic systems, contrary to reputation, easily opened by fluid
    transport, 28, 81

U-Pb/Rb-Sr comparative dating, pre-selected dates, still usually
    discordant, 30; see also 17

U-Pb zircon dates, concordant-yet-contradictory string of, 52-53

U-Pb zircon method, once believed virtually foolproof, 34-35

U-Pb, abrasion of zircons, see abrasion technique...
    evaporation technique, see evaporation technique...
    uncertain closure temperature of, 58

updating of dates, rationalization, see rejuvenation

uplift histories, derived from dates, admittedly baseless, 10

uranium content, not predictive of inferred closed-system behavior, 82-84

uranium, leaching of, probable cause of "very old" FT dates, 93; see also 33

uranium-lead dating method, see U-Pb

U-Th-He method, advocated revival of, 16

Vardiman, Larry, 6, 87, 96, 107

watches, few malfunctioning, see few malfunctioning watches, myth of

Whitcomb, John C., 13, 35-36, 87, 93, 108

xenocrystic contamination, *ad hoc*, euphemism for "too old" dates, (see
    below)
    Ar-Ar date rationalization, 21, 44, 48, 54, 74-75, 77
    FT date rationalization, 21
    K-Ar date rationalization, 19, 30-31, 48
    U-Pb date rationalization, invoked *ad hoc*, 82-83; see also 33, 39

xenocrystic U-Pb zircon, assumed closed system in, 53, 82

xenocrystic zircons, U-Pb date rationalization, the *rule*, not the exception,
    33, 96

xenocrysts and xenoliths, obvious, dating of, special pleading and, 49,
    74-75

young rocks, ostensible, difficulties of K-Ar dating of, 7

younging up, dates, non-evidence for validity, 18, 20-23, 94-95
    duplicated by non-radiogenic chemical species, 18, 23, 95

zero ages, bogus anti-creationist argument about, 24
    hidden from publication, 24

zeta, FT dating and, 14

zircons, "too young," FT dating, 46
    abrasion, see abrasion technique, U-Pb zircons
    optical properties, special pleading on, 82-83